Techniques of Value Analysis and Engineering

Techniques of Value
Analysis and Engineering

LAWRENCE D. MILES

Manager, Value Service, General Electric Company

McGRAW-HILL BOOK COMPANY, INC.

New York   Toronto   London   1961

TECHNIQUES OF VALUE ANALYSIS AND ENGINEERING

9 10 11 12 13 14 – M P – 9 8 7 6

41925

THE MAPLE PRESS COMPANY, YORK, PA.

To HARRY ERLICHER, *whose unusual foresight pierced the future and who created opportunity*

To W. A. SREDENSCHEK, *whose support and leadership provided challenge and inspiration*

To ROY FOUNTAIN, *whose engineering genius, limitless creativity, constant objectivity, and treasured personal friendship transformed problems into opportunities*

To engineer extraordinary JOHN HORN, *whose deep understanding, penetrating questions, and invaluable assistance contributed richly to the thoughts in this book.*

PREFACE

Accomplishments of a most astonishing and profitable nature accrue from effective use of the techniques of value analysis taught in this text. Thousands upon thousands of cases from actual practice, from small businesses and large, from mass production and job shop, from product redesign and product research and development, verify this, as the examples cited throughout the book will indicate.

Created for one specific purpose—identification of unnecessary costs —value analysis is a novel procedure for deriving much-needed results; this it does through a common-sense approach which yields startling efficiency.

Anything new or novel commonly accomplishes its specific purpose through a new arrangement of familiar things. Consider the automobile, for instance. It was created largely through a rearrangement of known components such as iron, copper, paint, fabric, wheels, and engines.

The same components, with a few others added, were again in later years rearranged into the airplane, creating a new product and increasing efficiency—if transporting people over long distances with comfort, safety, and speed is the purpose—five to ten times.

Similarly, value engineering is a creation born largely through the rearrangement of known concepts, plus the addition of a few new ones. It is used with knowledge from many technologies for the specific purpose of efficiently identifying unnecessary costs.

This new system is increasing the efficiency of its specific task manyfold.

The winning golfer has learned the effective techniques for driving, chipping, and putting and uses them all—each correctly and at the proper times. Similarly, the identification of unnecessary cost is most effective, efficient, and economical when all the proper techniques are learned and correctly used.

In achieving better value, there are two separate opportunity areas:

1. The identification of costs as unnecessary
2. The decision making which will eliminate the identified unnecessary cost

The techniques in this text are specific to area 1, the identification. They are applicable in the predesign stage, the design-concept stage, the design stage, the procurement stage, and the manufacturing stage, as well as in later cost-improvement stages.

Success in marketing a product is, to an important extent, dependent upon its degree of (1) performance equality or leadership and (2) value equality or leadership when compared at any time with its competition.

Industry generally has rather well developed and successful techniques and procedures through which improvements in performance are planned, researched, developed, and incorporated into the product.

In contrast, additions to value, i.e., identifying and eliminating unnecessary cost, proceed on a "do as well as we can" and "when we must" basis.

The objective of the concepts and techniques of value analysis is to make possible a degree of effectiveness in identifying and removing unnecessary cost which approaches the effectiveness of identifying performance improvements for the product and incorporating them into it.

The terms value analysis and value engineering are used synonymously.

Lawrence D. Miles

Contents

CHAPTER 1 *Value Analysis—Philosophies, Concepts, Basic Steps, Approach*

1-1. *What Is Value Analysis?*

Value analysis is a philosophy implemented by the use of a specific set of techniques, a body of knowledge, and a group of learned skills. It is an organized creative approach which has for its purpose the efficient identification of unnecessary cost, i.e., cost which provides neither quality nor use nor life nor appearance nor customer features.

Value analysis results in the orderly utilization of alternative materials, newer processes, and abilities of specialized suppliers. It focuses engineering, manufacturing, and purchasing attention on one objective—equivalent performance for lower cost. Having this focus, it provides step-by-step procedures for accomplishing its objective efficiently and with assurance.

Value analysis serves all branches of an enterprise: engineering, manufacturing, procurement, marketing, management. It results in the development of applicable specific information from the practically limitless stores of industrial technical information and skill for use in providing better value, i.e., lower costs, for appropriate products and services.

Value analysis is *not* a substitute for conventional cost-reduction work methods. Rather, it is a potent and completely different procedure for accomplishing far greater results. It improves the effectiveness of work that has been conventionally performed over the years, as it fills in blind spots. Quite commonly, 15 to 25 per cent, and very often much more, of manufacturing costs can be removed by effective application of the teachings of value analysis.

EXAMPLE: A typical simple example of the latter statement is the case of an electrical control. It worked very well indeed, but its cost was too high. Sales had dropped off. The makers brought the control in for value analysis with a statement which said, "We give you this with tongue in

1

cheek; we don't think that another penny can be taken out of the cost, but we're desperate."

In applying the value analysis approach to the device, one of the first parts to come up for review was a wire clip which held the cover on. It was made of phosphor bronze and cost $7,000 a year. The value specialist asked, "What is the function? How does phosphor bronze contribute to that function? It is a material that is commonly used when a part has to flex millions of times. But this clip is flexed only when the cover is removed for servicing—an average of six times in the life of the product." By changing to spring brass, the same job could be done for $3,000 a year, that is, for less than half.

FIG. 1-1. Temperature control.

The cover itself cost 4 cents, an expenditure of $40,000 a year. Its function was to keep extraneous material out of the small mechanism. The entire control was mounted inside another enclosure. Using a plain piece of laminated plastic reduced the cost from 4 cents to 1.5 cents each, and out went $25,000. Many similar findings were made as the analysis of the complete device proceeded.

The new approach, applied after conventional cost-reduction treatment, eliminated obvious, but hidden, amounts of unnecessary costs. No essential function was impaired, no "cheapening" was effected. The product was modified to represent better value.

No Reduction in Quality, Safety, Features, Attractiveness. Inherent in the philosophy of value analysis is full retention for the customer of the usefulness and esteem features of the product. Identifying and removing unnecessary cost, and thus improving value, must be done without reducing in the slightest degree quality, safety, life, reliability, dependability, and the features and attractiveness that the customer wants. Too often in the past, an endeavor to remove cost without the use of professional tools for accomplishing the project has resulted in a lowering of quality. Therefore, it must be clearly understood from the start that accomplishing better value does not mean reducing quality to a point where it is lower but may just get by. No reduction whatever in needed quality is tolerated in the professional grade of value work.

Experience shows that quality is frequently increased as the result of developing alternatives for the accomplishment of the use and esteem functions.

1-2. *What Is Value?*

Value means a great many things to a great many people because the term *value* is used in a variety of ways. Also, it is often confused with cost and with price.

In most cases, value to the producer means something different from value to the user. Furthermore, the same item may have differing value to the customer depending upon the time, the place, and the use.

Value, then, is a broad term. It can, however, be divided into various kinds, each of which is describable. It is often divided into four kinds, which are here listed. Useful to us in value studies are the first two.

Use value: The properties and qualities which accomplish a use, work, or service

Esteem value: The properties, features, or attractiveness which cause us to want to own it

Cost value: The sum of labor, material, and various other costs required to produce it

Exchange value: Its properties or qualities which enable us to exchange it for something else we want

Value is not inherent but is determined by a number of things. To be useful in identifying and eliminating unnecessary cost, value becomes a measure of the appropriateness of the costs involved. Value is stated as *the minimum dollars which must be expended in purchasing or man- ufacturing a product to create the appropriate use and esteem factors.*

Value of a product may be considered the appropriate cost to accomplish the use and to provide the proper esteem. We are concerned with use value as *the lowest cost of providing for the reliable performance of a function* and with esteem value as *the lowest cost of providing the ap- pearance, attractiveness, and features which the customer wants.*

Maximum Value. Maximum value is probably never achieved. The degree of value in any product depends on the effectiveness with which every usable idea, process, material, and approach to the problem have been identified, studied, and utilized. The purpose of the special techniques and special knowledge of value analysis is to bring, with less expenditure of time and cost, more of the better value combinations into focus.

Normal Degree of Value. In normal usage, value is considered good if the product contains somewhat better combinations of ideas, processes, materials, and functions, costwise, than competition; it is considered bad if, because the opposite is true, lost sales volume results. It is readily seen that this method of determining the degree of value comes too late and has serious limitations.

Selected typical products have been subjected to a concentrated and overnormal amount of attention in order to determine more nearly the amount of unnecessary cost they contain when compared, not with competition, but with the optimum combination of available ideas, processes, materials, and design concepts. Such studies have shown that unnecessary cost which can be so identified varies between 25 and 75 per cent of the product cost.

The reader must recognize that these unnecessary costs are not hanging like pears from a pear tree for those who wish to pluck, but rather that identification and removal are the reward for a well-organized effort utilizing effective value-oriented tools and involve appropriate use of money and competence.

1-3. *Importance of Value*

In a free enterprise system, with competition at full play, success in the business world over the long term hinges on continually offering the customer the best value for the price asked. Competition, in other words, determines in what direction one must go in setting the value content in order for a product or a service to be competitive with that which is offered by others to supply the same wants or needs.

This best value is determined by two considerations: performance and cost.

Over the years, it has been generally recognized that an acceptable product must serve the customer's needs and wishes to the degree that he expects; that is to say, the product must have *performance* capability. In recent years, it has also come into clearer focus that the cost of producing must be such that the customer can buy the product at competitive prices. This introduces the *value* concept.

Cycles in the History of a Product. In general, the production of a product involves three cycles. First is the *research and development stage* in which knowledge is extended toward innovation to create new func-

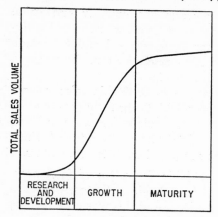

FIG. 1-2. Product maturity cycle.

FIG. 1-3. Optimum change in use of performance engineering and value engineering skills as product matures.

tions, to provide additional functions, and to accomplish existing functions more reliably or efficiently. This is the stage in which ways and means are sought to fill new needs, to execute new functions, and to improve functions already being performed in one way or another. The resultant products are awaited with anticipation, and if successful, they are sold in sufficient numbers to support continued performance studies.

Then comes the second cycle, the *growth stage*. The product, having proved that it fills a need, gains in customer demand, and competition enters the field. In this stage, it becomes evident that the product must be produced at lower costs in order to sell it competitively in sufficient quantities.

The third cycle, the *maturity stage*, is reached when the product has matured fully. Research and development are no longer making large contributions to the efficiency with which

FIG. 1-4. Effect of timing and degree of change from performance-oriented skills to value-oriented skills on sales volume of any one producer. Shaded area shows extent to which producer's sales are controlled by his decision in this matter.

functions are accomplished, to the life of the product, or to the addition of new functions. Thus the prime task of the manufacturer becomes one of tackling the value part of the job so well that product leadership will be maintained primarily by having performance equality and value leadership. This means that more dollars must be committed to identifying unnecessary costs and arranging for their removal and that more competence in the form of people and other resources must be assigned to work on the value part of product leadership.

Whether a business continues to increase in profitable sales volume or starts to decrease, then drops out of the field, is normally governed by the degree to which it recognizes this shift from performance to value emphasis at the right time and by the effectiveness with which it shifts its use of resources and competence, as compared with its competitors.

EXAMPLE: Kitchen waste is an unavoidable derivative of food preparation and consumption in the normal household. In the early days of civilized living, it was quite common to dispose of this waste by feeding it to pigs, by burying it in the ground, or by employing other simple methods. As the mode of living progressed toward town and city settlements, the problem was solved by organized provisions for garbage collection and removal. Less than half a century ago an awareness developed that there was a need for a better and more sanitary way of handling kitchen waste. Research and development was implemented to solve the problem, and the goal soon became one of reducing the waste, at the location at which it was produced, to a form in which it could be directly disposed of.

This effort, which included experimentation with chemicals, with combustion, etc., culminated in the process of grinding the waste into a pulp that could be disposed of in a sewerage system. Thus the research and development stage brought forth today's household garbage disposer.

The original product soon gained users' acceptance, and in the growth stage that followed, refinements were made and the cost was brought down to a level at which the demand was sufficient for profitable production.

In a relatively short space of time, the number of producers of garbage disposers rose from the original one to more than a dozen. The maturity stage was reached, and profitable production of the appliance hinged largely on eliminating unnecessary costs.

Value-oriented Work. It is seen then that the importance of *value work* —effort to provide better value—increases as the complete product cycle advances but that it always follows after the period in which the emphasis is on *performance work*—concentration to assure performance. New problems come into the picture because men have been hired, trained, and equipped with performance-oriented tools but the job has shifted to become value-oriented. A look at the list of all products which occupy human endeavor shows that there are large areas, such as the military, in which performance-oriented work is of the greatest vitality.

But, year by year, there is also an expanding list of matured products, and so value work has become of great importance for the successful operation of most businesses.

USE OF VALUE RESOURCES. Performance-oriented work is basically centered on using resources to accomplish new functions which are desired or needed by man. Value-oriented work is aimed at accomplishing these preestablished functions using less of the resources of materials and time. In reality, cost is a measure of the amount of resources expended. Value work, as a study of the use of resources to better advantage, helps to supply more needs of human beings per integer of resources. As such, it is a means of prolonging the prosperity of people by utilizing resources more efficiently.

In performance-oriented work, test results may cause abrupt changes in the attack in that unexpected directions totally contrary to the initial "feelings" of the researcher or designer may be indicated. In value-oriented work, on the other hand, the absence of test results allows feelings to continue to be a large factor in choosing the engineering and manufacturing alternatives which will establish the value level of the product.

VALUE WORK EXPANDS MARKETS AND JOBS. In the case of many products, the usage, and hence the volume in demand, increases in direct proportion to the lowering of cost; to say it another way, as customers find that they can exchange less of their effort for a particular product, larger and larger numbers will find it practical to do so. For instance, if the minimum cost for the rather complicated device known as the television set were around $1,000, the market would be much more limited than it is. At its present lower cost, more pleasure is provided for more people, and employment opportunities are multiplied.

The over-all results of the economic endeavor are promoted by the increase in volume that follows with lower cost. Entire industries have been built in which very much lower costs have been successively established while satisfactory performance has been retained. Take, for example, the electric clocks which today appear in many rooms of the home rather than in one room, as in former years, or the small electric motors which are now found in dozens of products for the home but which, a few years back, were rarities in private surroundings. These developments certainly could not have occurred on the basis of improvement in performance alone. The value has been improved, i.e., unnecessary costs have been eliminated, and the market has expanded, as have the jobs concerned with the production.

ELIMINATION OF HUMAN TOIL. In the area that includes the needs and services which people require and want for necessary daily tasks, much human toil must still be expended. Most of this work, however, can be accomplished by machines if only the limitation of their high cost can be eliminated. Effective value-oriented work in sufficient magnitude will bring the cost down, and equipment that eliminates tedious and difficult tasks will come into much greater use. A good example is the home laundry machine, which has been such a boon to millions.

ADEQUATE DEFENSE FOR LOWER COSTS. Adequate defense of a nation relies heavily on research and development to provide new functions more efficiently. This has been long recognized. But now it is becoming equally apparent that it also relies on effective and efficient value-oriented practices to identify and remove unnecessary costs so that adequate weapons will be available at less than bankrupting cost. An essential defense weapon eliminated by high cost lowers the country's military capacity, and the matter of reducing costs is one of national importance.

1-4. *Considerations for Improving Value*

As the twofold job of providing the performance the customer wants and of doing so at an appropriate cost makes progress through the product cycle from the research and development stage into the maturity stage, a number of factors are responsible for continued inclusion of unnecessary cost in the product. Some of these will be evident in the discussion which follows.

Who Contributes Performance and Value? Each individual involved in bringing forth a product contributes toward attaining the performance needed, and each must also, in his own area, contribute to the value of the product.

Beginning with the sales department, a representative contacts the customer and, by some means, learns what the customer wishes to buy and is willing to pay to get it. By stepping beyond the act of merely booking orders and giving the customer the benefit of his knowledge and experience, the sales representative can do a great deal toward attaining suitable performance combined with attractive value.

The design engineer next provides geometry and detail for the device. This establishes means for attaining the predetermined use and esteem values. In this endeavor, more than one useful solution commonly emerges before final selection. Decision making by the designer, therefore, requires much evaluation to arrive at the best combination of performance and value for the particular use.

Then, it becomes the task of the production engineer and the manufacturing expert to provide the tooling and facilities that will be most efficient for making the product. This takes an exhaustive review of both in-plant and outside equipment and practices to make a selection that will ensure the appropriate value content of the product. Usually this stage merges considerably with the previous stage so that the intended means of manufacture will be factored into design-detail decisions.

Finally, the management of the shop that actually builds the product must give the fullest consideration to all the elements that enter into the cost of production. This includes the very substantial element of materials, in the acquisition of which the purchasing department usually has an opportunity to make a significant contribution toward attaining a better value status.

The decisions of each of these various participants determine the degree to which the customer will be provided with the desired use and esteem values at the lowest cost. It will be seen that unnecessary cost is identified only to the degree that these participants secure the best ideas, the best information, and the best utilization of value possibilities—each in his own area.

Incorporation of Full Information at Each Stage. In each of the stages of the product cycle, it is readily discernible that, somewhere in the market, information exists which will aid in reliably accomplishing the function at the lowest cost. Such information is pertinent to the decisions being made and, if passed up, cannot be appropriately factored into the decision. It follows that extra cost enters in at each stage in which there is a lack of consideration of any applicable information.

Effect of Time Shortage. It seems the way of life that time is short. This is particularly true in the cycle of a product. Until a particular need appears, at least in an undeveloped form, people in the sales area have no way of sensing their customers' requirements. Then when a need arises, there is a rush to provide a proposal to satisfy the need and to do so effectively as quickly as possible, before competition has a chance to gain a hold on it. As the product then moves into the design-engineering area, deadlines must often be met which definitely do not permit complete searching, testing, and securing and utilizing information which would result in accomplishing customer use at the lowest cost. The same situation exists in purchasing, in manufacturing, and in all other areas of the business. Thus a shortage of time, by the very nature of the problem, is the cause of inclusion of unnecessary costs.

Lack of Measurement in Value Work. As emphasized previously, decision making in performance-oriented work can be based on tests and measurements. In contrast, value-oriented work at each stage of the product design and manufacturing cycle cannot be accurately measured. Therefore, after what the individual considers a reasonable effort using the value tools and the time and information he has, decisions are made by judgment with respect to the manufacturing and engineering alternatives. Again it is seen that, if any of these decisions bring about poor performance, tests will show it. If, on the other hand, they bring poor value, there is no immediate way of making that evident. Consequently, performance-oriented work is normally more efficiently and effectively accomplished than value-oriented work.

Case Study

DEALING WITH TIME AND VALUE

A control, consisting of a cube of 8 inches of electrical and mechanical equipment actuated by some knobs and operating levers, was in the process of manufacture on an order for 400. Time schedules were so short that, although the engineers and others attempted to provide as much value as they could take in stride during the stages of design, tooling, and buying of materials, nothing could be allowed to interrupt or delay production. The question was raised, "Should value analysis techniques be applied to this job now that it is under way?"

One of the engineers involved said, "Let's try the value analysis techniques on it and see what they provide." Another said, "This is a 'dead horse.' We may never make another one. Let's not waste time on it." Still another said, "This is like a post-mortem. But let's not forget that the purpose of the post-mortem which is performed on the dead is to gain information which will provide better life to the living." This viewpoint prevailed, and a value engineer was assigned to work with the design engineers in making a value audit.

The various assemblies, subassemblies, and parts were studied to determine precisely the function they contributed to the over-all product and to develop alternatives which would accomplish the functions at better costs. The results of the post-mortem were startling. The function of the assembly and of part after part could be provided for one-fifth to one-tenth of actual costs. Some of the *before* and *after* costs for the various assemblies and parts were:

Before	After
$4.54	$0.46
0.42	0.07
2.14	0.57
0.53	0.02
1.85	0.28

The value alternatives suggested are those provided by the engineer who studied the job. He believed that they would perform exactly the same tasks with the same reliability. In most cases, where parts were involved, the costs applied to practically identical parts. In others, it was a matter of using functional components which were found to be available rather than using custom-built items. For instance:

A small metal knob costing $2.25 operated a miniature potentiometer. In standard catalogues, plastic and metal knobs were found which performed the total function slightly better for 25 cents each.

A rather large assembly supporting an emergency control lever cost $20.33. Its functions were provided for $8.12.

This was one method of dealing with time and value. There are other methods, some before-the-fact, which are often applicable.

Interestingly enough, a subsequent order was received for this type of control. Since it was a military product, it was quite naturally modified in some respects. Just the same, the engineers were able to take the report on the post-mortem study page for page and to include in the new design the benefits of thirty of the forty-five specific value alternatives suggested. Of course, one considerable gain was accomplished in the new design because it could be "built in" prior to original tooling. *Post-mortems can be direction indicators*.

Human Factors. Lack of sufficient communication, misunderstandings, and normal frictions between human beings become increasingly responsible for unnecessary costs in the more complicated products and systems. With no intent to underrate the good work of average people, it must be recognized that the average job is accomplished by an average man and therefore will, in general, be of average grade. The average man can accomplish his job more effectively if he is supplied with special tools which are designed for him and not for the genius. It is, therefore, basic to the philosophy of value analysis that vastly improved tools should be provided which encompass much additional potential for the average man.

Impact of New Processes, Products, and Materials. The constant and accelerating flow of new ideas, new processes, new products, and new materials can, when properly applied, aid in establishing the desired use and esteem values at a lower cost. This leads to the conclusion that when a product is designed and tooled and is on the market, it is already advancing toward becoming obsolete, valuewise. Better tools for value-oriented work will help to incorporate more of such new information sooner and thus minimize the value-obsolescence problem.

1-5. *Concepts of Value Analysis*

Customer use values and customer esteem values translate themselves into functions as far as the designer is concerned. The functions of the product which cause it to perform its use and to provide the esteem values wanted by customers can be clearly identified and distinctly divided into the two categories.

Identification Knowledge. A universe of knowledge and a system of techniques oriented toward creatively searching and effectively identifying value alternatives can then be established.

Classes of Functions. The use values require functions that cause the product to perform, while the esteem values require functions that cause the product to sell. Both are of recognized importance and both enter into value analysis. Conversely, no cost should be included in the product without adding a function either causing it to perform or causing it to sell. Where function consists of two parts—that which causes the product to perform and that which causes it to sell—the value in dollars becomes the lowest-cost combination of design, materials, and processes which will reliably accomplish these functions.

Value Established by Comparison. Value in dollars can then be established by comparison, both for the composite of all functions and for each individual function.

Objective. The one objective that we are concerned with in value analysis is providing equivalent performance at lower cost. Cost is related to the function, service, or operation purchased by that cost.

Case Study

FUNCTION: RADIATION SHIELDING

A new laboratory under installation was to contain very powerful X-ray equipment for deeply searching large forgings and castings for hidden defects. Providing for the protection of adjacent areas from radiation was required. For this, the drawings included a concrete wall, 7 feet thick and 14 feet high, in the shape of a horseshoe outside of the building. The best bid on this wall was approximately $50,000. The contract was taken to the works manager for his initialing. Recognizing his responsibility for the area, he told the manager of the laboratory that he would approve the contract. However, he said, "If you decide to move the laboratory, you will take this concrete away with you and get it out of our way." This was an unexpected condition to which the laboratory manager was unprepared to subscribe. He called in a construction supervisor and asked him what he could do to work out the problem. The construction engineer, who had not worked with problems of radiation, was astonished to see in the plans an enormous amount of concrete, seemingly idle and carrying no load. Inquiring into the function of the concrete, he was advised that it was to stop radiation.

Having studied value analysis function-based techniques, he thought in terms of "what else would stop radiation." He asked whether dirt would stop it and was advised that it would if it was provided in sufficient quantity, which was found to be a mound 14 feet high and 14 feet thick. Bids on it showed that it could be installed for $5,000; of course, the works manager immediately approved. The use, at the proper time, of the function-based value analysis techniques resulted in a superior product, namely, a grassed-over earth mound, at one-tenth of the cost of a solid concrete wall. *It pays to inquire into "what else will do."*

Timing for Value Work. Functions can be clearly identified nearly as well before actual design of the product as after design. Alternatives can be nearly as creatively developed from blueprints as from actual models. Therefore, much value work can be done before original design and before purchase of original tooling.

This statement should not in the slightest degree detract from the importance of realizing that after design and after various product parts and assemblies have been proved by actual usage it will be profitable to use the value analysis approach again. Periodically during product life, important cost elements should be identified with the functions which they perform, and further engineering and manufacturing alternatives should be developed with the aid of value analysis knowledge and techniques. This will make possible, in many instances, changes that will eliminate large amounts of unnecessary cost which, for various reasons, eluded the first round of value decision making.

Basis of Determining Value Content. Understanding the desired function of a product or item or the expected performance of a service is the basis for determining value content. Such understanding is acquired from detailed studies of the ultimate aim of a design project. When the design is complicated, the appraiser may need to seek the assistance of others to arrive at a firm understanding of the function or aim. In these cases, good human relations is a vital link in the chain that leads from the aim through the techniques of analyzing and weighing to the final evaluation. It follows that power to interpret, ability to analyze, and capacity to devise techniques combine with talent for cultivating good human relations to constitute principal attitudes needed in value analysis work.

Drawing on Available Competence. Hand in hand with the objective of attaining equivalent performance at lower cost goes recognition of the need and importance of drawing on the knowledge of others to reach the goal. Throughout the country, as in the rest of the world, practically limitless funds of specialized knowledge in every field exist. Value analysis implies that maximum use be made of such knowledge. The experts of specialist organizations stand ready, and should be allowed an opportunity, to apply their skills and materials to obtain the desired function economically and reliably. Their suggestions should be sought and provided with a dollar sign for evaluation. In that way, value analysis becomes an engineering and manufacturing tool which reaches into the boundless supply of technical information and provides opportunities for suppliers of functional materials and functional products to suggest their application for specific job requirements.

1-6. *Basic Steps of Value Analysis*

In the process of obtaining lower-cost engineering and manufacturing solutions and alternatives, three basic steps are used:

1. Identify the function.
2. Evaluate the function by comparison.
3. Cause value alternatives to be developed.

To help the reader recognize that these basic steps serve as the first tools for effective value analysis, a further discussion of them follows.

Step 1: Identify the Function. Any useful product or service has a prime function. That function can usually be described by a two-word definition such as, provide light, pump water, indicate time, exclude dust, support handle.

In addition, there may be secondary functions involved. A light source may be required to resist shock, a pump for domestic use to operate at a low noise level, a clock or watch to provide attractiveness, an umbrella to be useful as a cane, a dust enclosure to allow access to interiors, and a handle support to provide for locking.

We may take, as another example, an electric refrigerator, which has the prime function of preserving food by electrical means. The added features of revolving shelves, a butter conditioner, storage space in the door, etc., are secondary functions.

Once the functions have been determined and evaluated in terms of primary and secondary nature, we can proceed to examine the cost of each with the aim of determining its appropriateness or of finding some other, lower-cost way of accomplishing that particular function. A basic ground rule in this connection is that we must accept the assumption that the device or part is in principle what is wanted to provide the function. Otherwise, we may go too far afield. Turning back to the refrigerator, we must assume that an electric refrigerator is what is wanted and not an icebox or some other means of preserving food.

In this functional approach, it will often prove helpful to also separate the parts and their costs into functional areas. If we take a device like a large electric switch, for instance, we can break it down into functions:

Electrical parts	Support
Mechanical parts	Finish
Case	Appearance
Cover	

From this breakdown, a definite picture is derived of the cost of the

Electrical function	Enclosing
Mechanical function	Assembly

These cost figures will indicate what areas hold the best promise for profitable value analysis.

The step of identifying the function is the value analyst's initial tool. In some cases, just the clear use of this step prompts ideas and information which result in better value. For example, a round bronze casting

3 inches in diameter and ¼ inch thick, with a center-drilled and splined hole, was found to cost $16. What was its function? It fitted on a valve stem, and its function was to facilitate opening and closing a valve by hand. In other words, $16 was expended on providing a handle to open and close a valve. Nearly everyone has seen valves with suitable handles and realizes that whole valves can be bought for $2 or $3, so one is motivated at once to "do something about it," namely, to look to valve experts for a better answer. By just this step, a similar valve handle of equal effectiveness, readily available, was produced for a cost of 60 cents.

Step 2: Evaluate the Function by Comparison. Value being a relative rather than an absolute measure, the comparison approach must be used in evaluating functions. The basic question, "Is the function accomplished reliably at the best cost?" can be answered only by comparison.

The larger and more complicated the object undergoing analysis, the greater the number of comparisons necessary to make the analysis sufficiently comprehensive to establish the best value for each included function. This means analyzing a series of basic functions, each discovered by breaking the assembly down into its subunits, components, and parts. In this way the problem becomes, perhaps one of comparing the use of one material with that of another, the style of one part with that of an equivalent, the application of one process of manufacture with that of another, and so on. It may be a matter of comparing metal with plastics, screw-machined parts with lathe-machined equivalents, or stamping with spinning to determine how the needed function can be obtained reliably at the lowest cost.

It can be said almost without fear of contradiction that, if there is no comparison, there is no evaluation. All evaluation results from comparison of some kind: in some instances, comparison with standards; in other instances, comparison with similar items; and in still others, comparison with partially similar items. If, in the pursuit of better value, functions have not been identified and these functions have not been evaluated by comparison, then the process has not been value analysis but merely cost analysis.

This vitally important step, "evaluate the function by comparison," is perhaps best recognized by looking at a few illustrative examples.

EXAMPLE 1: *Where use value is of prime importance*

What is the value in dollars of a nail? We find, by comparison, the answers to such questions as: What precisely are the functions with respect to use, convenience, life, etc., which are needed from the nail? Then, what alternative ways are there of accomplishing all those functions with the same reliability? And finally, what is the cost by these alternative methods? The value of the nail cannot exceed the cost of the least expensive alternative method of accomplishing all its functions with equal reliability, as established by comparison.

What is the value of a brass screw? First, all functions of use, of appearance, of convenience, of endurance, etc., must be clearly established. Next, other combinations of materials, processes, and products which will reliably accomplish the total purpose are compared. When the costs of these alternatives have been developed, the cost of the least expensive alternative that will reliably accomplish the total function establishes the maximum value of the screw. And, indeed, the screw must be available for that cost, or informed consumers will buy other products and discontinue the use of the screw.

What is the value of an electric switch? Again, with the total functions of the electric switch in clear view, a search should be made for other means of reliably interrupting a circuit under the same conditions. Some of these alternatives may be more costly and some less costly. If some less costly are found, then the makers of the switch may well expect marketing problems because the shortcoming of their switch is established by comparison.

EXAMPLE 2: *Where esteem value is of prime importance*

Total dollar values are normally established by comparisons which include both the use factors and the esteem factors in function. In most products for industrial applications—from the nail up—the use function holds primary importance. A great variety of other products, of which the electric clock is one, must, besides accomplishing their use functions reliably, have appearance, attractiveness, and perhaps other interest factors which cause customers to buy them; these we may group broadly under the term *esteem*. Consider here an item such as a suit of clothes. The use value derives essentially from the functions providing warmth and comfort, while the esteem values consist substantially of the functions yielding appearance, attractiveness, and conformity to social custom. Also, these values can be established by comparison. A thorough search would probably identify means for securing the warmth and comfort functions of a $50 suit of clothes for $10 or $15. This can be developed by comparing all alternative means of securing the same warmth and comfort. To then arrive at the total value of $50 for the suit, we must add the $35 or $40 which represents esteem value. Here too we are concerned with comparison. If there are better ways of providing at lower cost all of the attractiveness, appearance, conformity to custom, etc., which are contained in the suit, then the suit does not represent good value at $50; only lack of knowledge on the part of the customer causes him to buy it. An informed user will change to the alternative choice which has been developed by comparison.

Evaluation, then, is seen to be a result of the comparison involved.

It will later be seen that the quality of the comparison is governed by the techniques used, the applicability of the particular techniques, the effectiveness with which they are used, and the fund of knowledge which is applied in conjunction with them.

Step 3: Cause Value Alternatives to Be Developed. (For the development of effective value alternatives, the thirteen value analysis techniques described in Chapter 3 should be followed.)

Realistic situations must be faced, objections overcome, and effective engineering, manufacturing, and other alternatives developed.

"But there is no other way to do it" is a common statement made, and believed valid, by responsible decision-making people in many areas. Although stated with finality and emphasis, what is really being said is, "I don't know of any other way to do it, and I don't believe there is another, equally effective way." Anyone engaging in value work must recognize that it is his responsibility and opportunity to begin at this point and, without unduly or unnecessarily ruffling human feelings, bring forth substantiating facts. This implies the use of techniques which will penetrate the subject further, in the direction of securing the desired functions for lower cost, and which will produce, in tangible form, information that may alter these "feelings" and "beliefs" which govern decisions.

In the search for, and selection of, alternatives, attention must be constantly focused on function and not merely on a material, part, or device as such. Unless this is done, it is easy to fall into the trap of considering an alternative that may impair the designed-in function and thus fail to meet the fundamental requirement of value analysis that the needed function must be accomplished reliably at the lowest cost.

Case Study

CONDUCT ELECTRIC CURRENT IN STEEL?

In a control device it was noted that costly nonferrous materials were used for certain parts which could be very economically made from ferrous materials. In a function evaluation, it was discovered that there were, in general, two functions involved: the mechanical function plus the function of conducting electric current. The amount of current was small, and the engineer applying value analysis techniques to evaluate functions collected information to determine if there was any basic reason why steel could not be used for these parts. He was told, "It is poor practice to conduct electric current through steel. We never do it. For current conduction we use nonferrous metals." He questioned this "design" premise on the basis of the numerous common applications in which electric current is conducted through steel, for example, in the track rails of an electric railway system. On the basis of the comparative conductivity of the nonferrous materials and of the steel which would provide the lower-cost alternative, he made specific suggestions. In finishing this work, he noted that steel was used for one important current-conducting member, and naturally he inquired, "Why, since you have advised me that you believe it is not good practice to conduct electric current in steel?" He was told that in the particular application in which steel was used the temperature was so high that a nonferrous metal would not hold its temper and shape, and it was necessary to use steel in order to properly accomplish the function at all.

Clearly focused, what the statement meant was, "We are using copper-based materials for the easy conducting jobs, but where such materials will not perform, we use steel." The suggested change to conduction of the current through steel was made, and the product was greatly simplified. Besides, costs were reduced, and because of the new and greater simplicity, reliability was increased. *Habits often lead astray.*

1-7. *Value Analysis Approach*

The value analysis approach requires, first of all, that valid and complete answers be developed for the following five questions:

1. What is the item?
2. What does it cost?
3. What does it do?
4. What else would do the job?
5. What would that alternative cost?

These basic questions serve the end of uncovering needed pertinent facts. With the establishment of answers to them, the foundation is laid for developing objective data for presentation to the decision makers. Hence the importance of understanding and effectively using these questions cannot be overemphasized.

What is the item? This question is usually quite readily determined from objective data.

What does it cost? Here the answer is often obtainable from effective and meaningful cost data, but sometimes such costs are difficult to obtain. This will be further developed in technique 2 of the thirteen value analysis techniques presented in Chapter 3.

What does it do? For the moment, all else except precisely the question, "What does it do?" must be disregarded. This means that we put aside such questions as:

What machines does the factory have?
What processes does the factory customarily use?
What special skills do the factory people have?
What special skills are available in the drafting and planning organizations?

What equipment must be liquidated?

What buildings must work be provided for?

What people in what areas must be kept busy?

Admittedly, all these additional questions embrace considerations that will enter into decision making, but at this stage of value analysis, the establishment of sound criteria for decision making is handicapped if any of these questions are allowed to interfere with the effective generation of objective data such as, "It conducts current," "It excludes dust," "It supports the operator," "It separates dials," "It mounts the motor," "It mounts the control."

What else would do the job? This is not a superficial question; it is a penetrating one. The comprehensiveness of the answer to that simple question governs, to a high degree, the effectiveness and the grade of value work being done. No matter how skilled the searcher and no matter how diligent and creative his search, there will always remain alternatives which he did not bring into focus, many of which would have accomplished the total performance reliably at very much lower cost. To ensure good value content, many of the special techniques and much of the special knowledge of value analysis must be used in getting substantial answers to this question. The approach here is to search intensively for alternatives by:

Studying handbooks

Perusing trade literature

Telephoning people who might have pertinent information

Writing to specialists and to companies who might know of effective alternatives

Focusing intense creativity sharply on the precise task to be accomplished

Refining the results of these creative sessions and searching further for additional information

Unless this phase of the work is effectively and penetratingly done, it cannot be hoped that the product will have more than an average degree of value.

What would that alternative cost? Handbooks are full of information on the properties of various products and materials and suggested uses for them. Notably absent from most of these is cost. This is quite understandable. Costs vary from time to time while the properties of materials and their functions are relatively stable. Furthermore, as our civilization has developed, it has been a basic necessity to find materials which, within the appropriate size and weight range, accomplished the necessary functions. Therefore, the handbooks contain the information needed for these pursuits. When value is the objective, it becomes vital to have

440

meaningful costs for decision making. Hence the question of the cost of alternatives must be effectively and objectively answered.

Meaningful costs may be obtained from a variety of sources or from a combination of sources:

The cost department
Cost analyses
Catalogues
Suppliers of products or materials
Special cost studies

But since, in many instances of good value work, materials, products, and processes will be utilized in different ways, really meaningful costs often must be worked up for the job. This does not mean that it is necessary to have perfection in cost data at this stage in the cycle. Costs within a range of plus or minus 5 per cent will usually be sufficient, and often, costs within a range of plus or minus 10 per cent will help to determine whether the particular value alternatives are of sufficient interest to warrant more exact cost determination and further study.

At the risk of appearing too emphatic about this important point, the value specialist must not be too concerned about the comment, "Beware of the situation in which precise costs are not provided." His concern must rather center on statements such as, "Tools are too costly; it is not even worthwhile to provide an estimate on them" or "The quantities are so small that we know the process will not be practicable; therefore we will not provide an estimate" or "We have studied this a number of times and always found it impracticable; it is therefore not worthwhile to prepare an estimate on it now." Such beliefs and habits of the past often lock in large amounts of unsuspected and unnecessary costs.

Case Study

Value Analysis Techniques Certainly Cannot Improve the Value of 10,000 Bolts!

This was the challenge put forth by a manager whose department used ten thousand ½-inch steel bolts, 12 inches long, with a square head on one end and a square nut on the other, produced by totally standard processes. It is typical of the normal action by the normal person when confronted with a different approach to any situation with which he already has a certain measure of experience. The tendency is to examine what is wrong with it. Experience has taught us not to accept different solutions without careful examination unless we are prepared to be embarrassed by the unsuspected shortcomings of the proposed change.

The challenge was an interesting one for the application of the value analysis approach, which developed the following:

The bolts were used for making cable reels. The ends of the cable reels were wood disks, 3 feet in diameter. Several of these bolts, with washers under the heads and under the nuts, were used on each cable reel.

One of the best suppliers of this type of material was approached and given an appropriate understanding of value analysis. He was advised of the use and function of these bolts, and he, in turn, expressed the feeling that there were benefits to be gained. He was anxious to develop them in detail for this particular bolt. He then provided two interesting suggestions.

First, since one end of the bolt was the same as the other in use (both going through similar ends of a wood spool), an alternative was a threaded stud with two nuts rather than a bolt with one nut. The supplier advised that such studs could be provided with a short thread on one end and with the nut already chased on to the end of this thread, so that from the user's viewpoint, it would be very much the same as starting with a bolt. He stated that the cost would be approximately 15 per cent less.

As a second alternative, he could readjust the machine slightly to provide a substantial flash of metal under the head which would perform the washer function. Obviously, the flash would not be as neatly round as a punched washer, but it could be provided with appropriate area and thickness so that the complete purpose of the washer for this function could be well served. He stated that, if this alternative was used, the necessary adjustment of the machine for the relatively short run of 10,000 bolts would add a little cost which would be offset by the elimination of the normal trimming operation, and they would be able to sell the bolts for the same price as the standard product. The benefit to the user, then, would be in the elimination of the cost of the washer on one end as well as in the complete elimination of the bolt and washer assembly work.

Either alternative would have been good, but in this particular case, the first alternative was immediately chosen because there was need for short delivery on the particular order and the suppliers' upsetters, which would coin the head, had a heavy future schedule. The result was that the supplier was able to provide the needed threaded studs with the nut on one end almost instantly and at a 15 per cent reduction as compared with the cost of the normal bolt.

The value analysis approach had proved its profitability.

The Planned Approach. Value analysis presupposes the use of a planned approach for intensive and effective utilization of every applicable technique to overcome "stoppers." This requires the development of sufficient skill in the application of enough techniques to bring into clear view a liberal number of value alternatives.

The soundness of this statement may be illustrated by a look at the following case involving a strip hinge.

What is the item? A metal strip hinge about 8 inches long has holes in the flattened portion for fastening it on a door and has one edge rolled so that a hinge pin can be inserted. It is made by stamping and forming, by a manufacturer who has proved his reliability in the field of hardware, in quantities of 500,000 per year.

What does it do? The item mounts a door on an appliance; the requirements are that it must be rugged and reliable, must be made uniformly enough to permit ready and reliable assembly, and must come from proven source. Lack of the hinge would stop the entire appliance

FIG. 1-5. Hinge.

production line with resulting work delays for thousands of people and large amounts of unexpected cost for the manufacturer.

What else would do the job?

1. Use other manufacturers' hinges. This solution was thought to be not too promising because purchasing had already secured quotations from others and had made a selection of the lowest-cost reliable supplier. His facilities and his ability to meet schedules had been examined. He had proven himself. To study the value of this item again was judged by many to be ill-advised.

2. Make it of a different material—plastics, for example. Great resistance existed against even an investigation of this approach because, during the developing technology in the plastics field, many of the wrong plastics had been misapplied and none with appropriate properties for this hinge had come sharply into the view of the decision makers. There were fears of loss of customer confidence and of costly replacements. All of these and other considerations tended to prevent a thorough investigation of modern or available plastics which might accomplish the job.

3. Cast the hinge strip. Admittedly the quantities were satisfactory to make this or almost any other high-volume process practicable. Those experienced in the art of casting pointed out that the hinge strip comprised relatively thin sections over large areas; basically, this is not a design type in which castings excel. It was also pointed out that the need for the long hole would mean a very long and tricky coring or an equally difficult long-hole drilling operation for the hinge pin. Experience in the past caused casting specialists to believe that it would not be worthwhile to develop alternatives for these parts made as castings, and that was the stand they took when asked for specific information.

4. Make as a forging. Here the problem of drilling the long, relatively straight hole for the hinge pin discouraged effective work in providing alternatives in the form of forgings.

5. Weld a strip of metal edgewise to a piece of tubing. Here, hardware

and hinge engineers were concerned about the quality of the weld, the amount of flash, the deformation that would take place at welding, and the appearance of the finished job. Costs by usual welding processes would work out to be too high. To develop it and plan it through with special jigs and equipment would require time and study, and welding men believed that this was not the way to do the job anyhow. Therefore, it was very difficult, if not impossible, to get a useful estimate of the cost of tooling and of the finished parts. The estimate, to be useful, should be correct to within plus or minus 5 or 10 per cent.

6. Pass a strip of steel through continuous rolls and roll on the edge of the strip the section that would accommodate the hinge pin. Hardware engineers were concerned with the "springback," the variations in tolerance and dimension, and the burrs which would result as the continuous strip was cut into short segments. Then there was the possible necessity for additional operations to bore out, or ream out, the hinge-pin hole and to punch holes in the flat section. Maintenance of the roll equipment was another foreseen problem, as was the question of whether steel of the thickness required could be properly rolled. All these considerations tended to retard or prevent the preparation of any objective proposals showing the approximate costs of a strip made by this method.

Numerous other alternatives can be brought into view and they all must satisfy similar objections before one can proceed with a useful evaluation study.

It will be readily seen from the foregoing that the value specialist's problem is to:

Understand and apply each applicable step of an orderly planned approach.

Expect that, when requesting the development of new value alternatives, men who customarily make decisions in their own field and accordingly are not used to seeing the materials or processes used differently will feel that the approach is wrong. Hence they will be very hesitant about investing their important time in serious considerations for the preparation of objective value alternatives.

In value analysis, however, it is essential that this sort of normal negative not be allowed to stop the development of appropriate information. Numerous are the examples in which large improvements have been made promptly after overcoming this type of reluctance and actually securing meaningful value alternatives.

What would that alternative cost? In the case of the hinge, continuing steadfast and effective development of the suggested alternatives brought into focus information which proved the last alternative very practical. The result was a 10-cent reduction in the cost of each hinge, and thus the payoff was $50,000.

CHAPTER 2   *The Value Analysis Job Plan*

2-1. *Need for a Plan*

Efficient actions rest on suitable plans. In actions in which cause and effect have immediate obvious relationships, good plans are the rule. In other actions which are more involved so that effects from the various parts of the plan are not so directly tied to their specific causes, plans often become haphazard and less effective.

As a simple example, the repetitive operation of getting into the car and driving to work in the morning involves carrying out a plan:

Open the garage door.	Get out of the car.
Open the car door.	Close the garage door.
Get into the car.	Reenter the car.
Close the car door.	Close the car door.
Insert the ignition key.	Engage the gear.
Turn the key.	Look again for children.
Depress the starter.	Depress the accelerator.
Engage the gear.	Enter the street.
Look out for children.	Release the accelerator.
Depress the accelerator.	Depress the brake.
Release the accelerator.	Change gear.
Apply the brake.	Depress the accelerator.
Open the car door.	

All the steps of this plan are followed every time and, normally, very good results are secured. Omission of any one of the steps would hamper the accomplishment of the objective.

In contrast, effort which is oriented toward identifying and removing unnecessary costs has commonly been carried out without an effective over-all plan that includes all essential steps. Besides, when it has seemed inconvenient or difficult to accomplish a step in the plan, the step has been omitted. For the achievement of high-grade results in the objective of removing unnecessary cost, it is no more possible to omit one

24

of the planned steps than it is to omit one of the necessary steps in the handling of the car and still achieve good results.

The reader will learn that, in effect, the value analysis job plan requires that the specialist:

Recognize and face the problem with the functions to be accomplished clearly in mind.

Secure the needed information.

Do the essential creative work.

Analyze the results of the creative work for the best choices of action.

Establish effective programs pointed toward execution of these best courses of action.

Execute the established program without faltering.

Accumulate and point up the results for decision and action.

2-2. *Phases of the Job Plan*

Phase 1: Orientation. The stage is set by establishing:

What is to be accomplished?

What is it that the customer really needs or wants?

What are the desirable characteristics with respect to size, weight, appearance, durability, etc.?

Phase 2: Information. Here, the concern is to:

Secure all pertinent information: costs, quantities, vendors, drawings, specifications, planning cards, and manufacturing methods data, as well as actual samples of parts and assemblies where practicable.

In the case of new products, secure all information that is available: all design concepts, preliminary sketches and drawings, preliminary cost estimates, etc.

Examine the basic engineering with the engineer—ask questions, listen, and develop through him a thorough understanding of the experience to date with the product.

Examine the basic manufacturing with the manufacturing experts—ask questions, listen, and study manufacturing methods which have been adapted for the operation in question.

Determine the amount of effort which should reasonably be expended on each of the important elements of cost in view of the quantities, costs, and other pertinent facts.

Phase 3: Speculation. Having acquired understanding and information, we have laid the foundation for the application of various techniques to generate every possible solution to the over-all problems involved, to the parts of problems, and to the individual problems. To derive the fullest benefit from our creative power, we must now:

Encourage free use of the imagination.

Arrange suitable brainstorm sessions and their equivalent.

Record every suggestion no matter how remote its probabilities seem.

Select items that hold promise of providing the biggest yield, pick out the main objections, and apply speculative thinking to methods of removing the objections.

Systematically explore a variety of materials, machine processes, arrangements of parts, etc.

Consult others who may contribute.

Utilize the various parts of any and all techniques that will help in effectively accomplishing this phase.

Phase 4: Analysis

Estimate the dollar value of each exposed idea.

Develop all the ideas with emphasis placed according to where the value seems to be and where the probability of accomplishment appears greatest.

Investigate thoroughly those ideas with large dollar values to objectively determine their good and bad points, and then seek to eliminate, overcome, or minimize objections.

Select the ideas and approaches which analysis indicates have the most promise.

Phase 5: Program Planning

Break the job down into a progression of functional areas, i.e., a fastening job, an electrical-contact job, a support job, a dust-protection job, etc.

Apply the applicable value analysis techniques as described in Chapter 3.

Select the best specialists for consultation.

Select the best vendors for consultation.

Establish a program of investigation which will provide the latest information on, and the latest capabilities of, each of the approaches that show promise, such as the casting approach, the fabrication approach, the plastics approach, the wire-form approach, etc.

Supply all needed information to the specialists and to the vendors in order to stimulate new, applicable, and effective solutions.

Phase 6: Program Execution

Pursue constantly, regularly, thoroughly, and intensively each of the avenues set up in the program-planning phase until all the suggestions have been appraised and evaluated.

Periodically provide more information and encouragement to the specialists and the vendors, and help them to overcome problems they find in applying their materials or processes.

Work with specialists and vendors until they come up with alternatives or otherwise terminate their efforts.

Make certain that their suggestions are received by men who really want the different solution to work. Only then will the suggesters carry their developments to successful conclusions and overcome minor difficulties which commonly arise when different methods of accomplishing a function are first considered.

Stay with each promising suggestion and help to overcome difficulties until definite, tangible, and usable results are secured.

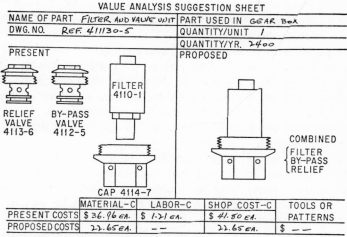

VALUE ANALYSIS SUGGESTION SHEET

NAME OF PART FILTER AND VALVE UNIT	PART USED IN GEAR BOX
DWG. NO. REF. 411130-5	QUANTITY/UNIT 1
	QUANTITY/YR. 2400

	MATERIAL–C	LABOR–C	SHOP COST–C	TOOLS OR
PRESENT COSTS	$ 36.96 EA.	$ 1.21 EA.	$ 41.80 EA.	PATTERNS
PROPOSED COSTS	22.65 EA.	– –	22.65 EA.	$ – –

ESTIMATED ANNUAL SAVINGS $ 45,960.00

COMMENTS
PROPOSED COST BASED ON QUOTATION FROM SPECIALTY VENDOR. THE ABOVE SAVINGS INCLUDE ONLY THE DIRECT COST OF THE PARTS ILLUSTRATED. FURTHER SUBSTANTIAL COST AND WEIGHT SAVINGS SHOULD RESULT FROM SIMPLIFICATION OF GEAR CASE CASTING AND MACHINING.

SUGGESTIONS–
COMBINE FUNCTIONS OF 2 VALVES AND 1 FILTER INTO ONE COMPONENT.

PROJECT GROUP: (F.WRIGHT) G.ROBINSON / A.TURNER / G. MARASKI
DATE: 6/16/60

FIG. 2-1. Value analysis suggestion sheet.

Phase 7: Status Summary and Conclusion. What will be most appropriate as a status summary depends upon the particular situation. If the design engineer or the manufacturing engineer has worked through the value analysis job plan on the product for which he will make decisions and take action, he can move immediately into decision making and action taking. If, on the other hand, as often happens, the work is done by an industrial engineer, a value engineer, a value consultant, or another person who does not personally make the decisions and take action, the method of documentation is of great importance. A suggestion sheet (see Figure 2-1) should then be issued. It should be concise, meaningful, and readable. It should be drawn in "manager's language" and should usually not be more than one page long to cover an important product or an important function. Engineering information and supporting data must not be a part of it but should be accumulated separately.

To repeat, the procedure should be to issue a concise, meaningful, and readable suggestion sheet covering each product, subgroup of parts, or individual part showing possibilities.

This suggestion sheet will present a simple before-and-after sketch of the part or assembly where practicable and pertinent information such as quantities used per year; material, labor, and shop cost; and suggested cost and tooling cost, if any. It should also have a statement describing the function of the part and suggestions in condensed form.

The suggestion sheet should be issued to the man designated by his manager to receive it.

The accumulation of supporting data, engineering information, and expositions from studies of pertinent manufacturing methods, manufacturing techniques, purchasing information, etc., should be directed to the proper person in the proper position so that he will be prepared when the time comes to take action.

When the suggestion sheet has been submitted and the supporting data have been directed to the proper points, the value analysis work on the project is completed. Prompt and unfettered work on the next job can begin.

2-3. *The Job Plan in Use*

The following example illustrates the application of the procedure described in the previous section.

FIG. 2-2. Electrical contact.

A SILVER CONTACT ASSEMBLY—TREATMENT UNDER THE
VALUE ANALYSIS JOB PLAN

1. *Orientation Phase.* The function of this assembly is that of operating an appliance on a 110-volt circuit. This requires making and breaking the

circuit several million times. It makes the circuit with a maximum starting current of 10 amperes and breaks the circuit with a maximum of 3 amperes and with known amounts of circuit inductance. It operates at ambient temperatures in a moderately dry and reasonably vibration-isolated environment.

2. *Information Phase.* The contact is found to be used in quantities of 1 million, and the amount of silver necessary to withstand the making and breaking of the circuit for the required number of cycles has been determined. The silver is purchased as a small part and is welded to the brass support. Drawings, specifications, vendors' names, costs, ordering quantities, and all allied information are available. The cost is $22 per thousand. As with other electrical contacts, the practice has been to provide the necessary amount of silver for the making and breaking surfaces and to support this silver on a copper base material which will readily conduct current and efficiently conduct away heat.

3. *Speculative Phase.* Every possible solution to the problem is now sought. By applying intensive creative imagination, in the neighborhood of, say, one hundred different approaches may be brought forth for consideration in the analytical phase. This is a likely result to be derived from a brainstorming session which might run along such lines as this:

QUESTION: How can the circuit with the established requirements of current, voltage, inductance, life, temperature, and other conditions be satisfactorily opened and closed a suitable number of times?

SUGGESTIONS:

1. Use steel strip.
2. Use steel strip to which silver is welded or brazed.
3. Use brass or copper strip.
4. Use brass or copper strip to which silver is welded.
5. Use steel wire.
6. Use brass or copper wire.
7. Use silver-plated wire or strip of iron, brass, or copper.
8. Use silver wire.
9. Weld silver wire to base metal of iron, brass, or copper.
10. Weld silver wire continuously to strip of iron, brass, or copper and cut off.
11. Weld silver wire continuously to iron, brass, or copper, cut off, and coin.
12. Weld silver strip to brass strip, cut off, and coin.
13. Weld shaped silver strip to brass strip and cut off.
14. Use silver rivets in iron, copper, or brass base metal.
15. Weld or braze silver balls to iron, copper, or brass base metal.
16. Buy present contacts more competitively.

4. *Analytical Phase.* This will produce comments like the following ones, which are typical though not complete.

Alternative 1: "Use steel strip." Steel has not been found satisfactory as an electrical-contact material required to conduct necessary amounts of current for the necessary number of cycles.

Alternative 2: "Use steel strip to which silver is welded or brazed." A strong belief by qualified technical people that nonferrous metals should be used, combined with a reasonable question concerning the amount of heat generated if steel were used, makes this one of the less desirable alternatives.

Alternative 3: "Use brass or copper strip." This is not considered satisfactory for the operating conditions.

Alternative 4: "Use brass or copper strip to which silver is welded." Probably the right solution, this is the way it is being done now. Later suggestions cover this arrangement in more specific terms.

Alternative 5: "Use steel wire." Probably steel-to-steel elements make and break contact unsatisfactorily under the specified working conditions.

Alternative 6: "Use brass or copper wire." Possibly a satisfactory solution; however, technical beliefs and much technical momentum back the use of silver as the face metal in making and breaking contacts under the particular conditions.

Alternative 7: "Use silver-plated wire or strip of iron, brass, or copper." This is probably a good alternative. If plating could be provided economically enough and thick enough at the points needed, it might accomplish the function for the lowest cost.

Alternative 8: "Use silver wire." This alternative is ruled out by high cost.

Alternative 9: "Weld silver wire to base metal of iron, brass, or copper." This is a workable approach to be further investigated.

Alternative 10: "Weld silver wire continuously to strip of iron, brass, or copper and cut off." This possibility should be investigated in connection with alternative 8.

Alternative 11: "Weld silver wire continuously to iron, brass, or copper, cut off, and coin." This should also be investigated in connection with alternative 8.

Alternative 12: "Weld silver strip to brass strip, cut off, and coin." This is a practical approach but probably not as useful as alternative 13.

Alternative 13: "Weld shaped silver strip to brass strip and cut off." A workable approach, this needs to be investigated in detail.

Alternative 14: Use silver rivets in iron, copper, or brass base metal." This workable approach should be further investigated.

Alternative 15: "Weld or braze silver balls on iron, copper, or brass base metal." A workable approach, this deserves further investigation.

Alternative 16: "Buy present contacts more competitively." Review of purchasing effectiveness is called for.

5. *Program-planning Phase.* From the foregoing, the indications are that actions should now be set in motion to further explore the possibilities of the alternatives identified. This requires programs to cover each

VALUE ANALYSIS SUGGESTION SHEET

NAME OF PART ELECTRICAL CONTACT	PART USED IN CONTROL
DWG. NO. A-1645	QUANTITY/UNIT 1
	QUANTITY/YR. 1,000,000

PRESENT — BRASS STRIP / PUNCHED / SILVER-BRASS CONTACT / CONTACT ASSEMBLY

PROPOSED — BUY LONG STRIPS OF PRE-BRAZED MATERIAL. / CUT OFF

	MATERIAL-C	LABOR-C	MFGRG COST-C	TOOLS OR PATTERNS
PRESENT COSTS	$ 1.00	$ .60	$ 2.20	
PROPOSED COSTS	.90	.10	1.10	$ NONE

ESTIMATED ANNUAL SAVINGS $ 11,000.

COMMENTS
BRASS STRIP HAS BEEN PURCHASED AND PUNCHED.
SILVER BRASS PRE-FORMED CONTACT BUTTON HAS BEEN
PURCHASED AND BRAZED TO BRASS. PART.

SUGGESTIONS—
PURCHASE STRIP BUILT UP OF PROPER AMOUNT OF
BRASS AND SILVER.
CUT OFF PUNCH HOLE, AND USE.
COMPLETELY INTERCHANGEABLE
CONTAINS SAME AMOUNT OF FUNCTIONING SILVER
AND BRASS.

Fig. 2-3. The electrical contact suggestion sheet.

of the alternatives thought to be the most likely ones to produce reliable and useful choices.

Accordingly, alternatives 7, 9, 11, 13, 14, and 15 will be assigned to particular specialists or suppliers who, it is felt, lead in the technologies involved. Effective ways of searching for and selecting such experts form the first need. Then, steps must follow to provide these people with all the pertinent information and with proper motivation so that they will propose whatever contacts they believe will meet this application and will also furnish costs. As for item 16, it will be assigned to purchasing for action.

6. *Program-execution Phase.* Whenever there is an attempt to accomplish a specific job in a different way, new questions arise. Each of the six suppliers or specialists must be given a definite individual to refer back to for more information and guidance in the adaptation of their technology to the precise function. Their questions must be answered promptly, and they must be assured that the user will match their efforts in endeavoring to work out any problems involved in making it practical to utilize the lowest-cost value alternative to reliably accomplish the function.

7. *Status Summary and Conclusion.* While the suggestion sheet often will cover several alternatives, only one of the alternatives suggested in this instance seemed to have a special merit. Accordingly, it alone is included in the sample suggestion sheet (Figure 2-3).

Case Study

THE PIVOT PIN

One morning's mail brought a little stainless steel pin about ⅟₁₆ inch in diameter and about ⅜ inch long. A manufacturing man sent it in with the following statement: "We are paying $3.65 per thousand—that's a third of a cent apiece—for 50 million of these a year. Is it good value?"

On receipt of the facts relating to this pin, we found that it was bought from a supplier, and on further study, it was determined that it was not worth that kind of money. We put this finding up to the supplier's sales manager who then, in a two-page letter, told us that the tolerances were so tight that they could do nothing about it. This motivated us to arrange for a meeting of the sales manager, accompanied by his factory superintendent (so we would have the facts), the engineer who had designed the pin, and the buyer who bought it.

Among the questions discussed at this meeting were the following:

1. What purpose does the pin serve? It is the pivot used to support the pinions and gears in an electric clock. Several of them are used in each clock.

2. How is the gear put on the pin? Pressed on. The pinions, made from thin, laminated, carbon steel, are blanked in a small punch press and pressed directly onto the pin. Gears and pinions are held in place by friction with the pin.

3. Why is stainless used? To avoid corrosion.

4. Why use No. 440 stainless which is twice as hard to machine as the others? Because it has 100 points of carbon and can be satisfactorily hardened.

5. Why harden it? In pressing on the tight gears and pinions, the surface of the pin otherwise is sometimes slightly scored, and as this surface serves as a bearing surface, the scoring would result in erratic and short life. The

sole function of the hardening is to avoid damage to the pin surface while
the gears are being pressed on. Since the pins are running in copper bearings,
it is felt that the steel would be sufficiently hard for good bearing operations
even without hardening.

6. If the gears are carbon steel and do not corrode or rust, why should the
pins? We tried carbon steel for the pins and it does corrode. The gears are
made of a very thin cold-rolled steel, and it seems probable that the supplier
uses some rust inhibitor in his process which is good enough. If we thoroughly
clean the pinion steel by acid or other method, it too will rust.

7. Why the chamfer *D*? To provide entry into the gear.

8. Why chamfer both ends? To save labor. Otherwise each pin must be
picked up and examined before it is located with the proper end up.

9. Why the flat *B*? The flat presses against the end plate and locates the pin
axially. It is desirable for the flat surface to be at a minimum in order to
reduce end friction.

FIG. 2-4. The pivot pin, greatly enlarged.

10. Why the radius *C*? The radius is for the purpose of connecting the
chamfer to the flat.

11. Why have both the chamfer *D* and the radius *C* when the combined
length of both is 0.010 inch and may, within tolerances, be as little as 0.005
inch? A chamfer or suitable radius is necessary to provide entry into the gear,
and a small end bearing surface is necessary to limit end friction. We presume
that the other details best fit into the manufacturing arrangement of the
supplier who helped to work it out. A desirable end from this viewpoint would
be a semispherical surface. However, such a surface would extend clear back
into the bearing and eliminate the cylindrical portion which is now the
bearing surface.

12. Why only ±0.001 inch on the length tolerance when it is observed from
actual assembly that there is an end play of around 0.015 inch on each pin?
Due to the build-up of tolerances, there may be friction between gear faces if
more than 0.001 inch is allowed. The tolerance on the studs which separate
the end plates is ±0.002 inch, and if it were more economical to hold them
to a closer tolerance than the pins, the tolerances might be reversed, allowing

+0.002 inch on the pin and making the stud to ±0.001 inch without adversely affecting the assembly.

13. Why only 0.00025-inch diameter tolerance? To provide dependable interference fit when mounting the gears and pinions.

14. There are other ways of providing the features which have been discussed. In general, what prompted this particular design? The part has quite a history; it was made by ourselves and possibly others. The present vendor showed particular interest and aptitude for the job, and some of the design details are prescribed to coincide with his manufacturing processes.

15. Why does the pin cost $3.65 instead of 45 cents per thousand? Because of the ±0.001-inch-length tolerance, the 0.00025-inch OD tolerance, the chamfer-radius end construction, the No. 440 stainless steel, and the hardening.

16. How is it made now? It is made of material in excess of the desired diameter and cut off too long. Then, after hardening, the ends are ground to length and the outside diameter is ground to size. There are twelve operations in the making of the pin.

17. How much does the stainless material alone cost? Forty-five cents per thousand pieces.

18. How much would carbon steel cost? Around 10 cents per thousand.

19. Can wire be purchased to the diameter tolerance required? Yes.

20. Will automatic screw machines cut it off to the ±0.001-inch-length tolerance? Probably not. We would expect ±0.003 inch from them.

21. How close will wire-forming equipment shear it to length? Good equipment will hold it to ±0.002 inch.

22. Why not cut it off on a form cutter which will provide, in one operation, the necessary chamfer, radius, and end flat? It might work. The problem would be to cut it off to the tolerance of ±0.001 inch and to maintain the form cutter.

23. Some cutoff methods would normally leave a small tip in the center. Wouldn't it be desirable to do so? We would expect so, providing the tip was closely enough controlled so that the distance from end to end of the tips would come within the length tolerance.

Based on this and other discussions, the vendor was requested to quote on the following five alternatives:

Using the entire 0.0005-inch diameter tolerance, which would also allow a substantial reduction in rejected pins. Also, inspection cost will be re-evaluated based on sampling methods.

Same as above except that wire of smaller diameter is to be used, reducing the number of passes from three to two and also reducing attendant losses.

Same as second alternative except that allowable length tolerance is to be 0.003 inch instead of 0.002 inch.

Same as second alternative except that allowable tolerance is to be 0.004 inch instead of 0.002 inch.

Same as second alternative except for the substitution of No. 1090 carbon steel for No. 440 stainless steel.

The vendor's quotation read: "Our production department has been doing a lot of work in connection with better and more efficient handling and feeding methods. This, plus the concessions discussed, has resulted in some rather startling cost reductions, which are reflected in the prices shown below."

PIVOT No. 41626-8

Method No. 1. Based on using ±0.00025-inch diameter tolerance, plus attendant drop in rejects and lower inspection costs, we quote $2.05 per thousand.

Method No. 2. Same as method 1 except that by using only two centerless grinding passes, we quote $1.90 per thousand.

Method No. 3. Same as method 2 except for a total length tolerance of 0.003 inch instead of the present 0.002 inch. This larger tolerance should allow us to furnish radius ends instead of slight flats. Using this method, we quote $1.79 per thousand.

Method No. 4. Same as method 2 except that to use SAE No. 1090 carbon steel instead of No. 440 stainless would allow us to quote $1.55 per thousand.

Method No. 5. Same as method 2 except for an increase in the length tolerance to 0.004 inch. Our costs would be the same as under method 3, so the same selling price would apply.

Subsequently, the engineers approved of alternative 2, and the cost went down from $3.65 per thousand to $1.90 per thousand, for a saving of $83,000 on a use quantity of 47 million pins a year. As will be noted, this accomplishment derived from:

Using all allowable diameter tolerance

Using smaller stock, and eliminating one centerless grinding pass

Charging for only sampling inspection approved by our engineers rather than 100 per cent

Eliminating some handling

It will be seen in studying the value analysis job plan that all parts of the plan are not necessarily used in connection with every function reviewed. However, all the parts are tested for effectiveness in application to the function being studied, and all those parts that appear useful are applied. This means that nearly every part of the value analysis job plan must be used to achieve high efficiency and a high degree of value.

CHAPTER 3 *The Value Analysis Techniques*

Successful value analysis effort, culminating in the elimination of unnecessary cost, depends a great deal upon skillful application of techniques that will identify unnecessary cost, remove obstacles, and provide a course of action that will ensure the development of value alternatives of merit.

Such a series of techniques has been developed and has proved capable of meeting real-life situations. Each of these techniques—thirteen in all—will be described in this chapter. In some cases, good results are obtained by using only one of the techniques, but in many more cases, more than one will need to be applied. The situation in each particular instance will dictate whether one, several, or even a whole group of techniques holds the best promise. That question will be further covered in Chapter 4 on the use of the techniques.

The reader will do well to acquire a distinct comprehension of each specific technique and its aim.

The value analysis techniques are:
1. Avoid generalities.
2. Get all available costs.
3. Use information from only the best source.
4. Blast, create, refine.
5. Use real creativity.
6. Identify and overcome roadblocks.
7. Use industry specialists to extend specialized knowledge.
8. Get a dollar sign on key tolerances.
9. Utilize vendors' available functional products.
10. Utilize and pay for vendors' skills and knowledge.
11. Utilize specialty processes.
12. Utilize applicable standards.
13. Use the criterion, "Would I spend my money this way?"

3-1. *Avoid Generalities*

All too frequently a good idea or proposition is swept aside by a good-sounding generality such as, "The farm is no good—never has been and never will be." This statement stops buyers, excludes investigation, and prevents change. Assume that we ask, "Specifically, what is wrong?" Perhaps it will be found that $1,000 worth of limestone will make it the best farm in the township.

Similarly, "This field won't grow potatoes. They never are any good; they have hollow centers. Don't waste any time or money trying to grow potatoes on it." By specifically inquiring why it won't grow potatoes, we might find that $5 worth of magnesium sulfate will make it top-grade potato land.

Such general statements stop progress in somewhat the same way that fog stops traffic. Although there is not necessarily any tangible obstruction in a fog, as a dense, unmanageable curtain it constitutes a good stopper. It is so general and so diverse that problems, if any, within it cannot be seen; nor is there any assurance that the fog shrouds no problems.

In industry, one commonly meets with generalities such as the following:

1. "Every detail of the design of this device has had a thorough review by a special, high-competence review team."

2. "The best manufacturing specialists in the United States have reviewed this and agreed that these manufacturing methods are the best and most economical."

3. "It's not practical to build dies for drop forging when quantities are less than 25,000 per order."

4. "It's not practical to build molds for casting in quantities of less than 5,000."

5. "We had to make these parts by hand because we can't pay for the tools with the quantities involved."

6 "We've made a thorough study of every conceivable way of doing this, and what we have is the only way it can be accomplished."

Recognizing every generality as a force for continuing the status quo, the first step must be to eliminate the generality by coming to grips specifically with "man-size" integers of the problem.

As an example, let us see how we may deal with generalities 1 through 6.

1. First, we must establish precisely what the over-all function is, and also what the partial functions are. By then intensively studying a specific function which is being accomplished, the "fog" will be penetrated. Alternatives which reliably accomplish the specific functions or subfunctions for lower costs will suggest themselves.

2. In this case, we must inquire specifically into what it is that manufacturing must accomplish—oriented, not exclusively to specified drawings, but rather to required functions. Having in mind a precise function, we can determine the manufacturing processes or skills which will result in a product that accomplishes the intended function with greatest reliability and lowest cost. Then the manufacturing problem can be broken down into a series of small, manageable integers, each of which can be studied intensively as a single item and in its relation to the others. For example, in a practical case the manufacturing processes were studied, planned, and put into effect on a water-cooled support and resulted in a cost of $90. Generalities certainly indicated that nothing more could be done on the manufacturing of the item. Application of value techniques to the individual parts and to possible combinations of individual parts showed that two important and costly parts could be combined and made by hydroforming. This provided a thoroughly reliable product, even more desirable in that it was somewhat lighter in weight,—and the cost went down to $36.

In another case, it was reported that manufacturing studies just completed had succeeded in removing a third of the cost of assembling a twelve-piece insulating support. Did the generality that the best manufacturing specialists had looked it over and had made their recommendation mean that little more could be done to lower the cost of manufacture? In the "what does it do" functional approach, it was brought clearly into focus that this item supported 2 pounds of weight, insulated by about 2 inches from a metal frame. An obvious question was, "Does it require twelve parts to insulate and support 2 pounds?" This examination, originating from a study of the manufacturing process, resulted in a very much simpler and equally effective way of accomplishing the total function.

3. In this case, the generality was, "It's not practical to make dies for this quantity." The fact is that:

Parts may vary in complexity.

They may vary in kind of material used.

Different suppliers develop particular skills in diemaking and machine setup.

Nearly each year sees advancement in the art of diemaking, and periodically progress is made in the type of machines in which the dies are fabricated as well as in the simplicity with which dies can be changed.

Different ways of heating metal are developed according to the size and shape of the raw material.

The important point is, "Precisely what is it that is to be forged?" Specifically, what equipment, what processes, what specialists in the industry can contribute to this particular item in the light of today's developments? Unexpectedly useful benefits result when these time-accepted generalities are turned into specifics and an action study is made.

4. As for the fourth generality, the same situation pertains as in the case of generality 3.

5. This generality is one of the substantial reasons why unnecessary manufacturing costs are retained in a wide variety of moderate- and lower-volume products. The idea that "the quantities are too low to liquidate the tools" is very widespread. There are, however, so many products and parts made in moderate quantity that the problem has generated its own solution. Specialists have developed processes for making special types of tooling, for using combinations of tooling, and for making quick changes in and out of the equipment, so that all of the generalities fall by the board. Here again, the question is, "Precisely what is needed? Who is most likely to have the best answers? Where are they? How do we get their specific technology applied to this specific part or function or group of parts?"

For example, a small weld segment, about the size of the palm of the hand, was made from ⅜ × 3-inch bar stock. One end had to be cut to an irregular contour. Quantities were 3,000 per year. For several years it was made by manual effort on power equipment. It cost $1.41. The generality was, "For material ⅜ inch thick, tools cost entirely too much to consider buying them to produce a quantity of only 3,000 a year." When this generality was discarded and vendors of the type who specialize in "low-quantity stampings" were approached, it was found that, with a tool cost of $75, they could produce the segments for 39 cents each. The yield in this case, after it was determined to not accept the generalities trap, was $3,000 a year for a $75 investment.

6. The last item was, "This is the only practical and reliable way of doing it." Here again, let us establish what is to be accomplished. What are the subfunctions which must be accomplished in order to achieve the over-all function? Precisely what are the alternatives for accomplishing these subfunctions, and what are the relationships between them? With the total general problem thus divided into its integers, the generality applying to the whole is no longer applicable. Where this particular generality has protected the status quo for a period of time, the yield from the use of value analysis techniques is usually especially large.

To summarize, avoid the generalities trap. Recognize that if a generality exists it has probably deferred effective value action in the past. Proceed to break the situation down into specific, man-size integers of function and cost. Then apply the appropriate value techniques and watch the results.

Case Study

DEVELOP SPECIFIC INFORMATION

For one application, forty thousand ¼ × 3-inch screws were required. It was necessary that they be threaded all the way to the head. Standard screws contained only a 1 inch length of thread, but they were purchased and then put in a screw machine for extension of the threads to the head. The costs became 12 cents. The arrangement satisfied all involved because (1) purchasing could buy available standard screws with no problems; (2) manufacturing had the equipment and welcomed the work which could be put on its machines; and (3) the engineers obtained the screw they needed. As is so often the case, all considerations except those of value were properly cared for. The use of value analysis techniques showed that the function was not worth 12 cents. Accepting no generalities as a basis for decision, suppliers were asked for bids on supplying screws with the proper full-length thread initially. This resulted in a change to buying the screws ready to use for 2½ cents each. The purchase and modification of standard products may be a good-sounding generality that does not guarantee best value.

A second and most important phase of the rule of dealing with specifics is to remember that specifics are needed to sell an idea and to stimulate action. To suggest or ask for a change to a less expensive material in a product without furnishing specifics is not the value specialist's way. His procedure must be to describe, with no ambiguity, the specific material, its characteristics, and how it is proposed to be used. Similarly, it is not enough to know that a casting, for example, costs $5. The specifics that count here are: how much of the total represents material, labor, extra costs for complicated coring, costs of scrap and rejects, costs of patterns or die maintenance, tolerance, flash removal and machining, inspection and handling, and the many other factors that contribute to cost.

Many times a sand casting is used because of a general opinion that sand castings are the cheapest method for producing short-run cast parts. Later it may prove that necessary machining operations price the part out of the market. Only by a specific analysis of cost can these details be pinpointed. Here, it is not enough to ask, "What does this part do?" The question should be, "What does this tolerance on the part do?" Be specific, not general.

Case Study

CRYSTAL OR WINDOW GLASS

In each area of activity, habits and accustomed practices prevail. Specific information, when developed, often leads to changes that bring large improvements in value.

In the drafting department of an electric clock factory, the word "crystal" was always used to designate clock faces, as a matter of habit. They were called clock crystals. This meant that drawings delineating the exact shape and dimensions of clock faces always specified these as crystals.

In the general auditing of freight bills, it became accepted practice to expect the crystals to require a very high freight rate. However, when the time came for making a special audit of freight rates, the question arose, "How does a clock factory use so much crystal?" The investigation which followed disclosed that the clock faces were indeed window glass, warmed and sagged. The investigation also brought forth the information that the transportation of crystal, a very expensive grade of glass, is extremely costly, while window glass, in any form, travels at a very much lower rate.

Crystal shipped "less than carload" costs 1.25 times the first-class freight rate, while "bent window glass," which correctly described the product being shipped, travels at only 0.85 times the first-class freight rate.

The result was that the name was changed on the drawings, in the specifications, on the orders, and on the bills of lading so that, instead of being wrongly called crystal, the material was correctly called bent window glass. The freight rate was cut by 32 per cent. *Always, "specifics" are important.*

Value analysis is an intensive study; its very basis is dealing, item by item, with specifics, not generalities. It requires reviewing every operation on a planning card; checking every radius, every corner, and every hole shown on a drawing; looking critically at operations performed and at material purchased but not used and diverted to scrap; and establishing all else that affects cost.

It follows that no effort must be shunned to get at and present the essential facts. This may seem like a big job because, while some of the specifics may be easily obtainable, others may take real effort to nail down. When this is the case, the value analyst will do well to remind himself that he may let an opportunity go by unless he gets together more specifics than anyone else may easily lay his hands on.

> *Whenever the objective is to promote beneficial change, always use specifics. Generalities serve only to prevent changes and protect the status quo.*

3-2. Get All Available Costs

Meaningful costs bear the same relationship to good value as meaningful tests bear to good performance. Unfortunately, it is not uncommon to find that far-reaching and important decisions are made without accurate and meaningful costs. In contrast, important decisions affecting performance are no longer made without meaningful test data.

To have available and use meaningful costs is more vital and more difficult than may be immediately apparent. It is vital because cost is influenced by every decision on every part, component, or subcomponent of a product. If meaningful cost is a criterion in each decision, then value may be secured. Otherwise, value is not obtainable.

There are a variety of reasons why it is difficult to obtain meaningful costs.

Cost figures normally developed are for use in a basic system intended to ensure proper income tax accounting and proper over-all profit accounting for the total business and also to provide some manageable basis for liquidating necessary charges of all types. It is a popular misconception that these costs are meaningful for the purpose of decision making about engineering, manufacturing, or other value alternatives. They are not. They accomplish their intended purpose very well. However, when the purpose is important enough and the user understands the problems involved, they may serve as a basis for meaningful costs.

The resultant cost figures, however, bear little relationship to those provided by the normal cost system. As a homely example, the same types of materials are put together and the same types of processes are used in making vehicles of various kinds for the transportation of people. One vehicle, the automobile, is intended for transport on land and is very effective for that purpose. Another type of vehicle, or vessel, intended for transportation on water, accomplishes that purpose very effectively. A third type, intended for transportation by air, may accomplish its purpose very well with the same resources of materials, processes, and men's talents put together for its different intent.

So it is with cost systems. Anyone who believes that costs which have been put together in a form to accomplish one purpose can also be used for other purposes and so protect the business' interests arrives at a very faulty decision.

The cost situation is so involved that different people in the accounting business use different names to cover different combinations of the various types of cost. A few of them are:

Material cost	Decision cost
Labor cost	Shop cost
Overhead cost	Standard cost
Fixed overhead	Manufacturing cost
Variable overhead	Incremental cost
Burden	Variance cost
Prime cost	

What does each of these terms include? What does each of them mean? What types of costs are included in the terms used in the company involved?

Meaningful costs are difficult to develop because of the matter of overhead. In practice, nearly every machine and nearly every process actually consumes a different overhead. Still, for convenience of accounting, they are bunched together in some sort of grouping. How should the fixed overhead for the buildings, the depreciation, and the management of the company be apportioned? How should the work of maintenance people, janitors, service people, etc., be factored into individual costs? What effect on all of these expenses would different alternatives actually have?

The problem here lies in the fact that it is necessary to provide not only an answer that is satisfactory to the head of accounting or to the manager, but an answer that is also satisfactory to the economic system. An incorrect method of preparing so-called meaningful costs may be directly responsible for making wrong decisions which preclude good value in the product.

Another reason for the difficulty of getting meaningful costs is that habits, practices, and procedures are already established in most areas. People and machines are in place and things are being done in a certain way. Vested interests exist. Change often seems wrong to the people involved. Change always brings uncertainty and a measure of insecurity to the people concerned. Because means of allocating costs have been empirical and arbitrary, the tendency is to prolong the use of existing types of costs.

Does "labor cost" mean the amount paid to labor? Possibly, but probably not. It may include only part of the payment to labor; the remainder may be in a variance or other account caused by labor rate increases since the item was planned and the various costs set up.

Does the "material cost" show the amount which was paid to vendors for material? Perhaps so and perhaps not. Frequently, the accounting practice is to add certain overheads into this account. Someone must purchase, receive, inspect, and protect material. Additions of from 3 to 20 per cent to the actual material cost for these operations are not uncommon. Thus, the material cost may actually include some overhead.

Where labor and material costs include just the total of labor and material, are the figures meaningful? The assumption in this case is that the machines, the buildings, and the supervision are all in place and nothing needs to be added to the bare cost of the labor and material involved. The answer is obvious: These are indeed not meaningful costs. Obviously, the business results will be affected negatively by taking advantage of time, people, and facilities paid for in other budgets. Decisions made on this basis will not bring value to the product.

If we add overhead to labor and material, that is, if each part or product is assessed its share of the over-all overhead so that the item takes in the total of material, labor, and overhead, does the cost become meaningful? Certainly not in itself. Many items of overhead in the business continue, and will continue, regardless of whether the particular part or assembly is made on one machine or another machine, is made in one assembly area by one method or in another assembly area by a different method, or indeed is purchased from an outside supplier. Many more overhead items are affected in varying degrees, some rather directly and others most indirectly.

The purpose here is not to penetrate deeply into accounting practice—a subject on which text books are available—but rather to provoke recognition that the mere inclusion of overhead does not bring meaningful costs for value decisions.

What happens if we concern ourselves with labor and material plus partial overheads? It has been reasoned that overhead is divided into two groups: fixed and variable overhead. Fixed overhead takes in such items as costs of buildings and equipment; depreciation; and general management of the company, research, and other operations that will go on regardless of the value decision pertaining to any one product. Variable overhead covers the expense occasioned by the particular way in which the particular product is designed and manufactured, such as carrying charges of special machines and equipment used, foremen and supervisory personnel, and other items, exclusive of labor, which are caused directly by the particular manufacturing or design alternative chosen. Do we now have a meaningful cost? Perhaps the problem lies in the danger of using arbitrary or habitual percentages which may not in the slightest way show how the business is affected. For each engineering and manufacturing alternative, these various overheads are probably affected somewhat differently. Therefore, it becomes necessary to understandingly study the specific alternatives involved so that the amounts of overhead expense and other additions will be in harmony with the economic system and not necessarily with the practices of the past in the area involved. Any margin of error between what is believed to be meaningful cost and what is in reality the true economics of the way the business is affected is decreased value.

What then is meaningful? To prepare meaningful costs for the purpose of making correct value decisions, the true effect of the use of the different alternatives must be interpreted in terms of dollars for several areas.

How is the business really affected?

How is the product affected?

How will sales be affected?

How will other products be affected?

How will the company's future plans be affected?

How will the development of new technology be affected?

Attainment of the desired degree of reliable performance is commonly no problem except in the case of newer products that are the result of recent research and development, and these might embrace 10 per cent of the industrial production. *Where the problem does lie is in getting reliable performance at low-enough cost.* Cost is the important factor in decision making in every phase of product planning, designing, and manufacturing. For nearly every function and for nearly every manufacturing situation, there exist many alternative solutions, all of which will accomplish the purpose reliably. Proper selection depends upon meaningful costs, and only when such costs serve as an essential criterion in the decision making will good value be achieved.

Without meaningful cost, decisions will not, and cannot, be made to provide good value.

EXAMPLE 1: There are no costs. This is a normal situation when value analysis work is done before design. It forms a satisfactory starting point. Meaningful costs must be developed, however, for each of the alternatives that might be used.

EXAMPLE 2: Costs exist but are not provided. Seldom, if ever, is value work efficiently done if costs which exist are not brought forth. Getting good value is difficult. All possible help is needed. Knowing present cost sets certain floors and ceilings with relation to different types of alternatives. This saves time and helps show where the work will probably be most effective.

In contrast to performance-oriented work, it is often desirable, in order to secure good creativity, to avoid knowing how others have accomplished the desired function until some study has been made. Otherwise the thinking is often channeled into the types of solution that are known to have been used previously, with the consequence that excellent value alternatives which might accomplish the total function reliably for a small fraction of the cost are not brought into view.

To summarize, start out with the best costs that exist, understand them, know their deficiencies, and gain all possible benefits from them.

EXAMPLE 3: Data exist but only labor and material costs are provided. This situation is sometimes found in areas in which competition has not forced a high degree of value. Normally labor costs are known, as are material costs. Furthermore, it is known precisely how much of each applies to the product in question. The easy, habitual way is to accept these as the costs. No interpretation, no imagination, no direction, no forethought, and very little effort are required. In contrast, if some or all of the pertinent overhead figures are included, the questions arise: Which one? How much? What percentages? etc. These require thought, study, and understanding. Where only labor and material costs are provided, the action taken is usually justified by various forms of rationalization; for example, "Direct costs of labor and material are about all that are affected by a change anyway; overheads continue relatively the same."

Again, efficiency of value work is reduced to the extent that pertinent costs are not brought into the picture.

EXAMPLE 4: Decision cost—so called "out-of-pocket cost"—in make-or-buy decisions.

A general statement, specific enough to have some validity, is that meaningful costs for use in make-or-buy decisions will include:

Labor
Material
Variable overhead
Some amount of fixed overhead

Normally, all labor, material, and variable overheads are included. But, considering all of the effects on the business, on costs, on sales, on

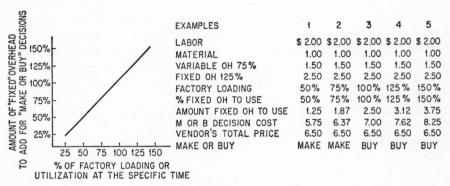

EXAMPLES	1	2	3	4	5
LABOR	$ 2.00	$ 2.00	$ 2.00	$ 2.00	$ 2.00
MATERIAL	1.00	1.00	1.00	1.00	1.00
VARIABLE OH 75%	1.50	1.50	1.50	1.50	1.50
FIXED OH 125%	2.50	2.50	2.50	2.50	2.50
FACTORY LOADING	50%	75%	100%	125%	150%
% FIXED OH TO USE	50%	75%	100%	125%	150%
AMOUNT FIXED OH TO USE	1.25	1.87	2.50	3.12	3.75
M OR B DECISION COST	5.75	6.37	7.00	7.62	8.25
VENDOR'S TOTAL PRICE	6.50	6.50	6.50	6.50	6.50
MAKE OR BUY	MAKE	MAKE	BUY	BUY	BUY

FIG. 3-1. "Make it or buy it."

other products, etc., the question is: What percentage of fixed cost should be added to arrive nearly at an out-of-pocket cost which will show how the business will be affected?

Although there are many important factors, the most significant consideration normally used is the amount of work in the plant compared with its capacity. When machines or facilities are only partially loaded, it will be observed that some machines are idle, floor space is not filled, some people are on short time, and other people are obviously "stretching" less important work in order to make a full day of it. It is generally felt that the costs for make-or-buy decisions are lower in this situation than when the plant is working at full capacity or over. Figure 3-1 illustrates an approach that is sometimes used.

It will be seen that the amount of fixed overhead liquidated in the cost of the particular product is reduced as the plant load decreases to bring more work into the plant. Again, as the plant work load increases, the amount of fixed overhead applied in the comparison figures is increased, tending to minimize "keep-busy work" and to open up capacity for essential, productive, profitable products which must be manufactured in the area.

EXAMPLE 5: Decision cost involving make one way versus make another way in the factory.

The general practice is to use labor plus material plus variable overhead plus or minus significant changes in the way fixed overhead is affected.

In conclusion, the costs used often make the decision. Therefore, any wrong action taken in preparing cost means a wrong decision and resultant poor value in the product.

Case Study

UNMEANINGFUL COSTS USED FOR DECISION MAKING CAN BANKRUPT THE BUSINESS

Word was received that severe customer resistance had developed to hamper the selling of an important electromechanical control. Advices were that all the assemblies, subassemblies, and parts were laid out for study and that each was labeled with costs, quantities, etc.

Even first examination showed that costs were extremely high. For example: Twenty-cent items often cost 50 to 70 cents.

Two-dollar items often cost $4 or $5.

Three-cent items cost 50 cents.

Eight-dollar subassemblies cost $21.

Study was undertaken to determine why costs were so high. Some of the reasons follow:

1. Parts were being made on less than optimum equipment.

2. Parts were often made by skilled labor when they required none.

3. Inventories of some parts were extremely high.

4. A "blanket" fixed-overhead rate was used on all items whether the fixed assets used consisted of a screw driver or a $20,000 machine.

Interpretation

Cost figures which were used for decision making and which had been responsible for overpricing the product were not meaningful because:

1. The use of blanket fixed overhead regardless of the fixed assets used prevented decision makers from knowing how the business was really affected by the various alternative methods for accomplishing the necessary functions.

2. The job was used as a "filler" to take up the slack in the factory. Whenever machine time opened up or men had no other jobs, parts were made for inventory.

Labor costs were not meaningful for decision making between alternatives because they were often based on uneconomical short runs and on the use of much higher skill than the particular items required.

Setup costs were not meaningful for decision making because they were based, not on needs of the job, but rather on conditions of "factory slack absorption."

In fact, no costs—labor, material, or setup—were meaningful for decision making because they were based, not on the needs of the design or the job, but on other considerations.

3. The volume of the work in the factory was being reduced because, unfortunately, the selling prices of the product were being influenced by the summation of these costs.

Even a glimpse at the cost realities shows that included in these "carefully delineated" costs of parts, subassemblies, and assemblies were these costs:

1. The legitimate cost of producing the functional parts, subassemblies, and assemblies as they were designed
2. Completely extraneous costs for factory load balancing
3. Costs for totally unused items of fixed assets

It was decided that two activities would at once proceed.

1. Determination of appropriate costs, strictly applicable to the particular parts and assemblies being manufactured
2. Using the value analysis techniques, evaluation of all functions of the product

With the meaningful figures of cost for accomplishing the various functions by means of present designs and with a clear view of the value of these functions, alternatives were developed where poor value existed.

The result was practical alternatives as a basis for decision making which would reduce the total cost to less than half.

3-3. *Use Information from Only the Best Source*

Lack of full information and use of misinformation are frequently the cause of a poor degree of value. In recognition of this, the search for pertinent information in value analysis must be a continuing one, and likewise, the sources from which the information comes must constantly be weighed to ensure that they constitute the best ones available. The more diligent and effective the search for the best information, the better the value attained.

Questions by the score must be raised, and answers must be accepted only from the highest level of the best sources in each case. Some examples of the sort of questions that should be asked are:

Why is this square?
Why is it painted red?
Why does it have a double set of contacts?

Why is it "hogged" from solid bronze?

Why is there a 0.0001-inch tolerance on the diameter?

How does the customer mount the base?

At what atmospheric conditions must it work?

In what positions can it be mounted by the customer?

What limits its market?

What causes it to be noisy?

What benefits does the F4 finish on the inside of the cover bring?

Answers traditional to the thinking within any area are readily available. Experience shows that such pat, traditional answers must not be accepted. Whatever the pertinent question is, only the best source must be allowed to answer it. The following examples are offered in verification of this statement.

Who is the best source, the engineer or the sales manager? In the value analysis of a moderate-sized piece of electrical equipment, a partial inside cover was found which had a cost of $5. The analyst, in analyzing functions, could find no function for it. Accordingly, in reporting to the engineer in charge, he said, "This cover costs $5 and I can find no function for it." The engineer immediately answered, "It has no function, but the customers require it." The analyst at once recognized this as quite a normal situation, in which the engineer voiced his belief; in fact, he voiced the criterion on which the decision to retain this cover had been made for years. The analyst's suggestion, therefore, was, "Why don't we ask the sales manager why it is that the customers require this cover if it seems to us to have no function." When the question was subsequently put to the sales manager, his answer was: "Does that cost $5? Take it off. I have only one customer who uses it. The others take it off and throw it away. I will see to it that this particular customer pays a special charge for extra equipment."

Again, who is the best source, the sales manager or the purchasing agent? At a manager's staff meeting, it was being determined whether or not it was practical to increase production of some appliances from 2,000 to 4,000 per week. The marketing manager said, "In this market we can now sell all we can make. However, with the shortage of steel, we can't get enough to support a schedule of any more than 2,000 a week." This statement contained what he believed, for the very good reason that he had made inquiries. He had talked from time to time with purchasing and had read in trade magazines about shortages of steel. Just before the group made its decision, the engineering manager said, "Shouldn't we call in our purchasing agent and get a direct up-to-the-minute reading from him on this shortage of steel?" That was done and the purchasing agent, like most competent men, knew more about "his business" than anyone else. When told that they wanted to increase the schedule to

4,000, he told them to increase it; he would furnish the steel. Thus, a loss of potential business was narrowly averted by merely going to, and accepting the answer from, the best source. What the purchasing agent did was to buy some of the necessary steel components in a partly finished or finished form, and by so doing, he properly utilized the steel allotments of various component manufacturers for whom he provided good business at the same time that he met his own quota of 4,000.

Who won't approve it, the Underwriters'? A value alternative suggested for a small transformer would reduce its cost 20 per cent and seemingly provide all the functions, as well as efficiency and reliability. The answer from the engineer was, "The Underwriters' won't approve the change." For the answer to the resultant question, "Why won't Underwriters' approve?" communication was made directly with the Underwriters'. The answer from the appropriate personnel in the Underwriters' office was: "Proceed with the change. Several years ago, under different conditions of application, we felt that the transformer should be made in a certain way. However, we have since changed this requirement as the added expense makes no contribution to safety or performance."

Case Study

THERE IS ONLY ONE SUPPLIER

A special instrument required a glass cover, about 10 inches in diameter, having a curved shape similar to a cereal bowl and having a ¼-inch hole through it. Its cost was $1.25, and the quantity used was about 20,000 per year.

The value analyst was told, "There is only one supplier for this type of part, and though we recognize that the cost seems high, we have little choice."

Realizing that the buyer in a specialty department was not the best source for knowledge relating to clock and instrument faces, the analyst asked the buyer at a clock factory if he could suggest suppliers for the part. The answer came back, "We have six excellent suppliers for this type of part." Drawings and specifications were sent to some of these suppliers, and the result was that, for exactly the same item, the cost became 50 cents rather than $1.25.

It always pays to locate and consult the best source.

3-4. *Blast, Create, Refine*

This is a special technique usually helpful in reaching value objectives. Its purposes are many. First, it serves to eliminate what is in immediate view so that the mind is no longer channeled and so that thinking in totally different, more effective directions is not stifled. Second, it directs thinking to basic considerations. Third, it provides a mechanism for building that which is needed on these basic considerations.

The use of the technique is often very painful to the originator of a design or a plan. His solutions are his brain children, so to speak. In arriving at them, a great deal of effort was expended. Studies were made, money was spent, the aid of others was solicited, and so on. With the concept evolved and the plan put together, the designed and manufactured product has truly become a part of the individual. To him, the idea of "blasting" is inwardly revolting. It is as though a part of his being were about to be destroyed.

These mental reactions are emphasized here because the whole technique of blasting, creating, and then refining is a mental, not a physical, one. It can be extremely productive when people are mentally trained to understand and use it.

In the technique, the function or functions are first brought into very clear focus. Then the possible means of providing the functions are reduced to oversimple terms. The necessary complexity is then added. Alternative means for adding the complexity come next. Where good-grade value is required, this procedure is necessary to eliminate the causes of why things are done as they are. The common controlling factors are the habits and knowledge of the people at the time the particular thing, whatever it be, was first done and when it later was modified as different processes and materials and other people came into the picture.

For example, the three-room house so typical in the Middle West in earlier days provided accommodations for living, cooking, and sleeping. Sanitary facilities were outside in a nearby building. This house was functional and appropriate to the circumstances of the time as they were then known and interpreted by the people involved. Later, a lean-to was added to include two sleeping rooms as both girl and boy children came along. There followed a lean-to for the hired man. When the family became overcrowded, another lean-to for the kitchen was added and the former kitchen was converted into eating space. With the advent of modern plumbing, a further lean-to was provided for a bathroom and the outside facilities were likely to be remodeled into a tool shed.

Intense study of any product shows that it is, to a greater or lesser degree, the result of such a chain of happenings. Even the new products that value work will bring forth will be, to some extent, of a similar nature.

This situation raises the following vital questions in the search for better value:

How can this chain of influence be periodically stopped?

How can a function needed today, in the light of today's knowledge, be looked at objectively?

The technique of blasting, creating, and then refining is specifically directed toward accomplishing these objectives. The aim of the three steps in the use of the technique are:

1. *Blast.* In this stage (keeping in mind the basic functions to be accomplished, but not expecting necessarily to entirely accomplish them) alternative products, materials, processes, or ideas are generated. These alternatives should, first of all, qualify for accomplishing some important part of the function in a very economical manner or, at least, serve as an economical base for modifications that are likely to accomplish an important part of the function. At the same time, the precise amount of the function which would be accomplished and the specific cost which would result are brought into clear focus.

2. *Create.* Using intense creativity, as described in section 3-5, this step should serve to generate alternative means by which the concepts revealed by the blasting can be modified to accomplish a large part of the function with pertinent increases in cost. In this creative part of the technique, definite integers of increased function are associated with definite integers of increased cost.

3. *Refine.* In this final step, the necessary created alternatives are added to the functions which would be accomplished by the blasted product. These are further sifted and refined, adding additional integers of function with additional integers of cost, until the refined product fully accomplishes the total function. It is not uncommon for the resultant newly constructed product concept to accomplish the total functions with the same reliability and over-all benefits for a cost of one-half to one-tenth of the original.

The following are examples of execution of the three steps. The selection of the three most common simple fasteners—the nail, the screw, and the bolt—is made purposely for the sake of clearness.

Nail. To blast a steel nail, let us compare its cost with that of steel wire of the nail diameter, which surely is capable of performing an important part of the function of a nail.

In our blasting of the nail, it is recognized that additional work must be done on the steel wire to make it accomplish the total function of the nail. Our next step must be to create, for review, a list of alternatives which will serve for the function of the head, such as (1) bend the wire at one end, (2) flatten it at one end, and (3) weld a small piece at one end.

In refining, we first look again critically at the total function of the nail. Second, we review the basic cost of the material from which the nail is made, as found in the blasting, and also the amount of function which the wire alternative fails to accomplish. Third, we develop the ideas arrived at in the creative approach to a point where the ones most practical can be selected for further consideration, and we then select one or two of the approaches which will provide, at a minimum cost, most of the required additional function. Fourth, we critically review the new approach, which embodies the blasted concept plus the created additions, and determine whether the function is totally accomplished with complete reliability. Also, we ask: Have the lowest-cost practical solutions been selected? If the function is not totally accomplished with complete reliability by the selected combination, we must refine further by adding additional increments of function and cost so that the new product becomes totally usable.

Screw. To blast a steel screw, it seems reasonable to compare it first with steel wire of proper diameter and then with the nail. In each case, we identify appropriate costs.

Starting with the alternative of a nail, we proceed to consider (1) cutting the thread, (2) rolling the thread, (3) coining the thread, (4) accomplishing the function of the screw without a thread, (5) coining a slot at the head end, and (6) milling a slot.

Again, we combine the best alternatives produced by the blasting and the creating, adding in each case the integers of function and the integers of cost. Then we study the precise function for which the screw is to be used and make necessary refinements by adding additional function and additional cost until the product will accomplish the total function completely and reliably.

Bolt. To blast a steel bolt, we may similarly compare it with steel wire or rod of the appropriate diameter and in the appropriate amount, then with a steel spike or nail, and finally with a steel screw. In addition, we study the function which is intended for the bolt and, if possible, draw comparisons with other basic ways of accomplishing the same fastening function at a much lower cost.

From among the blast alternatives, we may start here with the wire or rod necessary and proceed to (1) create alternatives at the end as was done in the case of the screw, (2) create alternatives at the head end, and (3) examine the function to determine what variation of alternatives can be provided for the particular application. In each case, we should attempt to bring into view, at least for preliminary consideration, a considerable number of alternatives.

For the refining, we follow the procedures described above in connection with the screw. The more complicated the product, the better are the opportunities for wide use of creativity and for searching investigation of value alternatives which will accomplish total functions reliably for very much lower cost.

The blast approach may often be used also on individual elements of the cost. For example, let us take the case of a counterweight that cost 6 cents.

Its function was to provide weight. It was used in a completely enclosed assembly with no parts other than its support near it. Simple analysis showed that its use value was 100 per cent and its esteem value 0 per cent. The amount of $2,000 per year was paid to grind a small flash from the casting. This flash did not affect the weight or the mounting or the environment.

The "function" secured for the expenditure of $2,000 was blasted and revealed that the grinding provided no use function. With no esteem function, any expenditure which does not provide a use function represents total waste. Accordingly, the grinding operation was blasted to zero and eliminated from the cost.

Looking back, it is seen that it was quite normal to accept the $2,000 cost because it is normal to grind the flash from castings. It is the way such things are done. It represents the way people who are used to handling castings operate. It is accepted by them, on the basis of their years of experience, as a normal, proper, and necessary operation to add to casting making.

The reader will learn to recognize that the accomplishment of outstanding results will depend, in some instances, upon expertness in the use of the "blast" portion of this technique; in others, expertness in use of the "create" portion will be largely responsible for extremely high-grade results; in still others, extreme expertness in the "refine" portion will bring forth the optimum results. It is important that the value of effectively using each portion, when and as it is needed, be understood and, further, that the emphasis in each case be placed where it is needed. The examples that follow will aid in recognizing the validity of this statement.

FIG. 3-2. Copper tubing.

EXAMPLE 1: A needed part (Figure 3-2) was a piece of ¼-inch copper tubing 1½ inches long. Its cost was 4 cents. Here are the results of applying the three steps of the technique.

Blast. The basic cost of the required amount of copper tubing at the mill was found to be ¾ cent.

Create. The first alternative was to draw the tubing straight at the mill, box it in 20 foot lengths, and ship it to the factory for cutoff. The second alternative was to draw the tubing but wind it in coils and ship to the factory for straightening and cutoff. The third alternative was to arrange to have the tubing cut off at the mill as it was drawn and so eliminate the need for boxing straightened lengths for a costly shipment or for coiling the tubing and having it straightened at the factory.

Refine. Putting together the costs, the figures for alternative 3 were:

$$
\begin{array}{lr}
\text{Material} \dots\dots\dots\dots\dots\dots\dots\dots\dots & \$0.0075 \\
\text{Cutoff} \dots\dots\dots\dots\dots\dots\dots\dots\dots\dots & 0.0010 \\
\text{Boxing and freight} \dots\dots\dots\dots\dots & \underline{0.0017} \\
\text{Total (delivered ready for use)} \dots\dots & \$0.0102
\end{array}
$$

Quite obviously, the third alternative appeared to be the proper one to subject to refinement. What refinement was necessary? In the particular application, it was essential that there be no burrs. Therefore, the cutoff equipment had to be inspected and samples of its work had to be examined for burrs. This examination proved that the high-speed cutoff equipment accomplished its work effectively without leaving burrs. The final result was that the cost for the part changed from 4 cents to 1.02 cents.

EXAMPLE 2: The clamp bar shown in Figure 3-3 is made of steel, $1 \times \frac{1}{2}$ inch, with two $\frac{1}{2}$-inch threaded holes. It is 2 inches long. Required quantity is 4,000 per year.

What is the function? Half concealed inside heavy equipment, this clamp bar performs a basic function which could be provided by two $\frac{1}{2}$-inch nuts. It does, however, also provide the secondary convenience function of compensating for the fact that there is no space in which to insert a wrench to hold individual nuts during the tightening operation. Further, the clamp bar is desirable to keep individual nuts from becoming loosened during the use of the equipment. The over-all function, then, consists of a holding function, approximately equivalent to that which would be performed by two nuts, plus some type of secondary fastening function, such as could be provided by welding the two nuts together, welding them to a common piece of metal, or pressing them into some sort of holder which would keep them together.

FIG. 3-3. Clamp bar.

Blast. The basic function for which this part was designed, we find, could be accomplished by two nuts which cost $1\frac{1}{2}$ cents each. Hence, the value of the basic function is 3 cents. This represents a typical blast finding. We have an alternative which will provide an important segment of the function, though it will not accomplish the over-all function. To do that the two nuts must somehow be fastened together.

Create. How to fasten the nuts together is the subject of the second step, and we arrive at these solutions:

1. Weld the two nuts side by side.
2. Weld the two nuts to a piece of wire.

3. Weld the two nuts to a piece of sheet metal.

4. Press the two nuts into two holes in a piece of sheet metal.

Approximate costs for the above alternatives are brought into view.

Refine. Particular complications or problems to be solved in each case are now generally considered. While so investigating, we find that a vendor makes and sells weld nuts of the proper size. Further, we find that the factory has proper facilities for making a small stamping and for welding the two nuts into the stamping. The result of the blasting, creating, and refining is the double nut assembly shown in Figure 3-4. Its

Fɪɢ. 3-4. Clamp bar.

Fɪɢ. 3-5. Radio-frequency transformer.

cost is 8 cents, while the cost of the clamp bar had been 32 cents. In other words, by applying the technique, an alternative is provided which reliably accomplishes the over-all function for one-fourth of the cost.

EXAMPLE 3: Here we are concerned with a small radio-frequency transformer (Figure 3-5) about twice the size of a grain of wheat and costing 39 cents. It is used in large quantities. What is the function? The normal function of a transformer is to effect a useful transfer of electrical energy between two coils. For that purpose, one coil of wire is brought in close physical proximity with another coil of wire. In this type of product, it is most profitable to divert the thinking from the end function to the structural function. Basically, the problem then becomes one of reliably holding two coils of wire in an appropriate physical relationship. In this case, "holding" was found to be accomplished by winding both coils of wire on a very small spool. Four almost microscopic holes were then drilled in the ends of the spool, and the four necessary ends of the two coils were threaded through and pulled out of these holes. Study showed that the two coils of wire accounted for less than 10 cents of the cost. The cost of the spool, the drilling of the ends, and the threading of the wires through the holes in the end made up the bigger part of the cost.

Blast. Use only the two coils of wire. Put the two coils on a toothpick-size piece of wood or plastic.

Create

1. Discontinue drilling the spool ends and the subsequent threading of the fine wires through the holes.

2. Use a drop of adhesive to hold the wires in place.

3. If the spool ends are not to hold the wire, they will not be needed, and so we can discontinue using the spool.

4. Use a straight piece of suitable plastic or insulator material, wind on the coils, and secure the wires by a drop of appropriate adhesive.

Refine. By using only the coils as indicated from the "blast" step and the small insulator and adhesive (alternative 4) to maintain them in rigid relationship to each other, the electronic function can be accomplished at considerably less than half the original cost. However, we are now short of a means of supporting the assembly in the equipment. To provide for this, an additional small mounting part can also be secured by the drop of adhesive, as shown in Figure 3-6. The new cost is 19 cents. The annual cost, which had been $78,000, is now $38,000.

FIG. 3-6. Radio-frequency transformer.

EXAMPLE 4: GASOLINE TANKS for United States Navy landing craft. This represents one of a number af very important examples that resulted when the U.S. Navy Bureau of Ships first applied this "blast, create, refine" technique to the procurement of 1,000 landing craft. The function was to reliably contain 200 gallons of gasoline in a landing craft. The noncombat life of a landing craft is eight years.

Blast. Use four 50-gallon standard drums.

Create

1. A standard tank similar to the 250-gallon oil tanks in domestic use.

2. Tanks of rubberlike material, such as are often used in aircraft.

3. Special, but simply made, welded tanks.

4. If iron for drums or tanks is not suitable, add appropriate coating.

Refine. The use of four basic 50-gallon drums to contain the fuel at a cost of $25 was refined by applying alternative 4, the use of appropriate coatings to provide the required reliability and life. This brought the cost to $80. The four drums accomplished the total function with at least the same reliability as the former one large tank of special high-cost alloy steel.

As a result of applying the technique here, the $80 gasoline containers were adopted to replace the $520 special-alloy tank. The return to the taxpayers was $440,000—the difference between $520,000 and $80,000—on this one procurement.

EXAMPLE 5: In military equipment of the radar type, it is often necessary to have a control for centering a spot on the televisionlike screen. This "joy-stick" assembly (Figure 3-7) consisted of a mounting plate about 6 inches square with a small lever about 4 inches long extending through the center. This lever could be moved in any direction, and as it was moved, it electronically caused the spot on the screen to move in the same direction. In back of this plate were suitable gears and mountings for the lever and for four potentiometers: two operating at right angles to the other two. The total assembly cost $127. The potentiometers which accomplished the electronic function accounted for $3.60 of this cost. For the required simple, unprecise manual movement of $4 worth of electronic gear, $123 worth of mechanical gear was used.

Fig. 3-7. Radar-control mounting.

The over-all function was that of electronically providing decreases in certain currents and increases in others so that the spot could be guided to the center of the screen. For the purpose of providing better value alternatives, this total over-all function is best divided into a number of subfunctions which become quite manageable valuewise. Basically, the mechanical functions of the device consist in mounting four small potentiometers with an operating handle so that the handle can be moved through the proper range to adjust the potentiometers for proper operation.

Blast. For this item, with which the hand moves a small lever until the eye sees that the spot is in the center, it would seem that a very simple mechanism for mounting the lever and the potentiometers would accomplish the total purpose and would be low in cost.

Create

1. A standard or a modified ball-and-socket mounting with suitable linkages to operate the potentiometers

2. A simple "double axis" mounting with the axes at right angles

3. Standard control levers with their mountings, as already provided and available for other applications

Refine. A study showed that the principal reason for the high cost was that the potentiometers had to be moved through 300 degrees to get their complete variation, and to that end, it was necessary to have a considerable number of gears back of the panel in order to magnify the 90-degree motion of the lever through the panel. It was further found that a plus or minus 20 per cent variation tolerance was properly specified for the potentiometers, because in this application, any specific benefits from close tolerance would be canceled out by differences in the motion of the hand.

The vendor was asked for quotations based on providing potentiometers which would vary through the same range with a motion of 90 degrees. This he was able to do, but the potentiometers became "specials" and a cost increase of 10 cents was added to each. Therefore, instead of $3.60 for the four standards, $4 would have to be paid for the four specials. A basic model was promptly provided for $11 to meet other physical conditions of the equipment. This was further refined to an interchangeable component which met all of the operating specifications and which had the same reliability at a cost of $30. Three-fourths of the cost was removed and all of the performance reliability continued. This is a typical result of applying the technique.

To summarize, the very useful value analysis technique of blasting, creating, and then refining serves first to bring the needed functions sharply into focus. Then the means being used or planned to accomplish these functions are critically reviewed and blasted by comparing them with processes, products, or materials which would accomplish only part of the function but which would have a small fraction of the cost. This is followed by an extensive and intensive creative effort in which a series of significant alternatives for accomplishing the total function or each part of the function or for causing other methods to perform satisfactorily are brought into view. In a subsequent refining effort, the total needs for the application are objectively considered in the light of all the information developed in the function study and in the blast and create phases, and a suitable combination of alternatives is established for reliably accomplishing the total function at a cost lower than that existing.

Case Study

THE ELECTRIC CONTROLLER

Electromechanical controllers, approximately $1 \times 1 \times 2$ feet in size, were required in quantities of 1,000 per year. The product performed its function well and had received good acceptance in the market for several years. With the constant march of progress, it was apparent that the selling price would have to be lowered, which in turn meant that costs would have to be lowered.

A team of men from the engineering, manufacturing, purchasing, and cost department was assigned to go over the controller in detail. Their work culminated in the reduction of costs by about 10 per cent. While this reduction was adequate to meet the market conditions at the time, it certainly allowed no leeway for the unexpected. Hence the manager, who had heard of the value analysis approach, arranged to have a man make a value audit of the product using value analysis techniques. Starting again with the functions performed by the assemblies, the subassemblies, and the parts and evaluating these functions, value alternatives were developed which would reliably accomplish these functions.

Some of the items, together with the particular changes affecting them, were as follows:

Small hinges were made by buying an extruded section, drilling the hole for the pin, and then drilling mounting holes in the flat portion. The cost was 28 cents. By using a ⅛ × 1-inch steel strip, cutting it to length, rolling it at one end for the hinge pin, and drilling it for mounting, the cost became 10 cents.

A steel hub 2½ inches in diameter and ¼ inch thick, with a ¼-inch hole drilled in the center and six small holes drilled around and near the outer circumference to serve for mounting two small 6-inch diameter by ¹⁄₁₆-inch-thick aluminum dials, cost $1.27. The search for a specialty product which would perform this function revealed that aluminum companies sell slugs, i.e., round pieces of aluminum punched from sheet stock, for use in impact extrusion machines making toothpaste tubes and a wide variety of similar containers. It was found that one of these slugs, 2½ inches by ¼ inch in size, could be secured for 4 cents. However, it was slightly cupped, and the judgment was that for the application in question it needed to be flat. This could be accomplished by a flattening operation costing 1 cent. The operation of drilling the center hole and the smaller holes for mounting the dials came to 8 cents, giving a total of 13 cents instead of $1.27.

Plastic cams, ¼ inch thick by 2 inches in diameter, having the equivalent of saw teeth, approximately eight per inch, cost $1 each. By reviewing the product with the plastic supplier, it was determined that orders placed approximately twice each year rather than more frequently in very much smaller lot sizes, as had sometimes been done, resulted in a price of 20 cents.

A ⅝-inch ID by ⅞-inch OD by ½-inch-long collar drilled and tapped for a radial set screw cost 36 cents. It was made on a screw machine. By changing the raw material to a heavy-wall tubing which was cut, burred, and provided with a drilled and tapped radial hole, the cost came to 10 cents.

A special jam nut cost 20 cents. A standard jam nut of the same general description costs 1 cent. However, the distance across corners of the standard jam nut was slightly too large—¹⁄₃₂ inch—to avoid interference with the smallest-size gear which, under some conditions, was used in the mechanism. A slight modification was made in the mounting arrangement, and the cost became 1 cent.

A small spur pinion, approximately ⅝ inch in diameter by ⅝ inch long, was being machined. Its cost was 65 cents. A supplier was found who could provide the pinion stock of the proper size and thread so that the factory merely needed to cut it off and burr it in order to produce an interchangeable pinion for 40 cents.

Three switches and a switch mounting plate were purchased from the same supplier for 85 cents. They were routed to the factory and put together into an assembly. The cost of the assembly was $1.33. The particular supplier was asked to provide the assembly ready for use, shipping only one part instead of four. This eliminated much inspection, mounting, handling, storing, etc. The supplier offered delivery of the assemblies ready to use at $1.

A bracket in the form of a U was made of ⅛ × 1-inch steel bar. The base of the bracket was about 6 inches long, with each end turned up approximately 2 inches. Some suitable holes were drilled. The cost of the bracket was 48 cents. In studying the reason for the high cost of this bracket, it was found that one operation—a special straightening and sizing of the ends to hold the distance between the two bent-up ends within extremely close tolerances—accounted for 12 cents of the cost. This sizing operation was said to be required so that the assembly would immediately go together under all circumstances. Inspection and study of the assembly area showed that a mallet was kept nearby. The operator said that it was used on all of the brackets in assembly. This element of obviously unnecessary and noncontributing cost was eliminated, and some other improvements were also made, with the result that the cost became 17 cents.

A bearing block was made by buying extruded material, cutting it into lengths approximately ½ inch long, and drilling a large mounting hole for the bearing and two transverse holes for mounting the block. It cost 65 cents. It was found that a piece of ⅛-inch steel sheet, with two holes drilled in what would serve as a flat section for mounting and a large hole swaged to receive a flanged bearing in a section that was bent up at right angles, would accomplish the function with the same reliability for 20 cents. It was further found that the bearing which was being used cost 11 cents, whereas a suitable flanged bearing would fit ideally into the assembly and cost 3½ cents.

The device contained a dust cover which was open at the bottom and hinged on the side and cost $5. As reported elsewhere in this text, the cover appeared to have no function, but the engineers believed that it was necessary to provide it on the product in order to please the customers. It was found that only one customer wanted it, so the item was eliminated except for that one customer, who then paid for it as special equipment.

A large assembly called a motor plate pointer assembly was made of ⅛-inch steel approximately 5 inches on each triangular side, with a welded pointer rising several inches and with teeth cut on one edge. Its cost was $1.80. In the value study, its function was evaluated at considerably less. A review of the cost build-up showed that these steel parts were being copper plated, chemically blackened, and then lacquered. Newer processes for chemically blackening steel directly, to provide good surface protection and a good appearance finish, were investigated and resulted in a decrease in cost to 80 cents.

A panel costing $2.28 was also carefully investigated. Each point of specification which caused increased cost was studied, and such actions were taken as were desirable and possible. Among others, care was taken to control the ordering quantities to eliminate unnecessary setups. The cost decreased from $2.28 to $1.

All these and other changes, none of which in the least affected the needed function, were responsible for a 40 per cent reduction over and above the 10 per cent removed prior to the application of the value analysis techniques. Tooling costs in this case were almost negligible—less than one-fourth of the annual saving.

3-5. *Use Real Creativity*

The technique of using real creativity is based on the commonly accepted conviction that creativity, in lesser or greater degree, is a human trait. By putting this trait into free play a surprising number of ideas for the solution of problems can be generated.

It has been generally said that there are at least eight ways of doing practically everything, and people intent upon exercising their creative ability commonly hold this belief. They recognize that creativity is not given a fair chance when a person becomes satisfied that a certain procedure is the *only* way. Therefore, they strive to keep away from merely criticizing a given solution and rather strive to weigh the other seven ways. For instance, when they face a motion which is accomplished, say, mechanically, they may proceed to investigating doing the same thing by electrical, electronic, hydraulic, thermal, or chemical means. By such an approach, new and better solutions are brought into view.

In value analysis, the application of available creative power is a potent tool to draw on as soon as the function desired in any particular case has been tied down to specifics. At this point, the question of foremost concern is: What else would do the function or in what other ways could it be reliably accomplished? The answer to that question needs to be established before hope can be had of sifting out the lowest-cost solution for optimum value.

This, then, means that our interest must now be centered on bringing forth the ideas that may spring into mind as possible alternative choices, regardless of what degree of practicability they may appear to hold at first sight. The more extensive the list of such ideas we can produce for subsequent evaluation, the greater the prospect of a profitable return on the creative effort we make.

The most common obstacle to deriving results from attempts to be creative in developing ideas lies in the natural tendency to let judicial thinking interfere with mental explorations. For that reason, the main requirement in applying the creative technique is to stay away from being judicial in the first stage of the process. Unless that be done, progress is soon retarded by sentiments such as "It can't be done," "It won't work," or "Specifications won't allow it." Such negative thoughts hamper a free flow of imagination; the things that they imply must be left to be explored in a subsequent step.

Another obstacle to getting creativity into action is the tendency to associate creative thinking with intricate and complex problems. The fact is that even the simplest problems benefit from being dealt with creatively. The thing to guard against here is the application of creativity in the wrong directions. For example, in one case on record the problem was to seal off a 3-inch pipe. Here the designer chose to be creative by laying out a special pipe plug that served the function well indeed, at a manufactured cost of $15. Had he applied his creativity to searching out the best plug for the purpose from available supplies, he would, no doubt, have chosen to purchase a perfectly serviceable plug from a local plumbing dealer at $3, thus avoiding a needless outlay of $12 that returned no value.

A third cause of restricted use of creative thinking is often found in the difficulty people may experience in getting a chain reaction of ideas ignited and then sustained. In such instances, experience indicates that a brainstorm session with, say, three or more participants, works wonders. In the competitive atmosphere of such sessions, one individual's idea soon stimulates other ideas both in the mind of the individual himself and in the minds of his associates. The extent to which this happens is indicated by the following yields of two group-brainstorm sessions. In the one case, the problem was "how to detect that someone is at the front door and wishes admission." The record of that session showed a total of 109 different ideas for solution of the problem. The other instance had to do with how to join together two electrical conductors. Here, the record was comprised of 140 varied ideas.

Sight should not be lost, though, of the fact that an individual by himself can stimulate his own imagination or creative thinking by very simple expedients. For instance, anyone confronted with the problem of how to best join two flat pieces of material may derive helpful suggestions from merely glancing observingly around the ordinary office. As the eyes pause on the paste bottle, the cement tube, the Scotch tape roll, the paper stapler, the hole punch, or the clip tray, the mind is automatically directed toward the alternatives of pasting, cementing, taping, stitching, riveting, and clamping the pieces together.

Case Study

No Waste

A shift lever bracket (Figure 3-8) on an appliance was used in quantity and made of ⅛-inch-thick steel 3 inches wide. A die the size and shape of the required part was used. It blanked each item as required from the material, leaving a slight amount of trim all around. The part cost 11 cents. Its function was evaluated at between 2 and 3 cents.

In the creative phase of study, dozens of possible approaches were listed; for example:

Make of wire form
    Plastic
    Standard angle
    Flattened tubing
Eliminate it
Combine with the handle

One phase of the creative study developed suggested changes for the tooling used in making it. One suggestion was to cut off the piece instead of stamping it out. It was then discovered that the part had an unusual symmetry in that its edges were parallel and its top and its bottom could be identical. A new punch was made which would provide identical tops and bottoms to the part and which was itself the size of the required stamping. A slightly narrower steel

Fig. 3-8. Normal stamping operation with one piece formed at each stroke of machine and waste around edges.

Fig. 3-9. Improved stamping operation with two pieces formed at each stroke of machine and no waste material.

material was ordered so that there would be no waste on the sides, and the stamping operation would change to a cutoff operation. Since the stamping die was then exactly the size of the part required and either the bottom or the top would cut the shape required, the material was moved the length of two parts at each stroke and the punch acted to shear off one part with its leading edge and another with its following edge. The result, as shown in Figure 3-9, was that instead of one part with each stroke and waste all around, two parts were secured with each stroke and no waste whatsoever was made. Cost became 2 cents each.

Whether the application of creativity is exercised by the individual alone or in group brainstorming the important factor, as already indicated, is to let no judicial thinking eliminate any idea that comes to mind, regardless of how ridiculous it may sound at first. Every idea that emerges spontaneously deserves to be jotted down for further consideration. What this means, then, is that whenever the ready flow of ideas stops, each idea on the record must be evaluated in terms of what effect its development may have on the ultimate goal. A farfetched idea may then appear to hold the best promise of yielding the most substantial benefit in its developed state. Thus that idea, rather than the idea that seems the easiest to develop, may be the one to concentrate on, with due consideration to the time factor involved. In this connection, it is well to bear in mind that development work on one idea frequently leads to other ideas of even greater benefit. Hence no idea should be forsaken until an attempt has been made to develop it to the extent that time allows.

EXAMPLE 1: The United States Navy's bulkhead-penetration project culminated in the use of a combination of fiber supports and epoxy-resin sealing by air-gun extrusion. Compared with the standard variety of metal bulkhead penetrations, the cost of the new method came to one-fifth of the earlier cost and opened up opportunities to make sizable savings, more than $70,000 a year in one naval shipyard.

EXAMPLE 2: Application of squirted-in self-vulcanizing material to take the place of ready-made rubber gaskets resulted in a cost reduction from 11 cents to 1 cent per seal. This solution went back to someone's in-quisitively asking himself, "Wonder what use I could make of the jar-sealing gaskets that my wife buys for practically nothing at the dime store?"

A wealth of material is available in published literature on the subject of creativity and on how to exercise it in problem solution.[1]

Experience proves that the value specialist invariably profits in varying degrees from appropriate use of the technique of applying real imaginative creativity.

3-6. *Identify and Overcome Roadblocks*

There is hardly a person living who has not been impressed by the effectiveness with which some product accomplished its purpose, only to be superceded some time later by modifications which performed the same function much more reliably at a much lower cost. It is normal to accept, as being "near perfection," the good work which has been done on something that accomplishes its purpose well today. It is shock-ing to later learn that the same functions could have been performed so much better at a lower cost even at the earlier date.

Why, then, were these functions not accomplished at lower cost earlier? Something prevented it. Most likely, continuation of the study involved ceased, as did work that might have resulted in improvement. Design and manufacture were centered on the product as it was. In some

---

[1] The student of value analysis will do well to explore references such as Alex F. Osborn, *Your Creative Power,* Charles Scribner's Sons, New York, 1951; *Applied Imagination,* 1953, by the same author and publisher; Eugene K. Von Fange, *Professional Creativity,* Prentice-Hall, Inc., Englewood Cliffs, N.J., 1959.

instances the material or process that would yield the function at a lower cost was nonexistent at the time of the earlier design. Experience shows, however, that, in nine out of ten cases, applicable processes or materials or perhaps special products did exist and could, in fact, have been included in the earlier design and manufacture.

The natural question here is: Would not benefits have resulted from putting into earlier use such processes or materials which accomplish

"Roadblocks" surrounding every decision are deeply rooted in the realities so well expressed in Samuel Foss's Poem "The Path of the calf".

Path of the Calf *

"One day through the primeval wood
A calf walked home as good calves should;
But made a trail all bent askew,
A crooked trail as all calves do.
Since then three hundred years have fled,
And I infer the calf is dead.
But still he left behind his trail,
And thereby hangs my moral tale.
The trail was taken up next day
By a lone dog that passed that way;
And then a wise bellwether sheep
Pursued the trail o'er vale and steep,
And drew the flock behind him, too,
As good bellwethers always do.
And from that day o'er hill and glade,
Through those old woods a path was made.

The years passed on in swiftness fleet,
The road became a village street;
And this, before men were aware,
A city's crowded thoroughfare.
And soon the central street was this
Of a renowned metropolis;
And men two centuries and a half
Trod in the footsteps of that calf.
Each day a hundred thousand rout
Followed this calf about
And o'er his crooked journey went
The traffic of a continent.
A hundred thousand men were led
By one calf near three centuries dead.
They followed still his crooked way;
And lost one hundred years a day;
For thus such reverence is lent
To well established precedent."

FIG. 3-10. The path of the calf.

the total function more reliably, perhaps more simply, and at lower cost? Checks indicate that the answer is usually "yes."

What, then, stopped action for better value in nine out of the ten cases? Roadblocks—occasionally real but mostly imaginary.

The purpose of the technique of identifying and overcoming roadblocks is to help develop these situations and prevent value work from so often stopping short of adopting accomplishable value alternatives.

A roadblock, as that term is used in the present connection, is a decision which prevents timely development of appropriate value alternatives. The cause of it may be a lack of information, acceptance of wrong information, or a wrong belief. These factors cause the decision maker to decide that it is not wise for him to continue to work toward lower costs at the particular time. The sort of roadblock in question occurs after tests have shown that the performance objectives have been met. Value objectives, being less clear and not as measurable, are given secondary consideration, and decisions tend to be made to proceed with the drawing up of the designs, with the building of tools, and with manufacturing.

Some of the common roadblocks met with are:

There is no better material.

This is the best process considering quantities.

There is probably no better way of doing it and we are short of time anyway.

This has been proved to work. We won't change it.

Underwriters' wouldn't approve any other arrangement.

This is the result of a lot of study. It will be far better than competition.

We changed that a few years ago and got into an epidemic of trouble. We are not changing it again.

We had to maintain interchangeability.

You can't beat an automatic screw machine for any part that it can make.

We have ten turret lathes; we certainly make money by designing to keep them busy.

There is no other source of supply.

We can't pay for the tools.

It doesn't make sense, but it's policy.

We know more about this than anyone else.

There is no plastic with those properties.

It is impractical to make castings that small.

It costs too much to change the drawings.

The customers like it this way.

It is important to bring these roadblocks clearly into the open and to recognize that they usually represent the honest beliefs of the men who make the decisions. To achieve improved reliability, simplicity, and lower cost in these circumstances, more correct information must be injected into the situation with proper timing and presentation so that the decision maker will use it.

EXAMPLE 1: Rather large quantities of asbestos paper were used for one application at a time when asbestos was in short supply and was, besides, a costly item. Its function was to catch paint drippings in a dip-painting line. When the value consultant questioned the use of asbestos for this, he was told that it was the only material that fit the specification and had the approval of the fire-safety committee. The roadblock clearly was that the fire-safety committee would not allow the use of anything other than asbestos paper. New information was searched out from manufacturers of special papers, and when it was found that "nonburning" paper could be made, samples were obtained. Tests were made and the new paper proved to serve the purpose reliably. Based on this new information, the roadblock was overcome. The result was an improvement of value and a lessening of procurement problems.

EXAMPLE 2: A stainless-steel nipple for conducting water into electrical equipment cost 20 cents and was required in large quantities. It was manufactured by purchasing standard fittings and then modifying them. Manufacturing alternatives were later provided in the creative phase of a manufacturing value study. The finding was that the parts, made from tubing by semiautomatic machines, could be purchased for 5 cents each. The roadblock clearly was a statement put on the drawing for the guidance and instruction of the purchasing department. It said, "Purchase stainless fitting #AB 1025, modify as shown by the drawing." Again, with the roadblock clearly in view, action could, as is usually the case, be taken to overcome its costly effects. A review with the engineer disclosed that when the item was designed ten years earlier it was a relatively low-volume item, and the most economical way to provide the fitting was as specified. Sometime during the years, matters changed so that the opposite situation was now true. Of course, there was no reluctance on the part of engineering to immediately strike from the drawing this roadblock specification.

EXAMPLE 3: "IT IS PATENTED." A rather complicated arrangement was used to support about fifty pounds of rotating equipment on a high-volume product. Application of value analysis techniques quickly brought forth the information that a simple construction for the support would cut the cost by 40 cents and result in an annual saving of $24,000. However, the objection arose that the simple construction could not be used because it was patented. The roadblock came into clear view. Obviously, the simple construction should not be used if it were covered by a valid competing patent and if licensing could not be arranged for at a cost substantially less than $24,000. A patent search was initiated, and soon the attorney reported that there was no patent in existence that read on the simple construction which would most effectively and economically accomplish the function. This eliminated the roadblock and allowed action to simplify and improve the design, with the additional benefit of eliminating the $24,000 of unnecessary cost.

The fact remains that this "belief," until corrected, was just as effective in adding $24,000 to the cost as some additional customer requirement or additional new feature would have been.

EXAMPLE 4: "UNDERWRITERS' WON'T APPROVE IT." A very simple and functional design for a socket to hold a light bulb was suggested by a value analysis study. The verdict of the engineering people of one company was that the design would accomplish the function reliably but that it would never be approved by Underwriters'. Hence it was not adopted. Again the roadblock was in clear view. It is interesting to note that a socket incorporating the main features of this proposed design was put on the market by another manufacturer a few months later. It bore the stamp of Underwriters' approval as it should have, because it accomplished its function with total reliability and total safety.

This specific technique of identifying and overcoming roadblocks is another item in the kit of tools which is positively essential for the professional value engineer to learn to use effectively.

Case Study

It Won't Work

Truth is indeed often stranger than fiction. A most interesting and typical example of such a situation is the case in which 800 small brass cams were required per year. These cams were being machined from ³⁄₁₆-inch brass material, and because of their unusual shape, the machining operations did not lend themselves to any simple mechanical routine. Because the quantities were so low, it had also been determined each time a change was considered that it would certainly not be economical to purchase tools for stamping them out.

The value engineer, in looking at the job and in creatively searching for alternatives, felt that it was worthwhile to consider the use of a Kirksite die. Kirksite resembles lead and is commonly melted and poured into a die around a model of the part required. When it has set, it is hard enough to be used for a tool to blank out a good quantity.

A manufacturing methods engineer, whom the value analyst succeeded in interesting in the project, decided it had a chance of working and thought he would like to try it. Hence, he asked his boss for a shop order of $50 to give it a try. He didn't get it. The boss said, "It won't work." Meanwhile, the engineer's interest in the project grew, and he went on to tell the boss's boss what he had in mind and said he wanted the $50 to try it. Again he was told, "It will never work." By now he had become so enthusiastic about the idea and so involved in it that he decided to run the risk of going to the top and telling the manager of manufacturing about it. This he did; once more he asked for the needed $50 shop order, only to be told that he couldn't have it because "it wouldn't work."

During the following few days, the idea stayed with him, and his frustration turned into constructive emotion. He decided he would do it anyway and charge it to another shop order which he already had.

It worked. The demonstration was amazing. He decided to get the worst over first by telling the manager of manufacturing, and when he did, he was immediately given an opportunity to demonstrate. The amazed manufacturing manager called in a number of his subordinates and they were given the same demonstration. These people, in turn, called in a number of their engineers for a demonstration. Each time a few pieces were run off and checked for dimension.

An interesting happening was that, at the end of the day when the parts were viewed, it was decided to send them to the storeroom for use in production; as they were counted, it was found that they made up enough parts for two years of production.

After a roadblock is identified as such and eliminated, it appears very simple; prior to this, however, it is formidable and totally stops action.

Case Study

UNDERWRITERS' WON'T ALLOW IT

An electronic control contained twelve binding screws. The function of these screws was to hold small wires in positive contact on their terminals. Quantities were 50,000 controls per year which meant 600,000 screws. The screws cost $6 per thousand although they were very similar to screws which cost $2 per thousand.

Why this three times increase in the cost? The answer was that although $2 per thousand would buy small No. 8 screws of the proper size and type, the specifications called for No. 8 screws with smaller No. 6 heads. This made the screw a special. The use of technique 12, "utilize applicable standards," showed that two-thirds of the cost might be unnecessary. When the question of "why?" was raised, the answer from technical people involved was, "Underwriters' requires a No. 8 screw." Examination of the assembly showed that, as it was made, the head of the No. 8 screw was slightly too large to facilitate assembly in the installation of one of the twelve screws. Hence No. 6 heads were put on No. 8 shanks for all of the screws. When the question was properly explored with Underwriters', its answer was, "We felt it desirable to specify a No. 8 screw so that it would have a large-enough head to make extra-positive contact with the small wires."

Now that this roadblock was illuminated with more facts, it was obvious that putting the large shanks on the screws at three times the cost made no contribution of any kind. As a result, Underwriters' was asked to reexamine the application, and it subsequently approved a screw which cost $2 per thousand—one-third of the cost—as totally functional and safe.

In this case, as in many others, better answers did not come forth until technique 6, "identify and overcome roadblocks," was applied.

3-7. *Use Industry Specialists to Extend Specialized Knowledge*

Getting an acceptable degree of value means accomplishing functions as well as competition does. Getting good-grade value means doing it better. The former is accomplished by getting answers as good as competition's; to accomplish the latter, better answers are required.

The question, then, is how to get better answers. The procedure is as follows:

Establish clearly in the mind exactly what is to be accomplished, i.e., precisely what functions are desired.

Place better alternatives before the decision makers.

Get an action pattern established so that the information on the best alternatives will be promptly used in decision making.

In providing better answers for the accomplishment of each function, we must first ask: What technology is involved? For instance, does the problem primarily involve:

Circuitry:
    Electrical
    Magnetic
Conduction:
    Electrical
    Hydraulic
    Heat transfer
Design:
    Arrangement
    Styling
Mechanics:
    Gears
    Linkages
    Servomechanisms

Metals:
    Corrosion-resistant
    High-temperature
    Heavy-duty
    Lightweight
Nonmetallics:
    Paper
    Plastics
    Rubber
    Wood
Processing:
    Material removal
    Forming
    Joining
    Packaging

The quality of the answers suggested is dependent upon a number of things. Obviously, one of the most vital is the depth of penetration of the subject matter brought to bear on the problem. If we take the known penetration of any one technology as 100 per cent, what depth of penetration into each applicable technology can be expected in any specific instance? Is the answer, say, 25 per cent penetration? Probably not—or at least not in more than a certain few technologies. In most cases it is reasonable to assume that we get down considerably lower.

Let us assume that the personnel concerned with developing and selecting engineering and manufacturing alternatives which establish the degree of value in their product apply a knowledge penetration of 10 per cent on the average. The quality of the answers then arrived at, compared with the answers which could be obtained with available knowledge applied, cannot be good. Special knowledge in depth in the areas involved must be brought into the work to a greater extent before decision making. Furthermore, it must be remembered that knowledge, techniques, and processes are continually being developed in each technology and that only the specialists know of those which have become practical within the last year or two. Of still greater importance is the fact that these industry specialists are continuously working on advancing knowledge in each technology. The developments they complete one year will begin, perhaps, to come into usage the next year and will gain increasing use during the years immediately following. Only by bringing these specialists into touch with the functions needed in the product can the better answers derived from the latest within their technology be obtained so that a good or excellent degree of value may be ensured.

Case Study

DO IT LIKE AN INDIAN

Scarcity of stainless steel and innovation in attractive anodized finishes for aluminum made it advisable to seriously consider a good welded-aluminum construction for an appliance shelf.

After a few months of study, however, it appeared that the project should be abandoned because of an inability to weld suitable aluminum which would take an acceptable finish with sufficient dependability.

One engineer dissented, saying, "I don't think we ought to quit. Why don't we try doing it like an Indian would?" When questioned by the engineering manager as to his meaning, he said, "I only mean that an Indian wouldn't weld it, because in the days of Indians, they didn't have welding."

He was put in charge of the job. His first action was to utilize the value analysis techniques to obtain, as quickly and efficiently as possible, all of the industrial know-how from industrial specialists. This resulted in visits to two fence manufactures to learn approved practices in bending, crimping, twisting, and otherwise fastening wire to wire.

So much technology new to the appliance business but, in fact, old to the fence business came into immediate focus that before long practical designs had been developed, tested, proven, and put into production with retention of the desired aluminum construction.

For his accomplishment, the engineer received a special award from his company—a personal gain further recognizing his benefit to his company.

The concept of drawing on industrial specialists to extend the use of specialized knowledge is so simple and straightforward that it ought to be one that is followed as a rule rather than as an exception. That, however, is contrary to the facts. There are several reasons why this is so.

1. Unfortunately for the cause of value, contributors commonly have pride in what they do. Each individual, when he receives an assignment, becomes interested in it, intrigued by it, and challenged by it. He puts his body, his mind, and his emotions into it, and often he develops several answers. When tests show that they, or at least one of them, will work, he develops "pride of authorship." He may have attained neither excellent nor a good degree of value, but physical tests do not show that up. Therefore, he proudly supports any related projects of engineering, manufacturing, purchasing, or management, and the product is born.

2. In the past, when a good degree of performance was required but there was little emphasis on a good or excellent degree of value, it may or may not have been necessary to call in help. Just the same, it has become a quite well accepted practice, if performance problems continue, to call in industrial specialists to help solve the performance problems. In contrast, relatively few people as yet have become used to drawing on the technology of such specialists in order to get better answers which will improve reliability, provide simplicity, and result in lower cost. Habits and attitudes of the past work against this simple expedient.

3. Supervisors and managers, lacking sufficiently broad vision, may interpret the action of drawing on specialized knowledge as a sign of weakness. Even today, superiors will occasionally measure their people by their individual ability to solve the problems they meet up with without calling in extra help. Such an attitude may have been excusable in the past when there was so much less depth of knowledge in the various technologies and when the primary effort was performance-oriented. The fact remains that it has led to staggering, and sometimes bankrupting, amounts of unnecessary cost in products.

4. Individuals sometimes lack recognition of the existence of more knowledge pertinent to their work than what they have at hand.

5. People often do not know where to go to get more knowledge pertinent to their work, although they may feel that it probably exists.

6. The additional knowledge costs money. When a man buys an automobile, he sees, tests, and evaluates the automobile, then pays his money for it. He knows, in general, what he will get before he makes the decision. The exact opposite is true in the case of acquiring the help of technical industrial specialists. If the accomplishments they can provide were known beforehand, their services would be unnecessary. But the fact that their services must be solicited and will cost money before their contributions can be known is a strong deterrent to their use.

7. Securing more know-how may mean delay, especially if it is called in belatedly at quite a late stage of product development. It seems

much easier to go ahead with plans as they are. The product is known to have performance, attractiveness, and suitable features, and often it is assumed that the value is good. That is particularly so when some ingenious moneysaving ideas may have been developed in the course of the value work.

EXAMPLE 1: HEAT-TRANSFER ENCLOSURE. A complicated metallic enclosure of a space, approximately 2 cubic feet in volume, had the primary function of transferring and dissipating heat from the equipment which it contained. It had fins and other elements of design and construction for accomplishing this main function, which it performed very well. It dissipated the necessary amount of heat and helped to make the product perform entirely satisfactorily. It was made in moderate volume, and its cost was $74.

During a value program, a heat-transfer specialist was invited to look into the application. The result was that, within a week, design and manufacturing concepts were provided which accomplished the total function more simply with less weight and with complete reliability for $16.

EXAMPLE 2: THE LINKAGE. As today's products become more and more adjustable and more and more automatic, the development of simple, reliable, low-cost, effective linkages is changing from an art to a science. It is true that virtually any engineer can develop a linkage that will perform any job. The variation comes in the complication, reliability, and cost. It is not unusual for the number of parts to vary from five to one and for the cost to vary from ten to one.

A linkage used for a lifting mechanism, in moderate volume and in rather heavy equipment, had proved thoroughly reliable in accomplishing its performance function. The cost of the linkage, based on the usual volume, was $285,000 per year. During a value study, a linkage specialist was asked to review it and submit suggestions. In a week's time, he came up with sketches and suggestions for a linkage which completely retained the reliability and performance characteristics and, in addition, provided further simplicity, at a cost of $90,000 per year.

EXAMPLE 3: GYROS. In a military product in which weight was very important, gyros were used for a specific function. Since cost controls quantities in military purchasing, it too was an extremely important factor. During a value study, electronic specialists examining the functions to be provided advised that an electronic circuit would accomplish the total function of one of the gyros and eliminate weight, provide simplicity, and do away with large amounts of cost. The result was important improvements to the weapon.

The reader will recall that the greatest causes of roadblocks which are responsible for stopping at cost levels as they are instead of continuing projects until very much lower cost levels are attained are:

Lack of information
Wrong information
Wrong beliefs

The technique of using industrial specialists to extend specialized knowledge is usually essential in penetrating roadblocks to achieve very much lower cost levels and very much higher value levels.

> *To get top-grade value, it is essential that needed functions be clearly identified first. Then, the best of industry specialists must be appraised of the function to the end that they contribute their knowledge and technique to the securing of the simplest, most reliable, and lowest-cost means for accomplishing these functions.*

3-8. *Get a Dollar Sign on Key Tolerances*

Why are tolerances specified? The simple answer here is that tolerances are specified *where* and *as* required to obtain a necessary fit or to allow essential assembly. Nevertheless, confusion often causes tolerances to be called for unnecessarily, as illustrated by the following answers to inquiries from actual cases.

The designer or draftsman "thought" that the tolerance he specified was needed to obtain required fit.

The designer or draftsman didn't know, but to "make sure," he included a close tolerance or precise specification.

The designer "thought" it to be standard practice to specify tolerance.

Tolerances were included to avoid an "incomplete" drawing.

The designer "thought" the tolerance used would not increase costs.

The designer "thought" the tolerance to be in harmony with available economical materials specifications.

Variations of raw material in past years made it "seem" necessary.

Interchangeability with former products made it "necessary."

The way mating parts were joined, it was "required."

Case Study

Is the Value $60 per Thousand or Is It $1 per Thousand?

A small precise part resembling the top half of a shingle nail was used in quantities of 700,000 per year. The cost was $60 per thousand—6 cents each. What would a shingle nail cost? Perhaps ½₀ cent?

The part was found to be made of carbon steel, to have a very precise head, and to have a ½-thousandth tolerance on the shank part.

In operation, it acted as a valve. The exactness of the head was quite important. The function of the shank was the normal one of locating the functioning head.

The precision in the head was adding to performance.

The precision in the shank was adding only to cost.

The shank precision made manufacturing the part a very costly job.

Suppliers who specialize in economical manufacture of that type of part were shown the item, shown its performance, shown the precision needed in the head, and shown the function of the shaft.

The result was a quotation of $1 per thousand. The shank would be held within a tolerance of two thousandths.

The engineering group could see no reason why this alternative would not work and proceeded to find out why the ½-thousandth tolerance was specified in the drawing. The draftsman recalled a discussion of it with the engineer at some previous time, when they had both decided on the ½-thousandth tolerance. The reason neither could recall. Tests were made. No benefit resulted from shank precision. The change was made, the identical function was obtained, and the cost was reduced to one-sixtieth of the former cost.

Close tolerances, when they conform to standard practice and are provided automatically from properly adjusted machines, do not add substantially to increased cost in a good many cases. Often, however, from any list of tolerances, there are one, two, or three which produce shocking increases in manufacturing cost. These must be known for proper decision making.

The real objectives of tolerances, of course, are:

To assure a product which will work, i.e., provide use functions
To provide a product which will sell, i.e., provide appearance functions
To provide a product which can be manufactured at lowest cost

Regrouped as follows, these objectives become more readily applicable as a guide to study and to decision making.

To provide use functions reliably at lowest cost
To provide esteem functions reliably at lowest cost

On each tolerance called for, it is essential to raise the basic value analysis queries of:

What function does it provide?

What does it cost?

For efficient use in identifying unnecessary costs, these questions are here best reversed.

What does it cost?

What function does it provide?

What the key tolerances are is the next point that must be nailed down.

If in reality the cost of the tolerance is found to be trifling or negligible, then it may be passed up without further consideration in the application of this technique. But if the cost it introduces is substantial and important, the function it provides must be brought into clear focus so that it may be subjected to all applicable techniques to creatively generate and crystallize value alternatives.

Fig. 3-11. Pole piece.

This process of associating cost with each function automatically locates key tolerances as far as cost is concerned.

For example, iron pole pieces used on speakers, as shown in Figure 3-11, were called for to these specifications:

Length, ½ inch ±0.002 inch
Flange, ¹⁄₃₂ inch ±0.002 inch
Diameter, ½ inch ±0.0005 inch
Perpendicularity of face of flange to axis of cylinder, ±½°
Finish:
    Surface of flange, F5
    Surface of cylinder, F5

The method of manufacture involved the use of an automatic screw machine making 2 million per year.

It is obvious that tolerances must be evaluated in relation to each method of manufacture or process which is being considered. In this case, a study of each tolerance as produced on the automatic screw machine—using the annual cost for the normal yearly volume—would promote proper refining and improving of that process.

The yearly increase in cost for each tolerance above that which the equipment would take in its stride at fastest speeds and with minimum maintenance comes to:

Yearly total part cost	$70,000
Special tolerance costs:	
Length, ±0.002 in	1,000
Flange, ±0.002 in	none
Diameter, ±0.0005 in	5,000
Perpendicularity, ±½°	2,000
Finish:	
Flange	4,000
Cylinder	6,000
All other costs	52,000

We now rearrange these costs. For example:

Finish cylinder..................	$6,000
Diameter, ±0.0005..............	5,000
Finish flange....................	4,000

Our study then proceeds along these lines:

What use functions are believed to be provided by the $6,000?

What esteem or appearance function does the $6,000 bring?

To what extent are these beliefs valid?

What alternate processes, tooling, equipment, or technology might reliably achieve the valid tolerance requirement for lower cost?

Next, the various applicable value analysis techniques are applied to develop lower-cost value alternatives for achieving the specified tolerances.

Similar studies are made for each other significant item of tolerance cost, and then we examine other processes for manufacturing the part, for example, cold coining. A preliminary review shows these figures:

Yearly cost of parts.............	$50,000
Tolerance costs:	
Length, ±0.002 in.............	20,000
Finish flange, F5..............	10,000
Flange, ±0.002 in.............	none
Diameter, ±0.0005 in..........	none
Perpendicularity..............	none
Finish cylinder, F5............	none
All other costs..................	20,000

Proceeding with an analysis, a natural first question is: Why does length plus or minus 0.002 inch cost $20,000 extra?

The answer is: Because automatic slug shear cutoff cannot be used; special precision cutoff is required.

Now then, what function does the $20,000 buy? Answer: none. The flange of the pole piece is located on the magnet. Magnetic flux comes up through this flange, turns out radially to the cylinder, passes through the cylinder sides into air, and then passes through the cylindrical voice coil which surrounds the cylindrical pole-piece section. The small end of the cylinder is adjacent only to air and a felt cover providing appearance.

What would modifying the tolerance on length from plus or minus 0.002 inch to plus or minus 0.005 inch do? It would eliminate $20,000 of cost and produce no change in either use or esteem functions.

Similarly, why does flange finish F5 add $10,000? What function does it buy? The flange is in intimate contact with the smooth, flat surface of the magnet. It is desirable to have metal-to-metal contact between each particle in the flange face and the magnet. Any roughness or unevenness on the flange face would result in voids between the metal surfaces and lower the efficiency of operation of the speaker. It is found that true flatness and a controlled high degree of fineness of surface can be achieved by a Blanchard grinding operation after coining. Hence real use function is purchased with this $10,000. That sum represents a useful, necessary, and proper element of cost until and unless another reliable value alternative can be developed which will accomplish it at lower cost. The operation is retained, and the yearly cost of these parts becomes $30,000.

If it is not known how to accomplish a specified tolerance in a potential value alternative, give each tolerance a dollar cost equivalent to the dollars of economy that the use of this tolerance prevents. For example, in the previous analysis, if no known way of obtaining the tolerance of length plus or minus 0.002 inch had been developed, tabulation of tolerance costs, based upon the cold coining process, would be as follows:

Length, ±0.002 in...........	$40,000
Flange finish................	10,000
Other tolerances............	none
All other costs..............	20,000

This clearly and appropriately directs attention to the tolerance which is "locking in" much cost and compels study and evaluation of the functions provided by the $40,000 followed by application of the appropriate value analysis techniques to the end of creating suitable value alternatives.

In summary, the important questions to ask in this technique are:

Is the reason for the tolerance valid?

What other design concept, if any, would make it unnecessary?

Is the means for reliably securing the tolerance the most economical?

3-9. *Utilize Vendors' Available Functional Products*

All products are developed to perform one or more main functions. The bicycle, the turbine generator, the airplane, and the baby's crib, for example, all serve principal functions for which they are purchased. Each main function, however, is accomplished by a group of subfunctions, each of which often has its own group of functional components.

The main function of the airplane is accomplished through a number of contributing subfunctional components—the wings, the motors, the body, the tail, etc. In turn, the functions of these various components are accomplished by their functional components. The wing function may be accomplished, for instance, by sheet aluminum, structural aluminum, or magnesium and by rivets, fastenings, hinges, and supports.

Often, need has fostered development and has resulted in specific functional products such as special hinges, special rivets, special tapered structural shapes, and special gasoline-containing bags, to mention but a few. The use of these products often provides a total function more reliably and more economically than specially designed components. When this is the case, design time and design cost are saved. Besides, proved products can be used without expending time or money for testing.

Available functional products commonly have low costs because the specialty supplier has a sufficient lead in his particular technology and sufficient manufacturing volume to produce reliable components most economically.

This all sounds so simple—but!

Practical circumstances and interfering factors combine to cause far too little use of available specialty functional products. Some of these circumstances and factors follow.

1. Individuals making assignments may not know or suspect that a suitable product exists, so they proceed to have the design and development work done.

2. Men given the assignments may not realize or suspect that applicable products exist. Hence they carry out the detail development and design of the functional product assigned to them.

3. "Do-it-ourselves" forces are strong in most every phase of human activity. The overpowering feeling is that "we can do it!" This is followed by costly and detailed redesigning of functional products which already exist.

4. "The boss assigned the work to me. He expects me to do it." Men are very hesitant about spending time or money in any direction other than the direct line of their superiors' instructions, as they interpret them. Slow success or failure in direct harmony with bosses' directions is not as damaging, by a factor of ten, to a man as slow success or failure following a different approach.

5. Often there exists a belief that using the functional products of others is evidence of a shortcoming or weakness and that it is par for the course to be self-capable and self-integrated. This is the same as contending that only the man who does not know how to swim gets a boat.

6. A normal human characteristic is the tendency to place too much confidence in what "we" do and too little confidence in what is done by others. Much excessive "do-it-ourselves redeveloping of the wheel" is backed by an erroneous feeling that better quality will thereby be assured.

7. A self-injuring belief is that to protect "proprietary knowledge" which no one else has, it is essential to design and develop all aspects of a functional product, though it often causes delayed design, uncertain

performance, and high cost. Occasionally, of course, such a situation may exist for short periods of time and will bring temporary benefits to offset the inefficient "do-it-ourselves" philosophy. In such instances, very critical reviews should frequently be made to determine when the proprietary secrets have ceased to be secrets.

8. Because the results that a search for functional specialty products may bring are not known before the search has been made, the tantalizing fear exists that, after time and money have been spent searching, no suitable product will be found and that it will be necessary after all to develop and design it.

9. "Do-it-ourselves" work can be planned. The objective, the resources, the effort, the expected results in performance, cost, and time can all be reasonably scheduled.

In contrast, search is more unsure; hence plans to search bring greater insecurity, and the feeling of insecurity in a job, activity, or project is a topmost reason for shunning the search approach. The task of locating something—who knows where—that may or may not exist, compounds insecurity.

10. Groups of people often have the belief that the accepted and proper system is to "do it ourselves." To do otherwise means to deviate from established procedure. Creative search for combinations of available functional products to accomplish the needed function is foreign to their basic beliefs.

11. Men don't know how to efficiently and effectively start the chain from no information on a particular functional product and quickly penetrate haze to build up a valuable fund of information on specialty-product availability, performance, and cost.

12. Often the belief exists that, in some way, various intangible, unidentifiable benefits come from designing bit by bit and, hence, that much special hardware ought to be made in in-plant manufacturing space. The feeling is that resultant increasing activity in the factory will increase profits, business stability, control of markets, and utilization of resources. In consequence, a search for available functional products is regarded as a search for something injurious to the business.

The foregoing factors will oppose effective searches for specialty functional products that quite commonly aid in eliminating substantial unnecessary costs.

Case Study

A Specialty Product Simplified It

Four thousand small hinges a year were made by producing an extruded metal section which was then cut off and drilled for a close-tolerance hole. A pin, also with very close tolerance, was inserted in this hole so that an interference fit resulted and always held the pin in place. The cost of the hinge and pin assembly was 30 cents.

It was recognized that the main function of the assembly was to act as a hinge and that a secondary function, produced by costly close tolerances, was to hold the pin in place at all times. The construction was brought to the attention of a manufacturer who would make the hinge from sheet metal and roll a suitable portion to receive the pin. His process was found to be very practical except that the tolerances would not be close enough for a suitable interference fit to hold the pin reliably in place.

In searching for ideas and alternatives to overcome this problem, thought was focused on the use of a rolled, tempered sheet-steel pin as available on the market in a variety of sizes. These spiral pins are made with a certain springiness so that, when driven into a hole, they will expand and retain their position. It was found entirely practicable to use such a spiral pin in combination with the sheet-metal hinge, and the total assembled cost came to 10 cents instead of 30 cents.

Available specialty functional products may be divided into two classes:

1. Products which most designers expect to buy
2. Products which, although they often accomplish a needed function at the lowest cost, are not commonly considered as items to be purchased

For clarification, a sample guide of products in these two classes, as compiled for one specific usage, is shown below.

Commonly, designers expect that applicable standards will be purchased to fill their needs, but they often overlook the opportunity to have the desired functions accomplished reliably at the lowest cost by also purchasing suitable specialty forms. (A functional product, in the present sense, may be a plain material, a part, or a composite figuring as a "building block" for more inclusive design combinations.)

ELECTRICAL COMPONENTS

Apparatus type
  Generators
  Motors
  Converters
  Rectifiers
  Switchgear
    Circuit breakers
    Control devices
  Transformers

Part Assemblies
  Dry batteries
  Capacitors
  Condensers

Potentiometers
Rheostats
Resistors
Coils
Contacts
Magnets
Commutators
Collectors
Slip rings
Brushes
Brush holders
Terminals
Electron tubes
Transistors

Part Assemblies (cont.)
  Electronic circuits
    Etched
    Printed
    Plated
  Antennas
  Microphones
  Headsets
  Loudspeakers

Insulating fabricates
  Cloth
  Fiber
  Glass
  Mica
  Paper
  Plastic
  Porcelain
  Rubber
    Impregnated

    Laminated
    Molded

Wiring devices and supplies
  Wire
  Conduits
  Cable
  Terminations
  Tapes
  Cordsets
  Harnesses
  Junction boxes
  Receptacles
  Sockets
  Plugs
  Switches
  Fuses

Instrumentation
  Test meters
  Performance instruments

MATERIALS

Ferrous and nonferrous
  Ingots
  Rods
  Tubes
  Sheets
    Rolled
    Stamped
    Punched
    Perforated
    Rigidized
    Sandwiched
  Plate
  Strip
  Shapes
  Wire
  Powder
  Castings
  Forgings
  Extrusions

Nonmetallic
  Asbestos
  Cork
  Felt
  Fiber
  Textiles
  Ceramics
  Glass
  Paper
  Plastics } Molded,
  Rubber } laminated, Extruded
  Chemicals
    Organic
    Inorganic
  Synthetics
  Paints
  Lacquers
  Varnishes
  Metalizers

MECHANICAL COMPONENTS

Machine type
  Blowers
  Compressors

  Fans
  Pumps
  Engines

Machine type (cont.)
  Motors
  Actuators

Parts type
  Housings
    Boxes   ⎫ Cast,
    Cases   ⎬ pressed,
    Covers   ⎭ deep-
    Caps   drawn,
    Cabinets   ⎫ fabri-
    Shields   ⎭   cated
  Bearings
    Sleeve
    Ball
    Roller
    Needle
    Jewel
  Shafts
  Keys
  Leadscrews
  Shims
  Retainers
  Spacers
  Gears
  Springs
  Couplings
  Clutches
  Flanges
  Sprockets
  Pulleys
  Chains
  Escapements
  Bellows
  Diaphragms
  Filters

Shock absorbers
Vibration dampers
Hangers
Brackets
Pedestals

Hardware type
  Bumpers
  Casters
  Handles
  Knobs
  Mesh
  Trim
  Fasteners
    Nails
    Screws
    Bolts
    Studs
    Tie rods
    Turnbuckles
    Nuts
    Washers
    Rivets
    Eyelets
    Staples
    Stitches
    Clips
    Straps
    Corners
    Hinges
    Latches
    Locks
  Name plates
  Tags
  Dials

SUPPLIES

Building supplies
  Cement
  Mortar
  Bricks
  Cast blocks
  Lumber
  Coverings
    Roof
    Wall
    Floor

Trim
Heating items
Conditioning items
Lighting items

Maintenance supplies
  Brooms
  Brushes
  Cleaning agents
  Buckets

Maintenance supplies (cont.)
- Pails
- Mops
- Rags
- Steel wool
- Waste
- Aprons
- Gloves

Plumbing supplies
- Piping
- Tubing
- Fittings
- Unions
- Nipples
- Plugs
- Nozzles
- Valves
- Faucets
- Gaskets
  - Cord
  - Cork
  - Felt
  - Rubber
- Sealing compounds

Office supplies
- Furniture
- Equipment
- Stationery items
- Office machines

Packaging supplies
- Bags
- Boxes
- Crates
- Skids
- Pasteboard
- Excelsior
- Shreddings
- Wrappings
- Cord
- Wire and straps
- Paste
- Tapes
- Labels

Shop stockroom supplies
- Abrasives
  - Cloth and paper

- Compounds
- Powders
- Grinding wheels
- Sanding disks
- Sanding pads
- Sanding planes

Adhesives
- Cements
- Glues
- Pastes
- Tapes

Compounds
- Caulking
- Cutting
- Dust suppression
- Impregnating
- Insulating
- Sealing
- Descaling
- Rust protection
- Marking
- Soldering

Gaskets
- Felt
- Leather
- Paper
- Plastics
- Rubber
- Fiber
- Metalized

Lubricating agents
- Greases
- Oils
- Compounds
- Guns

Tools
- Axes
- Hammers
- Pliers
- Screwdrivers
- Wrenches
- Chisels
- Planes
- Saws
- Punches
- Nail sets
- Hand drills

Shop stockroom supplies (cont.)

Augers	Shovels
Bits	Pickaxes
Drills	Rakes
Reamers	Hoes
Taps	Instruments
Dies	Gages
Fixtures	Calipers
Jigs	Micrometers
C clamps	Levels
Air guns	Rulers
Soldering irons	Squares
Torches	Scribers
Shears	Compasses
	Straight edges

Productive steps for locating available functional products are:

1. Learn and clearly understand the desired function, the basic step **in** the application of any of the value techniques.
2. Search directories such as:

   Thomas' Register of American Manufacturers
   > Thomas Publishing Company, New York 1

   Mac Rae's Bluebook
   > Mac Rae, 18 E. Huron Street, Chicago 11

   Swift's Industrial Catalog File
   > Swift's Catalog Service, 119 West 40th Street, New York 18

   The Engineers Buyer's Guide[1]
   > The Engineer, London, WC 2, England

   Consultation of these and other inclusive business directories may advantageously be supplemented by referring to specialized sources of the order of:

   Electronic Engineers Master—E.E.M. Tech Publishers, Inc., 60 Madison Ave., Hempstead

   and particularly specialty manufacturers' trade catalogs.
3. Search appropriate trade shows, including exhibits at professional societies' annual meetings and conventions; for instance:

   Metals Congress and Exposition
   > American Society for Metals

   Powder Metallurgy Show
   > Metal Powders Industries Federation

---

[1] The Engineers Buyer's Guide is one of many publications offering a listing of "Forthcoming Engineering and Industrial Exhibitions" in Britain, Canada, the United States, and most European industrialized nations. Another useful inclusion in this particular guide is a comprehensive listing of "Associations, Institutions and Societies Connected with the Engineering Industry in Britain."

Plastics Exhibit
 Society of Plastics Engineers
Design Engineering Show
 Machine Design Division, American Society of Mechanical Engineers
IRE Show
 Institute of Radio Engineers
American Chemical Society's Annual Meetings
American Welding Society's Annual Meetings
Hardware Show
 Retail Hardware Association
Instrument-Automation Conference and Exhibit
 Instrument Society of America
Machine Tool and Production Engineering Show
National Materials Handling Exposition
 Material Handling Institute
National Packaging Exposition
 American Management Association

This listing is but a sampling of the trade-show and convention type of affair that has proved a profitable source in the search for improved value alternatives. Innumerable exhibitions of this kind, covering practically every trade and profession, are held constantly both in the United States and abroad. Where personal consultation at such fairs is not practical, it pays the seeker of new and varied ideas to scan the widely published accounts of what is being shown.

4. Search trade magazines. Where library services are available, request searches by them if needed.

5. Contact, by writing or phoning, competent men in related businesses. Describe to them the functions needed and ask for guidance. Inquiries directed to a dozen or so of those who represent top thought and knowledge in any one industry will often bring a most gratifying yield.

6. Make chain inquiries. Select, say, three men who have the best chance of knowing where to locate what is needed and ask them for guidance. If they don't know the answer, attempt to get names from them of the top two men they would suggest. Continue this process as long as desirable. It is surprising how soon very complete and valuable information can be assembled from competent men in a wide variety of industries.

Once suitable sources of special functional products have been located, do not neglect to (*a*) assist the functional product vendor; (*b*) interpret the needed functions to him; (*c*) provide him with a broad and deep feeling for the importance of the various functions, for the various operating situations, etc; (*d*) help him to develop practical suggestions for using his product or combinations of his products; (*e*) secure tangible suggestions from him.

With the aid of a few examples, let us see how this procedure may work out.

EXAMPLE 1: An adjusting screw that cost 8 cents was used to facilitate adjustment of electrical equipment. In use, a stiff wire was hooked into the hole in the head. The screw was lifted against a spring pressure, turned as desired, and then lowered again, allowing the cross pin to drop into a slot and be held by it.

Manufacture of the screw required $3/16$ and $1/16$-inch diameter steel as the raw material. The larger piece required cutoff, threading, and drilling of two holes. The smaller piece required cutoff, assembly in hole, and staking.

FIG. 3-12. Adjusting screw.

The part was deemed so unusual that it was not expected that a vendor made such an item.

A review of the function—not of the part—brought forth the requirements:

A screw having a hole in the top, or other suitable arrangement, so it can be lifted and turned

A head arrangement that will be pulled back into the slot and held to prevent turning

A search of specialty products having these two characteristics uncovered the spade bolt shown in Figure 3-13. Its cost was $1/3$ cent (as

$1\frac{7"}{16}$

FIG. 3-13. Alternative adjusting screw.

FIG. 3-14. Spacer hub.

compared to 8 cents). It accomplished all of the functions reliably. It was readily available.

EXAMPLE 2: A spacer hub (Figure 3-14) that cost, in steel with machining and drilled holes, $1.27, was undercut and turned from steel bar.

Its functions were to mount two disks of aluminum, which were riveted through six holes, and to provide a mounting center for this disk assembly.

Again, few would expect to find as an available product an undercut steel disk of the right diameter and right thickness; probably no one would search for it and possibly no one would find it.

But what happens when we consider precisely what the function is?

1. Separate two 6-inch diameter aluminum disks approximately ¼ inch
2. Provide for mounting them securely in an assembly
3. Provide a center hole for mounting the assembly

A search for specialty products which could be readily adapted to accomplish these functions brought forth, among other alternatives, aluminum disks or slugs that can be bought in bulk in a variety of diameters and thicknesses for use in impact extrusion.

FIG. 3-15. Alternative spacer hub.

FIG. 3-16. Thin nut.

One such slug was of a suitable diameter and thickness. It cost 4 cents, but it was stamped from sheet and so was cupped, not flat. It cost 1 cent to flatten it and 8 cents to drill the holes. The total cost of the alternative (shown in Figure 3-15) was 13 cents.

EXAMPLE 3: A ⅞-inch diameter thin nut (Figure 3-16) cost 8 cents. Its function was to hold a small 1-pound assembly on its shoulder bushing between periods of use and not allow it to fall off while it was not being used. There was no load on the nut. When in use, the force of the work held the assembly in working position and the nut was not performing any function. A small radial hole was drilled and tapped in the nut for a setscrew to reduce the risk of its loosening.

It was made from hexagonal steel bar on which the necessary operations were:

Drill and tap the center hole
Drill and tap the radial hole
Cut off

What precisely was the function?

1. To hold one pound onto the bushing
2. To provide unusual vibration-proof features so that, under all conditions, the nut would not loosen

A search produced a specialty product for this exact function in the appropriate size and type, namely, a standard locknut (Figure 3-17) possessing exactly the needed characteristics. Its cost was 1½ cents (instead of 8 cents). Besides, tests proved this locknut to be more vibration proof than the former nut with setscrew.

Fig. 3-17. Standard locknut.

Fig. 3-18. High-temperature locknut.

EXAMPLE 4: A high-temperature locknut—castellated nut—(Figure 3-18), including the drilling of the shaft on which it was mounted and the safety wiring on assembly, cost $4.75.

The function was to hold a heavy, high-temperature part to a moving shaft which, to some extent, was vibrating.

Search brought forth a variety of locknut arrangements, most of which were judged unsatisfactory because of the extremely high temperature of the application.

A manufacturer of nuts using plastic locking rings was given the complete problem. His engineer said, "In our product line, we have a variety

Fig. 3-19. High-temperature locknut.

of locking materials used for this function. Each is especially adapted to different environmental conditions. We can provide one which is suited to the high-temperature operation in question. Of course, it will cost a little more than our regular product."

What he provided cost 23 cents and eliminated the need for drilling the shaft and wiring the nut. It is shown in Figure 3-19.

Thus identifying clearly the needed functions and then searching creatively for vendors of specialty products reduced the cost of accomplishing the total function from $4.75 to 23 cents per unit.

In summary, the steps in this technique are as follows:

Recognize that for most subfunctions suitable combinations of functional products already exist.

Learn how to identify clearly and review precisely the functions needed.

Learn how to locate specialty functional products.

Use them.

3-10. *Utilize and Pay for Vendors' Skill and Knowledge*

It is unimaginable that any user would design his own nails and buy steel to make them. Nails fall within a group of functional products that we are accustomed to buying.

Likewise, few users would design standard screws and buy metal to make them (unless quantities were large enough for continuous runs on the most modern of equipment).

Many users, however, will design special screws and similar parts and go on to buying metal and making them. The alternative is to inform suppliers, who have the proper general type of equipment and accumulation of skills, of precisely the functions that are required and knowledge of the limitations on size, weight, shape, stress, etc.

With such information at hand, suppliers will gladly provide suggestions and quotations. Often the costs of this procedure are from one-fourth to one-half the costs of the "do-it-ourselves" method.

The objective in product development is to get the best solutions to the problems involved in the shortest time and at the lowest cost.

The best solutions will accomplish the function the customer needs and will provide the appearance that he wants. At the same time, they will do so at lowest manufacturing cost and with a minimum of manufacturing problems or quality difficulties.

The technique of utilizing and paying for vendor's skill and knowledge yields exceptionally high returns when effectively used, for the following reasons:

Large amounts of special knowledge exist in every field, and much of this knowledge is not possessed by people in other fields.

Only a relatively small amount of the total special knowledge bearing on any technology exists in any one place at any one time.

Special machines, fixtures, tooling, and equipment exist in large numbers.

New developments known only to the engineers concerned with them are in progress in most good supplier's plants. They represent the best materials, processes, or parts to use "tomorrow" within the particular technology. They can be put to use only if the supplier is called into the job to which they are applicable.

Suppliers want their new developments to follow actual needs in the market and they are usually searching for practical new ways of applying their technology. They benefit and the user benefits by working together.

It is important to note that the use of skills and know-how of others in the field of securing new performance is quite commonplace and quite fruitful. Such use is motivated by tests showing that suitable performance has not been secured. Faced with known unsuitable performance, the search for better answers is self-forcing. In contrast, since value is not measured, simultaneous realization that better answers are required valuewise is lacking; hence the course of action often taken is to choose from the alternatives immediately at hand, and in reality, an integer of value loss results.

Case Study

THE THREE SPRINGS

An electrical control used three springs:

One 1 inch long by ¾ inch in diameter, plated steel, 23 cents; $23,000 per year

One ¾ inch long by ¼ inch in diameter, plated steel, 11 cents; $11,000 per year

One ⅛ inch in diameter by ½ inch long, tension loops on ends, phosphor bronze, 17 cents; $17,000 per year

A supplier who had an established reputation as a top specialist in good-value springs as well as for good performance in springs was invited to look at the job. It was suggested to the sales manager of this specialist vendor that he take the product, the drawings, and such other operating and specification information as could be provided by the engineers, have his technical people suggest precisely what springs to use, and then provide suggested costs for them. His answer was surprising: "I can't afford to do it."

When asked to explain his stand, he said experience had shown that when an engineer has had the drawing details and specifications of an exact spring made up, it is offensive to him to receive a quotation unless it is confined to precisely the geometry requested, and in the long run, the submittal of a quotation is injurious to the supplier who makes the suggestion. Only when the buyer who was taking part in the value audit of the product brought the sales manager into direct contact with the engineer and the engineer asked him to make a quotation did he consent to do so. The springs were of such a standard nature that they could be made on completely standard spring machines and the supplier offered to submit five sets of samples for each of the first two springs and two or three sets for the third. He said he would provide twenty-five samples each and would furnish both a sheet of descriptive information telling exactly what each spring was and a sheet of test data telling precisely what each spring would do. This he did. The engineer was amazed and delighted. The cost for the various alternatives generally ran from one-fifth of the present cost up to the present cost. After study of the test data and completion of some additional tests, springs were selected with the following costs:

$16,000 per year instead of $23,000 for the first group
$3,000 per year instead of $11,000 for the second group
$9,000 per year instead of $17,000 for the third group

Besides, a modification of material on the third group provided improved operation and greater stability throughout the life of the product. *Utilizing available supplier skills and capabilities pays off.*

The business of industrial suppliers is organized along one of two lines.

1. Make a product or provide a process which will accomplish some known and needed function or group of functions, and then sell the product or process. Examples are turbines, motors, lathes, hammers, airplane autopilots, printed circuits, photoforming.

2. Develop a group of skills, a body of knowledge, and a family of facilities capable of accomplishing certain types of functions or certain types of work, then merchandise this capability to those who have corresponding needs.

This second type of business is most vital to our economy but much more difficult to merchandise than a product or process.

The value analysis technique that we are concerned with here ties in principally with the second type.

To locate the best suppliers of this second category requires active and effective search on the part of the user, especially since a vendor cannot know what the needs are until he is located and told.

The search is not simple. The first half-dozen or so vendors to whom the needs are communicated may not be the few having the special know-how needed, and thus the results become negative. Particularly high yields will be in proportion to the skill and effort applied in using the technique. Again, a series of questions must be raised, such as:

What functions are required?

What processes might contribute?

What vendors lead in each area?

When the answers to these questions are established, the definite actions to take are as follows:

Get in touch with the indicated vendors.

Describe the technical situation clearly to bring out what is really needed—the various functions; the limitations of size, weight, and dimension; the essentials of strength and appearance; etc.

State the economic situation clearly and fairly.

If there should be a prejudice by decision-making people against using any item, such as, stampings, castings, forgings, plastics, aluminum, or whatever, and the vendor's interest lies in that particular area, tell him just what the situation is. If he is competing against in-plant manufacture, tell him so and tell him the basis of the competition. If the product, even after development, has a questionable market volume, tell him that too. Only then can the supplier appraise the total situation and decide what amount of his resources it will be good business for him to commit to the solution of the problem.

The next step should be to allow the vendor's technical people time to study alternatives, to develop and test new answers, and to make a solid and new contribution. It is vital at this stage that the vendor be given every opportunity to ask more questions about what is important and what is not important, and also that he be assured that his suggested solutions will be given attention by people who decidedly want the proposals to be satisfactory for the particular purpose.

Alternatives submitted should be reviewed objectively and the best-appearing value alternatives should be selected for possible further improvement. Objective information on shortcomings should be taken back to the submitter and help should be given him to overcome the objections, if possible.

Usually, of course, only one supplier can win, i.e., earn the business. Several may work for it, but one commonly earns it. That is the nature of doing business in the competitive system. The suppliers realize this before they start work, and they fully expect that the supplier with the best answers will get the order. All of this points up the great importance of completely advising them *before* they start work. They must be made acquainted with all of the "rules of the game" before they decide to go into it.

After a vendor has produced the best answer—one substantially better than the one used prior to his work on the project—he has earned the business and must be given the opportunity to retain it for a reasonable length of time to fairly repay him for his development work.

It is indeed wrong, and cannot be tolerated, to:

Draw up his ideas and send them out to other vendors for quotation
Allow factory personnel to decide that they can make it that way in the plant

Such actions will cause the best vendors to stop wasting their good technical talent on the products or processes of the manufacturer involved. Besides, they will thereafter turn to assisting his competitors instead of continuing to help him. Paying for his work by placing orders with him if he has contributed is not only the ethical thing to do but is also, selfishly speaking, the only course of enlightened, long-range self-interest.

EXAMPLE: HANDLE FOR MACHINE TOOL ADJUSTMENTS. An operator uses this lever to make necessary adjustments by turning it clockwise or counterclockwise. Screws in the ends have opposite threads, one right-hand and the other left-hand; hence rotation in one direction lengthens the handle and rotation in the other direction shortens it.

What functional properties are required?

A rigid handle to be axially expandable and contractable
A handle capable of 300 pounds pressure
A surface on the handle for ready hand grip

What process might contribute?

Machine from bar; knurl and tap
Machine from tubing; knurl, plug ends, and tap
Make from aluminum impact extrusions; plug open end and tap both ends
Make from aluminum extruding tubing; plug ends and tap
Make from sheet metal, rolled and crimped; plug ends and tap
Make from suitable plastic

What vendors lead in each area? Select one or two good vendors in each of the indicated areas, the number depending upon the importance and amount of business involved. Follow through the remaining steps of the technique, as outlined above, with each of them. Help each to apply his expert knowledge and facilities.

The results of the technique will now be apparent.

The special function required in the product will be reviewed in the light of the most advanced skills, techniques, and facilities within several technologies. All resultant alternatives will be unveiled before the decision maker to enable him to promptly increase the value of his product.

3-11. *Utilize Specialty Processes*

Generally speaking, all processes serve for one of two purposes.

1. They accomplish functions that can be performed in no other way.

2. They accomplish performed functions equally well but at much lower cost.

The second group takes in an extremely large number of processes which are of vital interest in value-oriented work and which will be the group for further study in this section.

All processes might further be divided into two classes.

1. Processes which are known and are reasonably well understood by those who are making decisions

2. Processes which are not known to the decision makers but which would be applicable and would accomplish the desired ends at very much lower cost

Again, it is this second class that we shall deal with. Let us first see how processes which will accomplish functions reliably at very much lower cost but are not known to the decision makers at the particular time may be brought into view and how their benefits may be utilized in value work.

Of course, what is a special process today commonly becomes the standard process of tomorrow. Therefore, a line between the special and the standard process does not really exist, the differences being a blending of shades of gray. For practical purposes in securing important benefits from the technique in question, the best definition seems to be that a specialty process is an applicable process which would reliably accomplish the needed function for significantly lower cost and which either exists or could, and would, be developed by some one who leads in the technology involved if he understood the need for it.

BEFORE   AFTER

FIG. 3-20. J bolt.

For example, to the design and manufacturing engineers who designed the J bolt shown in Figure 3-20 as a cut thread part costing 11½ cents each, the process of roll threading at a cost of 1½ cents would be a specialty process.

Similarly, the hollow-forging method would be a specialty process to engineering and manufacturing men who did not know that hollow forgings 2 feet in diameter and 10 feet long could be made with very high grade properties for $3,000 each after finishing machining to take the place of a similar part made from solid material at a cost of $6,000 each after machining.

The capabilities of specialty processes to accomplish functions per dollar of expenditure extend far beyond what is normally recognized. Such recognition by professional people engaged in technical value-oriented work normally lags about three years behind capabilities. General recognition lags about ten years behind.

A good estimate seems to be that the recognition of normal decision-governing design and manufacturing engineers lags about five years behind capabilities. It is the purpose of the technique under discussion to eliminate an important part of this five-year lag.

Most specialty processes go hand in hand with the never-ending development of special tools. As a simple example, perhaps at some point in the history of industrial development three types of hammers existed: one for work with stone, one for the blacksmith, and one for the carpenter. As a variety of work was brought to the carpenter, the familiar claw hammer was developed to facilitate the nail-pulling process. Successively, this tool has been further developed into a heavier hammer for the process of laying oak flooring and a lighter and very much differently shaped hammer for tacks, with the still further development of the magnetic head to make the tacking process even more economical. Similar developments have taken place in hammers for metalworking and other fields. Probably few engineers know all the various stages of development of the simple hammer, each for the express purpose of improving a building or manufacturing operation of a specific type, and generally for the main purpose of improving value.

For another example, the casting process starts with the basic sand casting and spreads into almost hundreds of different types of casting processes. Some of these are uniquely appropriate to achieving a certain function by the use of some particular metal or temperature range; others fit for the attainment of specified tolerance, lack of porosity, desired appearance or surface conditions, etc. A group of typical casting processes are:

Sand casting	Miniature casting
Precision casting	Die casting
Shell molding	Mercury cast
Permanent molding	Insert molding
Lost wax process	

Case Study

MOUNTING HOLES FOR PERFORATED SHEET

For an appliance, a ⅟₃₂-inch-thick galvanized-steel sheet, 1½ feet wide by 6 feet long, was used. To perform its function, it was necessary to punch 10,000 holes in each sheet so that it became perforated. This punching cost 68 cents.

To facilitate mounting the sheet, six more holes were punched near the ends at a cost of 28 cents, bringing punching cost to 96 cents.

The 10,000 perforated holes served an essential function in the appliance, while the six additional holes served merely for mounting the part.

When these required functions were brought into clear focus with men throughout the country who had specialized manufacturing know-how, a supplier of continuous perforating equipment showed that the material could be continuously perforated in the long uncut strip and that some of the holes could then be used for mounting.

Investigation showed that the ends were bracketed and that cutting through the perforated area would detract from neither usefulness nor appearance.

The change was made with a reduction of 59 cents per sheet in punching cost.

Application of the technique of utilizing specialty processes involves three steps.

1. Recognize that processes which would accomplish the desired functions for very much lower cost (*a*) may exist and not be known, (*b*) are being developed, or (*c*) would be developed if competent men in the technology knew of the need.

2. Put in motion actions which will increase the likelihood that specialty competence knows about, and becomes interested in, the needed functions.

3. Assign time and effort to stay with each item until the minor problems, minor objections, and minor misunderstandings which always arise in any new approach have been illuminated with useful and factual information. The aim here is to ensure that the results to be expected

FIG. 3-21. Special screw.   FIG. 3-22. Bracket.

from the status of science at the particular time will indeed be developed and made applicable to the particular project.

For a listing of typical specialty processes see Chapter 5. It should be recognized that such listings may lag from three to five years behind actual industrial capabilities. Also, available tables are useful guides but do not supplant the further step of making direct contact with individuals who lead in any technology.

EXAMPLE 1: The undercut screw shown in Figure 3-21 was being used in quantities of 20,000 per year. It was made on a screw machine from steel bar, was 2¼ inches long, and was undercut as shown.

A study of the functions revealed that the screw was a suitable means of accomplishing the functions, provided the undercut could be produced more economically.

A specialty manufacturer who produced cold-headed and roll-threaded screws was among the ones contacted and informed of the need. He did not have a process "on the shelf" which would serve economically but he took the following approach: "I believe I can adapt the roll-threading process to remove the metal from the undercut portion. I will try to first roll a thread and then roll another thread so displaced as to remove the metal left by the first process. Next, if necessary, I will complete the operation by rolling enough successive threads until the metal has all been eliminated." He became very much interested in adapting his process to the need, so he tried it and it worked. The cost with the use of this specialty process became 1½ cents each, not 15 cents.

EXAMPLE 2: The small bracket shown in Figure 3-22 was used in large quantities and served to support a small spring assembly in an appliance. It was made of steel on well-mechanized equipment. Nevertheless, the drilling and tapping of two small holes brought its cost to $13 per thousand.

The functional study showed that this was a simple and practical way of accomplishing the function, provided the cost of tapping the holes could be lowered substantially.

Search for a specialty process brought one forth. A supplier recognized this type of part as being sufficiently common in industry for him to build a good business by creating special equipment around it. In his special tooling, he bent the material and drilled and tapped the holes all in one continuous process. As a result, he quoted a delivered price of $3 per thousand for the identical part made from the identical material.

EXAMPLE 3: TUBE SUPPORT GASKET. A molded-rubber gasket, a few inches in diameter and costing 11 cents, was used in large quantities. The functional study brought forth a number of alternatives for accomplishing the function. Most of the alternatives involved the use of rubber or rubberlike material but not necessarily a molded gasket of the precise type used.

The search for an applicable specialty process identified a manufacturer whose equipment applied rubber directly to the needed parts in

BEFORE   AFTER

FIG. 3-23. Tube support.

plastic form. The desired result was obtained by placing a small machine in the production line and applying the plastic rubber directly to the parts in an operation that required but a few seconds. The total cost for a functional product of the same high quality as the former product became 1 cent instead of 11 cents.

All cases of the profitable use of this technique to accomplish functions for very much lower cost have the following in common:

1. No applicable specialty process is known.
2. There is no assurance that such a process does not exist.

3. The functions needed in the product, together with alternative means for securing the functions, are brought clearly into view for study.

4. Based upon the likelihood that such specialized processes do exist, or would be created if proper information were provided to the proper suppliers, a search is started and the information is furnished to men in the technologies most likely to contribute.

5. Work is done with these specialists to obtain further information, to overcome minor misunderstandings, and to change meaningless specifications to allow adaptation of the specialists' processes to accomplish the needed functions at very much lower cost.

Case Study

THE TEMPERATURE-SENSITIVE CONTROL

An electrical control, made in relatively large quantities, consisted of a copper tube about 2 feet long attached to a bellows. The tube contained a gas which was very sensitive to temperature. Expansion and contraction of the gas operated the bellows to open and close electrical contacts. The copper tubing, for most of its length, was ⅛ inch in diameter, but for about 4 inches at the far end, it was ¼ inch in diameter. It was believed by the engineers that the larger volume at the end was required in order to give the desired sensitivity of control. The full length of the copper tubing cost 10 cents or for a million per year, $100,000. Value work was started in a number of directions.

Cost analysis showed that the proper lengths of the two sizes of copper tubing cost 5 cents and the joining operation cost 5 cents, equivalent to $50,000 a year. This immediately focused attention on the process of joining which was accomplished by brazing. Searches for other processes of joining failed to bring to light any useful alternative. Hence the function was more clearly examined and it was found that what was needed was a small end about ⅛ inch in diameter for mounting to the bellows and a larger end to contain sufficient gas in the temperature control environment. It appeared that possibly what was in between did not matter. This brought forth the idea of using a ¼-inch tubing and the process of swaging it down. The cost would then become $70,000 per year instead of $100,000. That alternative started a chain of useful results.

One process investigated was that of starting to draw the piece ⅛ inch in diameter and then, by some ingenious way, automatically opening the die so that the 4 inches on the other end would not be drawn to the smaller diameter. This solution proved very feasible. Samples were provided and proved excellent; the cost would be $60,000 per year.

Meanwhile, the engineers working along with the job continued taking basic data and making basic tests to determine precisely the length of the larger diameter needed at the end to give the sensitivity required. In doing this, they discovered that, because of improvements in providing gas with very much better temperature sensitivity than had been the case in years past, the same control was attained without any enlarged portion on the end. The tests proved that the use of copper capillary tubing somewhat less than ⅛ inch in diameter throughout its length and without any enlarged section at the end provided the excellence of control needed. The cost of this tubing came to 4 cents each, or $40,000 per year. The search located two useful processes but the final best result came in this instance from eliminating the need for the process.

3-12. *Utilize Applicable Standards*

To include this technique in the work guides of sophisticated industrial people sounds almost too elementary. It gives the impression of something amateurish. It is like being "for motherhood and against sin." Of course, everyone is.

The reader will soon find, however, that the technique, once used, becomes very valuable. Some approaches for applying it successfully will be discussed.

Fig. 3-24. Standard tube socket.

BEFORE   AFTER

Fig. 3-25. Knobs.

The full meaning here includes not only use of applicable standard parts and processes but appropriate utilization of *parts* of standard products, engineering concepts, manufacturing concepts, manufacturing processes, and materials. It means, also, do not use standards that do not apply.

So much has been so effectively written in the field of utilization of standards that our intent will be not to repeat but rather to supplement. Perhaps the best instruction on how to utilize the technique will develop out of some specific examples.

EXAMPLE 1: A STANDARD PRODUCT. A special tube base costing $6.80 versus a standard tube base (Figure 3-24) costing $1.80 each accomplish the identical function with the same reliability. Naturally, after a search has been made and the standard is found, it is a matter of direct substitution.

EXAMPLE 2: A SPECIALTY PRODUCT. A small aluminum knob and pointer were machined for use on airborne electronic equipment. The cost was $2.25 per knob. The function was to provide for manual adjustment of a small potentiometer. Available specialty products (Figure 3-25) in the form of suitable plastics with metal inserts would accomplish the total function with the same reliability for 25 cents.

Once this information has been secured and it is known that the 25 cent knob is available and will accomplish the function with the same reliability, its direct substitution is a straightforward matter.

EXAMPLE 3: A STANDARD PROCESS DETAIL. A small spring was required to have hooks at each end (see Figure 3-26). One of these hooks, rather than being of the usual turn form, was of an elongated shape. The cost was 9 cents. A study of the cost showed that, by changing from the standard process of providing a spring end hook and going to the special process necessary to produce the elongated end hook, the cost of the spring was increased from 3 cents to 9 cents.

BEFORE   AFTER   SCREEN   PERFORATED METAL

FIG. 3-26. Springs.   FIG. 3-27. Shielding screens of wire mesh and perforated metal.

With this information uncovered, a study of the application was made, and it was found that, with a minor change in the location of the hole of the mating part, the standard spring-end process could be used. By this change, the cost of the spring dropped to one-third of its original cost.

EXAMPLE 4: DO NOT USE INAPPLICABLE STANDARD MATERIALS. Suitable standard wire screen was purchased, fitted, and properly mounted for an electronic shielding function in which a certain amount of ventilation was also essential. A study of the function of the screen and its adjacent parts, together with an evaluation of the mounting and the supporting functions of both the screen and the components, raised the question of whether the use of this standard screening was the most efficient way to accomplish the functions. Value alternatives were developed which deviated from the standard material in that they were based on using a solid material which had been subjected to a standard perforating process (Figure 3-27). The finding was that functions which cost 28 cents when the standard wire mesh was used could be performed with the same reliability by the perforated sheet metal at a cost of 18 cents.

EXAMPLE 5: DO NOT USE INAPPLICABLE STANDARD PRODUCTS. One million small eyelets were used in an electronic device. These eyelets were made of brass and cost $1.75 per thousand. Examination of the required functions showed that, while the eyelet accomplished the functions reliably, all of the features of the eyelet were not needed for this application. Discussions with eyelet manufacturers revealed that, with a quantity of 1 million, the eyelet machines could be adjusted and special runs made to provide special functional eyelets for the purpose in question at 80 cents per thousand.

From hundreds of examples in which standards have been reviewed—some used and some rejected—a few common criteria stand out for standard materials, processes, products, parts of materials, parts of processes, parts of products, etc.

Knowledge of standards of all types is the basic ingredient around which all deviations for the benefit of value improvement must be organized.

If cost and applicability data have not been developed with regard to the function required, the chances that the needed functions are being accomplished at near their lowest practicable cost are decreased considerably.

The matter of correctly selecting standards, nonstandards, or partial standards in products, materials, or processes is similar to all other phases of decision making. The principal task is one of first locating sufficient applicable information and then making correct decisions within the various shades of gray. This will result in sometimes using standards, sometimes rejecting standards, and often using certain standardized functions but rejecting over-all predigested standards.

Case Study

STANDARDIZE THE PACKING?

Although a range of sizes, stylings, and types of electric clocks were being made to fit into the decor of each room of a house, it was recognized that there existed a substantial market for a utility alarm clock. Therefore, one clock was designed and marketed which included a minimum of cost for producing esteem factors and features. It was a very successful product and sold in large numbers. During a value audit on the clock, one of the expense items investigated was the packaging. In line with techniques 7, 9, and 10, the best competence which could be found for this type of package was invited into the job. One of these packaging specialists was very enthusiastic and felt that he could provide a package with added marketing benefits to protect the clock even better and to cost decidedly less. Two weeks passed and nothing more was heard from him. When contacted by telephone he replied, "We stopped our study of that." When asked why, he said that in his investigation he was confronted by a man who had the assignment of promoting standardization. This individual held that the packages now used on the whole line were a standardized family of packages—all based on the same philosophy and with each deviating only as much as necessary to fit the individual clock. Therefore, to develop an alternative would be a waste of time.

Nevertheless, the vendor was encouraged to develop the alternative in line with his original plan, and this was done. The use of the suggested new package for this one extremely high volume clock would reduce costs $150,000 per year. With this full-blown value alternative in hand, the decision was promptly made to delete the particular item from the standardized group in order to decrease costs and improve the package. *Overstandardization does not bring the best value.*

3-13. *Use the Criterion, "Would I Spend My Money This Way?"*

It has been said that the system of value analysis concepts and techniques is organized and illuminated common sense. Most certainly, any successful individual in the competitive economy has learned to use common sense in applying the criterion, "Would I spend my money this way?"

The average person, in evaluating his own expenditures, is governed by the following typical conditions:

He has a limited amount to spend.

He strives to secure maximum use function and appearance function from his expenditures.

He expects to get such functions within reasonable limits in return for his expenditures. If that is not in view, he at once sets out to make appropriate changes or, at least, to do so when he again is ready to expend his funds.

He knows that he cannot get reasonable value in exchange for his resources unless he has value alternatives clearly established and uses corresponding information as criteria in decision making.

Before he spends his money, he will have clearly in view the relative use values, the relative esteem values, and their relative costs.

The reader may recall for a moment that, in achieving value, it is vital to do what makes the best sense. Any deviation from the answers that make the best sense results in either diminished performance or decreased value. Diminished performance can usually be identified promptly by tests. Decreased value, on the other hand, often remains to be identified by buying resistance. Even then, cause and effect are so separated that the particular answers which do not make good sense are not necessarily in clear view.

Both motivation and direction are provided by the effective use of the technique with which we are here concerned. Unless the answers by design engineering, manufacturing engineering, purchasing, and management in all areas involved in decision making can affirmatively meet the test, "If it were my money, would I spend it this way?" it should be seriously questioned that a good degree of value exists.

The application and effect of this technique will become more understandable as it is seen in a number of typical examples.

EXAMPLE 1: A 3-inch diameter hand wheel on a small valve cost $3. Its function was to provide manual opening and closing of the valve.

"If it were my money, would I spend $3 for the valve handle?" With this motivation, manufacturers who produced handles for valves were

BEFORE   AFTER

FIG. 3-28. Trunnion bolts.

sought out. It was found that hand wheels of the same size for the same function, specially cast and machined for this application and made of the same material, could be provided for 60 cents each.

EXAMPLE 2: A 200-gallon gasoline tank on landing craft, designed for a life of eight years, cost $520. Again, asking the question, "Would I spend $520 of my own money for each of a thousand 200-gallon tanks for this application?" brings motivation and direction for action. Certainly, in this day of standard containers, of protective coatings, and of ingenious practical solutions to functional problems, the answer in applying this technique would be "no." As was seen in the discussion of an earlier technique, the gasoline capacity was obtained by using four 50-gallon drums with a special coating for a total cost of $80.

EXAMPLE 3: A moderate quantity of heavy solid-steel trunnion bolts (Figure 3-28), approximately 8 inches long with hex heads 3 inches across flats and with a bolt section 1½ inches in diameter, were needed.

Round bar was purchased and the bolts were machined completely from it. The cost was $11 each. Does it appear to make sense to machine away all of this metal and arrive at such a high cost? Although the manufacturing people involved believed it was the only way that the bolt could be provided in this quantity, motivation from the question, "Would I spend my money this way?" caused a further search.

As a result, a hot-upset bolt blank already containing the hex head was found to be procurable, and the total cost of an interchangeable trunnion bolt which accomplished the total function with the same reliability became $2.28.

EXAMPLE 4: A hub and a shaft used in large quantity were machined and then assembled together (Figure 3-29).

In order to provide reliable assembly, very close tolerances were held on that part of the shaft which mated with the hub and that part of the hub which mated with the shaft. The assembled cost was $1.12. Value

BEFORE   AFTER

FIG. 3-29. Hub and shaft assembly.

study of this item followed the line of questioning the wisdom of being forced to provide close tolerances on two mating parts because of their relationship to each other. After assembly, the money paid for these close tolerances did not further contribute to the operation of the over-all device. Application of the technique of asking, "Would I spend my money this way?" developed the conviction that it simply did not make good sense. There must be a better design philosophy.

Study of the function was followed by a study of alternative methods of securing the function and also by a study of ways of connecting the two parts without the need for high-cost close tolerances. The final result was a change in the design philosophy eliminating the necessity of close tolerances. The hub was cast on the shaft, and the finished part, machined, interchangeable, and ready for use, then had a cost of 63 cents.

EXAMPLE 5: A SMALL SUPPORT CLAMP. On a high-volume product, a part ¼ inch in diameter was supported by a small clamp. As a consequence of technological advancement, a part ⅛ inch in diameter was found to be capable of accomplishing the total function with the same reliability and at a cost of $50,000 per year less than formerly. It was expected that the change would be made at once.

Several weeks later it was noted that the ¼-inch diameter parts were still being assembled which meant that the added cost of $1,000 per week was continuing to be incurred. Personnel conducting the value study asked why the change had not been made. The answer was that owing to the loading in the tool room a twenty-week cycle was required for tool changes, since a $350 change would have to be made in the dies to make the small supporting clamp. When sufficient facts were laid before the decision-making men, the condition which allowed an additional expenditure of $20,000 on the product while waiting for the fabrication of $350 worth of special tools was seen to be so contrary to "the way I would spend my own money" that corrective action followed immediately.

EXAMPLE 6: ASSEMBLY OF PARTS. It is normal for people to want to do things themselves. That is true in engineering, in manufacturing, in purchasing, in management, and in all other walks of business life. It is no surprise, therefore, to find that manufacturing people believe they should do as much as possible themselves in manufacturing a product. They feel that they can control quality and make improvements and can, in a variety of ways, benefit their employers and their customers by doing so. This general belief, like other general beliefs, produces decisions which, in specific cases, keep large amounts of unnecessary costs in products. In the present example, a group of parts was purchased from one supplier and brought into the plant for assembly into a subcomponent. The subcomponent was ultimately used in the over-all product. The delivered cost of the parts was 86 cents. The labor, handling, overhead, and inspection involved in testing added 49 cents, so that the factory cost of the subcomponent was $1.35.

In studying the value of this assembly in terms of the technique in question, the conviction was brought forth that it just did not make sense to buy a number of separate parts, receive them, inspect them, handle them, and reinspect them as an assembly which is then stocked and ready for later use. It would seem to make sense to buy one part, test one part, stock one part, and use one part when it is needed. The answer to the question, "Would I spend my money this way?" was negative.

The result was that an alternative proposal was developed with the supplier, based upon his assembling the parts and providing a finished and tested subcomponent. This saved so much handling, packaging, etc., in the supplier's plant that he was able to deliver the complete assembly ready for use at 88 cents, which meant that 47 cents of unnecessary cost was identified and eliminated through the motivation of this one technique.

EXAMPLE 7: MACHINE PARTS. For good and specific reasons, rules, regulations, and instructions exist in every area. The instruction involved in the case of the following example was: "Prevent unnecessary inventory."

For a "one-shot" order, the buyer received a requisition to purchase 5,000 screw-machined parts which would cost 10 cents each—$500 in total. Being trained in value techniques, the buyer immediately developed alternatives and determined that the part could be made also by the cold-upsetting and thread-rolling processes. The minimum order quantity was 15,000 at a cost of $300, i.e., 2 cents apiece.

This meant that the buyer was faced with the problem of either ordering a 5,000 quantity as instructed at an additional cost of $200 or bringing in an unwanted inventory of 10,000 and, in the over-all, saving $200. His instructions were clear. However, his belief in the application of the technique, "If it were my money, would I spend it this way?" would not allow him to follow instructions, so he developed an alternative. He issued the order for 15,000 of the parts at $300. He sent instruction to the receiving room that he was to be notified when this order arrived. He planned to go out and personally scrap 10,000 pieces on the spot. He reasoned that there would be no inventory excesses and that his company would benefit by the $200 reduction in the purchase cost.

As so often happens where actions of human beings are involved, an amusing occurrence took place. Here is what actually happened. Somehow the buyer's letter to the receiving room was mislaid and he was not notified as requested. As far as he was concerned, nothing further happened in this connection until the end of the year when he received the dismaying notification that he was charged with $600 worth of excess inventory on the part. Having correctly advised his accounting department to charge the total $300 against the 5,000 parts used, it had booked the 5,000 quantity in at 6 cents each and liquidated the total purchase price of $300 against the job. However, when the 10,000 excess parts showed up at inventory time, accounting again used the 6 cents per piece cost figure, and thus the buyer received the startling debit of $600.

EXAMPLE 8: THE 1-CENT CHECK. Although the illustrations used in this text generally refer to products and processes, the effectiveness of the techniques is in no way restricted to those areas. The present technique is especially helpful in many other connections. For example, an engineer who, during a certain month, had taken out various cash advances and submitted covering expense accounts and refunds unfortunately made an arithmetic error and returned to the accounting department 1 cent too much. In order to balance the books the accountants drew a voucher on a New York City bank to pay the engineer back the 1 cent. The average cost of this procedure, according to an investigation with the management of the accounting unit, turned out to be $5 per voucher because of a great deal of detail involved. Engineering and manufacturing people, often hard pressed to reduce overheads, were startled to find that a practice existed whereby so much money was spent to disburse so little. The reaction of each was, "If it were my money, I wouldn't spend it that way." The practice of incurring $5 of expense in order to pay 1 cent, or for that matter to pay $1, was brought into the open for very serious questioning by application of the technique.

The present-day endeavor to establish systems which, almost regardless of people, will produce good results is certainly a most worthwhile trend. No matter how well a system is planned to take care of certain situations, there still remains room for the individual—thinking clearly—to make considerable contribution toward improvement. It is for that reason that the present technique is included in value analysis. Unless it is used and used effectively, experience in practical life shows that large amounts of identifiable unnecessary cost remain unidentified.

CHAPTER 4   *The Use of the Techniques*

4-1. *Selection of Techniques*

As we have seen, the techniques are tools for efficiently identifying unnecessary costs and removing obstacles to better value. Usually several of these tools are used in each case. Furthermore, they are often used simultaneously with one blending into another. In such cases they may be compared with the tools used by a blacksmith. With his tongs the smith brings the heated metal to his vise for gripping in order to shape it with his hammer. Then he measures, uses the hammer again, measures once more, and perhaps applies the tongs to reheating the work for repetition of the process.

There is great similarity in the selection and use of the value analysis tools for the identification of unnecessary cost. As in the case of the blacksmith, very seldom can good work be accomplished with just one of the tools. Efficient value work proceeds along the lines of:

Choosing the appropriate techniques
Arranging them in best order for the particular job
Using each imaginatively and effectively
Ending the use of some and emphasizing the use of others as knowledge is gained
Continuing through the steps of the value analysis job plan until the useful information developed is suitably summarized to clearly point out directions for decision and action

It will have been noted that the value analysis job plan is a framework for using the three basic steps plus the specific applicable techniques in the approximately proper sequence.

4-2. *Example of Procedure*

The best explanation of the procedure in using the techniques in combination with the basic steps under the job plan may be by way of an

110

example comprising two items of an assembly (Figure 4-1). Item 1 is a stainless-steel button, and item 2 is a carbon-steel pin.

Basic Step 1: Identify the Function. This coincides with the "orientation phase" of the job plan.

The two items are parts of a heat-sensitive device which consists of a nichrome tube having a high coefficient of expansion and an inner, smaller, concentric quartz tube having a low coefficient of expansion. As the ambient temperature changes, the difference between the coefficients of expansion provides a motion which operates electrical control equipment. Item 1 is secured in one end of the nichrome tube, its function being to provide a self-centering receptable in which the ¼-inch diameter quartz tube may reliably rest. The function of item 2 is to transmit the motion from the opposite end of the quartz tube into the control device. Accordingly, it is necessary to provide one part which will be supported on one end of the tube, i.e., something in the nature of a flange, and another part which will extend about an inch beyond the other end of the tube into the control device, i.e., something in the nature of an elongated member, such as a portion of a nail. Also, a part is needed

Fig. 4-1. Item 1, centering support; item 2, centering pin; item 3, assembly.

which will extend into the center of the quartz tube for a distance of perhaps an inch in order to keep the quartz tube and the metal part now being studied in the approximate center, axially, of the nichrome tube.

Basic Step 2: Evaluate the Function by Comparison. It will be observed that this is a tentative evaluation which will be revised as the various techniques are used in greater depth later in the study. It will also be observed that we have now progressed into the "information phase" of the value analysis job plan. Before making even a tentative evaluation of function, it is necessary to know the quantities involved (50,000 per year), since quantities required have a major controlling influence on the number of processes that can be employed.

For the purpose of centering and supporting the ¼-inch diameter quartz rod, comparison may be made with a washer, perhaps 1/32 inch thick and ⅝ inch in diameter. Instead of the usual hole in the washer, a conically depressed center will provide the self-centering and supporting feature. The washer is evaluated by comparison with a standard stainless-steel washer, which would have a cost of about ¼ cent. However, since this would not be made in quantities as large as ordinary washers and would, perhaps, need some special tooling, a comparison figure of 1 cent is set. Thus we now consider the value of the function of item 1 to be approximately 1 cent, which is, in effect, the same as saying that it is believed that, considering every suitable process, material, and idea, the function can be reliably accomplished for that amount.

Item 2, when compared with a nail of about the same size, would cost ⅒ cent. Nails, however, are made in extremely large quantities, and a nail in its usual form would not be suitable. The head would have to be coined in the center, and a more refined point would probably be required. In that light, this function also is evaluated, by the adjusted comparison, at 1 cent.

Basic Step 3: Cause Value Alternatives to Be Developed. Suitable value analysis techniques that will cause value alternatives to be developed are now selected. In the present case, the techniques initially chosen are:

2. Get all available costs.
4. Blast, create, refine.
5. Use real creativity.
7. Use industry specialists to extend specialized knowledge.
9. Utilize vendors' available functional products.
11. Utilize specialty processes.
12. Utilize applicable standards.

While still in the "information phase" of the job plan, these facts are established:

Item 1 is made on a screw machine from stainless-steel bar; its cost is 6 cents. The applicable drawings, specifications, and planning cards are sought out.

Item 2 is made on a screw machine from ¼-inch diameter steel rod. Its cost, likewise, is 6 cents. Manufacturing and use information concerning it are also accumulated.

By now proceeding into the "speculative phase" and applying technique 4, "blast, create, refine," and technique 5, "use real creativity," a wide range of possible solutions is opened up. "Brainstorms" are conducted and different approaches are explored. Likewise, a start is made with the application of techniques 7, 9, 11, and 12.

First, the functional requirements and some ideas for accomplishing the functions are set forth so that specialists can search their available functional products and study the use of their specialty processes in relation to this need. Second, a search for applicable standard items is started.

In next moving into the "program-planning phase" of the job plan, certain programs are established. Two of them cover the following actions. Specialists who use the coining process and specialists who use the cold-upsetting process are encouraged to apply their particular knowledge and to adapt their processes for the functions of item 1 and item 2.

By the various steps of the "analytical phase," it is determined that one of the probable best selections for item 1 is the coining process and one of the probable best selections for item 2 is the cold-upsetting process.

In the "program execution phase," the suppliers selected are provided with every possible assistance to assure accomplishment. Since the assembly is small and is already in production, the suppliers are provided with actual assemblies as well as necessary drawings and, perhaps fully as important, with encouragement and with prompt answers to their questions.

In the "status summary and conclusion phase," suggestion sheets are made out from the results provided. These show that, with retainment of complete interchangeability of parts, the cost of item 1 can be reduced from 6 cents to 2 cents, and the cost of item 2 can be reduced from 6 cents to 1 cent.

Fig. 4-2. Centering support and pin after modification.

The sheets also indicate in general how to proceed to accomplish these results. Folders of supporting data are provided to appropriate people in the decision and action area to enable them to identify and promptly remove unnecessary cost.

It will be observed that the process is an objective, action-oriented, searching study of:

What is to be accomplished.

What is the best way of accomplishing it, i.e., the lowest-cost way of reliably doing it.

What are the best answers from the best sources using the latest knowledge and technology.

What clear information is to be crystallized for the basis of decision and action.

As skill is acquired, less attention is necessary in selecting the right tools or techniques. For the sake of effectiveness, however, each of the basic steps, each of the provisions of the job plan, and each of the special techniques should be well learned and should be applied as a well-arranged part of the user's procedure.

4-3. *Examples of Appropriate Progression*

- · 3 basic steps
- · 7 phases of the job plan
- · 13 techniques

To help in gaining familiarity with an orderly application of these tools, each is shown in its appropriate progression in the following example.

BEFORE   AFTER $2\frac{5}{16}''$

FIG. 4-3. A pulley for which drawings and specifications are available and an alternative pulley.

EXAMPLE 1:

	Basic step	Phase of job plan	Techniques
The item is a 2-inch diameter V-belt pulley (Figure 4-3) for light duty on $\frac{1}{4}$-horsepower motor shaft.	1	1	
It is planned to machine it from a 2-inch steel bar.	1	2	
Its planned cost is 60 cents.	1	2	2
Specifications and drawings are accumulated.	1	2	
There are no close tolerances.	1	2	8
Quantity will be 60,000 per year.	1	2	
Comparison with available pulleys which are similar but not precisely usable show the standard to cost 10 cents.			
An addition of 5 cents to add special requirements gives a tentative value for the function of 15 cents.	2	2	4, 5
Tools most likely to produce the best solution are chosen.	3	3	4, 5, 9, 11, 12
Searches are made for different ways of doing it; for different methods of fabrication and manufacturing; for different materials, processes, and ideas; for different approaches to the problem.	3	3	4, 5

	Basic step	Phase of job plan	Techniques
Search for standards. Get into touch with suppliers of specialty functional products. Show them the need and interest them in the job.	3	3	9
Get into touch with specialists using specialty processes, show them the need, and interest them in the job.	3	3	11
Analysis indicates that two alternatives may justify intensified study. They are: Modify vendor's standard Make as die casting in plant	3	4	
Get into touch with proper vendors and arrange for information to be developed on the basis of a standard product suitably modified.	3	5	9, 12
Arrange for manufacturing and cost alternatives to be developed for in-plant manufacture.	3	5	
Follow each of these alternatives, providing more information as needed and making more suggestions to help each succeed.	3	6	
Prepare a status summary and conclusion sheet showing original intended cost of 60 cents with two alternatives: Modified standard, 25 cents In-plant manufacture including tool liquidation, 23 cents	3	7	

As experience is gained, the steps become automatic, the selection becomes rapid, and without omitting any significant steps or techniques, efficiency and effectiveness are improved as the techniques blend into and through one another.

Another example of the use of the basic steps, the job plan, and the techniques may be helpful.

FIG. 4-4. Spacer stud.

EXAMPLE 2:

	Basic step	Phase of job plan	Techniques
The purpose of the stud (Figure 4-4) is to hold an electric motor on high-volume equipment and space a dust cover over it. It offers no appearance or esteem values to the customer. It is a use part.	1	1	

	Basic step	Phase of job plan	Techniques

Quantities are 400,000 per year. The material is steel. There are no close tolerances. It is made on automatic equipment from standard steel rod. There are no quality problems. Its cost in labor, material, and overhead is 15 cents.

Drawings, planning cards, and samples, including an assembled and a disassembled sample of the product using the stud, are at hand.

With the function clearly established as a holding function and a spacing function, comparisons are now made to place the value on each function. The cost of the holding function can be compared with that of a screw of similar dimension, which would be about $1\frac{1}{2}$ cents. The spacing function can be compared with a piece of tubing cut to proper length or a piece of flat metal rolled to form a spacer. In either case, the cost would be in the neighborhood of $\frac{1}{2}$ cent. Therefore, by comparison, the sum of the combined functions is evaluated at 2 cents.

Intensive creative work, using the brainstorming technique, follows to develop a wide range of possible alternative means for accomplishing these two functions. These means are listed. Although several useful alternatives were identified, only one will be pursued through the remaining steps of evaluation.

Discuss the requirements with industry specialists, search for vendors' functional products, provide information upon the functional need to vendors' technical people, provide information to suppliers having specialty processes which might be applicable, and search for standard products.

A supplier of cold, upset, and roll-thread parts proposed a suitable screw as shown in Figure 4-4 at $1\frac{1}{2}$ cents.

A supplier of rolled spacers, which were a specialty product for him, proposed a suitable cylindrical spacer at slightly under $\frac{1}{2}$ cent. This spacer and the roll-thread screw assembled together ready for use would be an equivalent part costing 2 cents.

A suitable program was set up with the supplier of the special screw so that samples

Basic step	Phase of job plan	Techniques
1	2	2
2	3	4, 5
2	2	5
3	3, 4	7, 9, 10, 11, 12
3	3	11
3	3, 4	9

	Basic step	*Phase of job plan*	*Techniques*
were made and provided. On a quantity of these were mounted the rolled spacer from the specialty supplier. With quotations and samples at hand, the move was made to the next step.	3		5, 6
Preparation of the status summary and conclusion sheet revealed: Initial cost, 15 cents Cost as changed, 2 cents Yearly reduction in cost, $52,000	3		7

4-4. Generality Stoppers

As may be quite obvious, it is seldom known in advance what technique or techniques may best produce the results sought. Nevertheless, it will be illustrated by the additional examples which follow that emphasis on a particular technique is often the key to the identification of large amounts of unnecessary cost. In these examples, the complete framework is omitted and only the parts of the evaluation being studied are detailed.

EXAMPLE 1: ELECTRICAL TERMINAL. The function was to facilitate reliable connection of wire to electrical equipment. The terminal, shown in Figure 4-5, was made from copper strip by fully automatic processes on a four-slide machine. It was used in very large quantities.

Effective value work on this item was retarded by a prevailing belief that "made automatically from sheet stock on high-speed four-slide ma-

BEFORE   AFTER

FIG. 4-5. Electrical terminal.

chines, it simply cannot be beat." Being a simple part, it was made from the lowest-cost form of its base material, copper strip. The controlling generality was that all experience of the past had proved this to be by far the most economical, simplest, most straightforward way to make that type of part.

In the light of technique 1, it was apparent that even effective attempts at good-grade value work were being stopped by this generality. Therefore, it was decided to temporarily disregard the belief and to develop objective data.

Using technique 11, it was found that a specialty supplier had so improved his processes that he could produce copper tubing for almost the cost of producing copper sheet and strip. He also possessed very ingenious machines for making a variety of fabrications from this tubing. Further, his organization possessed a high degree of skill in adapting its special equipment to the special needs of its customers.

This attack brought forth an interchangeable part accomplishing the identical function at sufficiently lower cost, with the result that the function was secured for $8,000 less per year.

The professional user of value analysis techniques will soon learn to recognize situations in which any one of the techniques does not fit and also that each technique, in its own right, becomes the real cause of accomplishment for those particular types of products and situations for which it is provided.

EXAMPLE 2: A part (Figure 4-6) machined from steel bar served the function of locating the ends of two compression springs. Quantities were 5,000 each year. It was produced, however, in conjunction with

BEFORE   AFTER   BEFORE   AFTER

FIG. 4-6. Spring-locating parts.   FIG. 4-7. Weld supports.

some other similar machine work. In the information phase, when costs were requested, the answer was that costs were "unavailable." It was thought that because the part was being made in conjunction with a number of other things on equipment which might otherwise stand idle and by workmen during setup time and in odd periods between other jobs, it really had very little cost and that it would be meaningless to develop its own specific cost.

Turning to technique 2, which emphasizes the importance of obtaining and understanding costs, it was decided to determine the cost. With this decision and the action that followed, the cost figure of $1.08 apiece became available. The effective use of technique 2 made it possible to follow up with other techniques, among them technique 7. The result was that a tool costing $1,100 was made, and an interchangeable part accomplishing the total function was then produced as a stamping for a total cost of 8 cents each.

It was only after emphasis was put on the proper use of technique 2 that the project opened up so that the remaining techniques could be used with a resultant return of $5,000 per year for an expenditure of $1,100.

A technique which often facilitates initiation of effective work is technique 3, "use information from only the best sources." Not uncommonly it happens that a source which may not be best for exactly the specific question proves best for a nearly related item or process.

EXAMPLE 3: Weld supports ⅜ inch thick were cut from steel bar as shown in Figure 4-7. The quantity was 3,000 per year and the cost $1.41 each. The irregular shape and the relatively small quantity combined to necessitate considerable work on each. The part was used as a "weld segment" to fit into an opening in large equipment where it was welded in place as a part of a homogeneous mass.

The manager of tool design said that, although admittedly the part was of an irregular shape which was costly to make by individual processes, the quantity was so small and the material so heavy that it was out of the question to consider making dies and punching out usable parts. When he was asked for an approximate estimate of the costs of the tools and parts for the process of punching out the part, his reaction, after reflecting briefly, was that "it would be a waste of time to figure the dies because it is a foregone conclusion that they will be so costly as to make the alternative useless." This came from a highly skilled man in the field of dies, die construction, and die costs. It was difficult not to recognize him as the best authority on the question. The fact was, however, that his experience was generally with large quantities, and he did not have up-to-date knowledge of small-lot stamping technology.

When technique 3 brought this clearly into focus, an estimate was requested from a supplier of small-lot stampings. For him, who always operated in the small-lot field, the case presented no problem. His quotation was $75 for tools and thereafter 39 cents each for parts. This, then, was a case in which application of technique 3 led to a follow-through with succeeding techniques, specifically technique 11. The investment of $75 brought an annual return of $3,000.

Since nearly every case requires the effective use of technique 4, "blast, create, refine," no specific example will be included here to illustrate it. Likewise, effective use of real creativity (technique 5) is required in almost every instance, and no specific example of its use should be necessary.

Application of technique 6, "identify and overcome roadblocks," is of the greatest vitality and importance. Experience has shown that in three-quarters of the cases occurring in practice, the development of effective value alternatives is stopped by failure to use this technique. It has also proved that when this technique does apply and is used costs of the order of one-half or less usually result.

Further, it will be understood that this technique is commonly useful in dealing with situations which may be developed by a number of the other techniques and, in addition, uncovers wide areas of "stoppers" which are not identified by any of the other techniques.

The injection of generalities represents a roadblock until they are identified and eliminated.

The absence of meaningful cost is a roadblock until it is identified and eliminated.

The acceptance of answers from sources which are not the best is a very effective and common roadblock.

Lack of ability to locate industry specialists, vendors' functional products, vendors with specialized skills, vendors with specialty processes needed, and standard products also figures as a roadblock.

If a good degree of value work is to be done, effectiveness in overcoming every one of these and dozens of other roadblocks must be developed.

4-5. *Interrelation of Job Plan Phases and Techniques*

Basic steps	Phase of job plan	Techniques used
1. Identify function	1. Orientation	
	2. Information	1. Avoid generalities
		3. Get answers from best sources
		6. Overcome roadblocks
2. Evaluate function	2. Information	1. Avoid generalities
		2. Know costs
		3. Get answers from best sources
		6. Overcome roadblocks
		8. Put value on key tolerances
		9. Use vendors' functional products
		11. Use specialty processes
		12. Use applicable standards
	3. Creative	4. Blast, create, refine
		5. Use real creativity
		13. Spend money as own
	4. Analytical	1. Avoid generalities
		3. Get answers from best sources
		8. Put value on key tolerances
		9. Use vendors' functional products
		11. Use specialty processes
		12. Use applicable standards
3. Create alternatives	3. Creative	4. Blast, create, refine
		5. Use real creativity
		7. Use industry specialists
		9. Use vendors' functional products
		10. Use vendors' skills
		11. Use specialty processes
		12. Use applicable standards
	4. Analytical	1. Avoid generalities
		3. Get answers from best sources

Basic steps	Phase of job plan	Techniques used
		6. Overcome roadblocks
		13. Spend money as own
	5. Planning	3. Get answers from best sources
		6. Overcome roadblocks
		7. Use industry specialists
		9. Use vendors' functional products
		10. Use vendors' skills
		11. Use specialty processes
		12. Use applicable standards
	6. Execution	3. Get answers from best sources
		6. Overcome roadblocks
		7. Use industry specialists
		9. Use vendors' functional products
		10. Use vendors' skills
		11. Use specialty processes
		12. Use applicable standards
	7. Status summary and report	

At this point, it may be useful to work through an example evaluation for the purpose of checking the techniques that it is necessary to use in order to achieve an effective result.

Basic Step 1: Identify the Function. A terminal (Figure 4-8) of a small electrical device receives and must reliably hold a No. 6 cop-

BEFORE   AFTER

Fig. 4-8. Electrical terminals.

per conductor wire. Although the wire is usually inserted by moving it parallel to its own axis, sometimes other means of fastening the wire makes lowering it into the terminal more convenient. It is desirable, therefore, to be able to open the top of the terminal under such circumstances. In starting the investigation of this terminal, it was found that the manufacturing department had a fairly large battery of automatic screw machines and the necessary milling machines to produce this terminal as a screw-machined and milled part. Accordingly, they felt it unwise to invest time and resources in investigating other methods, which might result in making this good equipment useless.

It was found that engineering was very pleased with the performance of the terminal. There had been some quality problems a few years earlier. When the nuts were tightened down too much, the prongs of the terminal would snap together and slip threads. This was corrected by providing a washer with a center tongue which prevented this snapping together. The product accomplished its function well. There were no longer any quality problems, and there was other necessary work at hand for engineering talent. Therefore, engineering was not disposed to solve this problem by opening up new design and manufacturing considerations. (The sales department was meeting customer resistance but was seeking its solution by attempting to develop more effective sales methods.)

The essential information had to be secured and these roadblocks had to be overcome by some means, or else the value work would have ended prematurely. Techniques 1, 3, and 6 were put to use.

Basic Step 2: Evaluate the Function by Comparison. It was found that the quantities had been large, and although they were decreasing, they were still very substantial. The cost of the three pieces, which included two screw-machined parts and the stamping, was 20 cents for each three terminals used on the device. Preliminary study included various terminals used in other devices and in other industries. Terminal specialists were consulted. Vendors of terminals were invited to make suggestions. The technical people of vendors' organizations were advised of the problems and of the needs. Manufacturers utilizing specialty processes which might be applicable were given an opportunity to understand the function needed so they could apply their processes and suggest appropriate alternatives. Applicable standards were searched.

The initial comparison with available products indicated that this function could probably be reliably accomplished for something in the neighborhood of 6 cents per set of three terminal assemblies if the best combination of ideas, materials, and processes was brought together.

A creative study was then conducted, and in it, every possible alternative, and even impossible alternatives that could be suggested, were listed. These alternatives included contributions which might be made by various materials, by various processes, by various design approaches, by various manufacturing combinations, etc. Preliminary evaluation of them confirmed the 6-cent function value.

Basic Step 3: Cause Value Alternatives to Be Developed. Now, having in view a 20-cent set of terminals with an estimated value of 6 cents, more extensive creative work was indicated. The suggestions which came out of the preliminary creative work were examined. Especially effective avenues of approach were selected. Creative effort was made to produce a larger range of alternatives to provide ways of accomplishing some of the most effective approaches and also to provide suggested sources for better information and for later approaches.

With this move, sufficient information was accumulated so that, in the analytical phase, good information from knowledgeable specialists and covering estimates, or quoted costs, made it practicable to narrow down the selection of probable best alternatives. The succeeding analysis indicated that a reliable terminal, which would be convenient to use and which would accomplish its function well and be most economical, would in all likelihood be made, not on rotating machinery, but on punch presses or stamping machinery.

Therefore, in the planning phase as well as in the execution phase of the job plan, emphasis was placed on working with industry specialists having appropriate skills and techniques. Also, more intensive studies were made along the lines of using vendors' functional products and applicable standards, including modifications of such products and standards. Technical people in the plants of vendors making terminal-type products from flat material were further assisted and encouraged to suggest alternatives which would utilize their company's materials. Several good alternatives were developed.

The status summary and report was issued covering an alternative made of one stamping, a piece of tubing, and a standard screw at a total cost of 9 cents per set of three terminals. The best alternative in this case, brought forth by technique 11, "utilize specialty processes," was provided by a vendor whose specialized equipment and specialized knowledge qualified him to furnish simple, high-grade, functional terminals capable of accomplishing the total function reliably at the lowest cost.

It will be observed that in carrying out this typical value study, which identified half of the cost as being unnecessary, substantially all of the techniques were used and most of them made an important contribution. Of course, since this was not a close-tolerance job, technique 8 served only for a check to make sure that the specification on the terminal did not include any close tolerances. After that, no further thought needed to be given to the tolerance question.

In practical application, technique 13, "Would I spend my money this way?" becomes a very important motivator to offset, in some degree, the roadblocks and stoppers which always exist. If the answer to this question is clearly and sharply "no," the specialist will surely resolve to select enough of the appropriate techniques to overcome whatever particular situation may be inhibiting the development of better value alternatives.

CHAPTER 5 *Special Knowledge Required*

In practically all fields of human endeavor, the operator, to achieve the very best results, uses special tools in combination with special knowledge. The difference between one field and another lies in the nature of both the tools and the knowledge.

The tools may vary from the physical kinds that, for instance, the plumber needs to execute his work readily or the surgeon uses to perform his tasks expertly to the more figurative tools that the successful lawyer cannot do without.

As for the knowledge required, it ranges from the practical training and experience that the skillful plumber works with to the intricate medical knowledge needed by the surgeon or the intimate acquaintance with law, human behavior, and prior court decisions that the lawyer must have.

This elementary situation also prevails as far as the value analyst is concerned. He too needs special tools combined with special knowledge to produce value alternatives which, by the process of comparison, identify unnecessary costs.

5-1. *Reach of Knowledge*

There is one basic difference, however, in the reach of knowledge required by the value analyst in comparison with the majority of other experts. Consider the income tax specialist, for example. He must have special knowledge in great depth pertaining to tax law, practice, and regulations involving a multitude of situations. Or consider the heat-transfer specialist who must possess accumulated knowledge in great volume pertaining to materials, heat conductivity, and practicable shapes and ideas for providing, preventing, or controlling the flow of heat. The need of both of these specialists is for comprehensive special knowledge, all pertaining to the relatively narrow bands of the applicable field.

In contrast, the special knowledge required for high-grade value work is extremely broad. It does not consist of knowledge in depth in any specific field. It is rather a matter of having the kind of broad knowledge that makes the holder recognize the multitude of technologies and product areas that he must explore to be assured of optimum performance and optimum value in his product.

As we have seen in the foregoing discussions, the tools for professional-grade value work are the value analysis basic steps and techniques which are used to identify the problem, organize it into solvable integers, and bring a number of ideas to play upon each integer. By applying these tools in conjunction with appropriate special knowledge, alternatives are produced from which a choice can be made, either in the design stage or in subsequent design reviews, to accomplish the desired function reliably and at the same time to include less unnecessary cost.

5-2. *Nature of Knowledge*

The special knowledge required in value improvement work consists of information on materials, processes, functional products, sources of functional knowledge, approaches to function performance, and practical ideas for economical function solutions. In other words, the value analyst's requirement is for knowledge in moderate depth penetrating each of hundreds of widely diverse fields.

Only through the best combination of materials, processes, ideas, etc., is it possible, in any given instance, to arrive at the solution that secures reliable performance at the lowest cost, as represented by the "best value" alternative.

To achieve this result, it is not enough to have a library of appropriate knowledge, for the simple reason that, however comprehensive it be, the collection cannot be expected to include all information having a bearing on the sought solution. With the continual, rapid expansion of new knowledge, the latest information on materials, processes, and the like is hardly ever to be found recorded. Hence channels must be developed and recorded for ready access to such new information.

In consequence, it is important that the value analyst's library of special knowledge contain not only as comprehensive as possible a volume of trade knowledge backed by efficient means for quick recall of needed information but also well-organized references to a maximum number of sources of special skills that may be consulted in connection with each problem. Even then, 100 per cent performance can only be approached because no known system will scan the collection to ensure that the best information is brought into play.

Often the best alternatives for accomplishing desired functions reliably for small fractions of their expected costs are found by extracting from the fund of special value knowledge an overlooked material, process, or available functional product or some combination of them. The effective solution to a problem is quite commonly so simple as to almost produce embarrassment and frequently finds expression in sayings such as, "Why couldn't I have thought of it before?"

Case Study

THE TIMER

Precision timers were used on precise electrical equipment. They accurately provided timing of from 1/10 to 20 seconds. The quantity was 1,000 per year. The use of value analysis techniques brought into clear focus the unnecessary costs included in the following examples. The reader will note the importance of familiarity with the particular special knowledge which efficiently brought forth each of the alternatives listed.

An iron casting was purchased for 21 cents. It was very complicated and had a great amount of machining on it. By the time all the machining was done, its cost was $1.76. It was found that a rather heavy stamping could be purchased from small-lot vendors instead. Tool cost would be $100—10 cents each on a year's supply—and the part ready to use would cost 20 cents.

A special cam-operated electrical contact was assembled from specially fabricated pieces of plastic laminate, brass strip, and contacts. It cost 86 cents each. A specialty vendor provided a switch kit which contained all these parts as standard items. Parts could be taken from the kit, then purchased in the quantities desired and put together by him from his standard parts; this provided a finished switch which had the same operating characteristics and which could be used with a slight change in the mounting arrangement on the assembly, for 16 cents.

A timing lever assembly was made from metal strip cut, formed, drilled, welded, etc., and one screw-machined part which was welded in. It required a great amount of handwork and cost $6.56 each. It was found, in searching for a way to accomplish this function at more nearly its value, that, instead of the steel strip, a basic stamping which formed a principal part of the assembly was provided by a low-quantity stamping vendor for 20 cents each with $100 tool cost—again 10 cents each on a year's production. Adding the welding, the riveting, and an available commercial rivet instead of the special screw-machined part increased the cost 10 cents, so that the total now was 30 cents, or 40 cents for the first year, instead of $6.56.

An interesting assembly was a small pawl about 2 inches long which pivoted at one end and was pressed by a spring at the other end into notches on the edge of a dial. In this way it acted to hold the dial in exactly preferred positions which were exact fractions of a second or of a minute. It was made of 3/32-inch-thick steel, suitably shaped. Riveted into it was a screw-machined part properly grooved to hold the end of the spring which pressed it against the dial edge. Its special shape, the making of the screw-machined part, the assembly, etc., brought its cost to $2. The value alternative which would most economically and reliably accomplish all the functions consisted of a stamping of the same size, again made by a small-lot stamping supplier. Instead of the screw-machined part, the metal sheet was blanked and a part of it about ⅛ inch wide and ¼ inch long was turned up at right angles. In the punch-press operation, a small groove was placed on the top of this portion which, with the groove, served to receive the spring and make the screw-machined part and its assembly unnecessary. The cost of tooling was $50—5 cents each for the first year—and the cost of the part was then 7 cents, for a total of 12 cents instead of $2.

The foregoing are samples of thirty subassemblies or individual parts for which functions were examined and value alternatives were prepared.

The over-all result was identification of enough unnecessary cost to allow production of the timer with costs reduced from $94 to $28.

The more extensive the accumulated special knowledge for value work, the faster and more efficiently the value work proceeds.

The special knowledge needed for explorations in the value phase is so broad that only its type can be illustrated in a discussion such as the present one, and the reader should realize that a hundred times more information than that which can be presented here is necessary for a high degree of value work. Whatever it is, the information must be in a form which, in so far as possible, can be referred back to for alternative means and ways of performing given functions.

To be most useful, the special information on materials and products must include data on the functions which the item will accomplish as well as on the types of new functions which it may accomplish. Also, the data must be associated with approximate costs or relative costs.

5-3. *Form and Constitution of Knowledge Fund*

In actual practice, persons engaged in value work have found it advantageous to accumulate the special knowledge needed in whatever form it usually can be obtained, such as handbooks, catalogues, charts, price lists, product and process descriptions, tables. But one factor that plays an important role in effective development of value alternatives is not commonly found in available technical or trade information, namely, the association between properties of materials and costs, as contrasted with the commonly indicated relationship between the material and its cost. In searches for alternatives to accomplish specified functions most economically, it is the relationship between properties and costs that is most useful.

Similarly, the most helpful process relationship is that between the properties of products produced by various processes and the cost of each process, including the material used. Again, this type of information is not normally incorporated in existing handbooks, catalogues, and trade information sources.

Were tables of relationships of functions to costs generally available, the required amount of special knowledge would be greatly reduced.

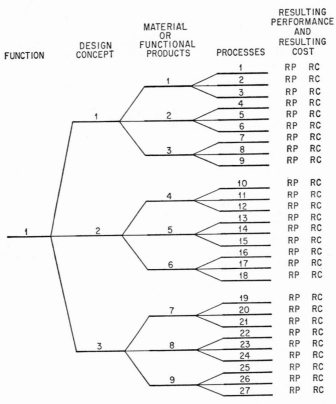

Fig. 5-1. Typical variety of combinations of design concepts, materials, and processes which will accomplish a specified function.

However, to establish the relationship of function to cost, a chain procedure is necessary, starting with function and proceeding to a design concept, then going on into certain products and materials and advancing into certain processes appropriate for use with these products and materials in this design concept. At this end of the chain, costs can be determined.

For recognition of the magnitude of the job of securing the desired performance at lowest cost, the reader may well examine the chart in Figure 5-1 which shows the necessary process which must be completed, beginning with a desired function and culminating in a combination of design concepts, materials, products, and processes which will yield the required function and to which a definite cost can then be attached.

For purposes of simplicity, let us assume that for a typical function three design concepts or approaches must be considered and that, for each approach, three different combinations of materials, products, or modified products must be investigated; further, let us assume that for each subcombination three sets of processes are possibilities. It will be seen that twenty-seven alternatives result in this case. In many instances, the average would be nearer four of each kind, which would mean sixty-four alternative ways, many of which would accomplish the required performance and most of which would be associated with different costs. As a general yardstick, it may well be that, to accomplish the normal function in industry, between twenty-five and fifty deviations may justify investigation. The required performance and the lowest cost may appear in any one of them.

It will be obvious that it is necessary to have included in the special knowledge extensive information concerning relationships and inter-relationships between functions, design concepts, materials, products, and processes. The problem of achieving functions reliably at lowest cost becomes the more complicated not only because the design concept influences and controls materials, products, and processes used, including the resulting cost, but also because the reverse is true; the resulting cost has an influence on the process selection, which in turn has its influence on materials and products, which again must influence the design concept. Continuous interrelationships must be cut and tried and changed, and the problem cannot be reduced to one of starting at point A and proceeding to point B with assurance that the road followed will be the shortest.

In a variety of valuable handbooks, design guides, and other sources of information, there will be found tables and charts of the relationships of:

Functions to design concepts
Products and materials to properties
Properties of products to functions
Properties of materials to functions
Materials to processes
Materials to costs
Products to costs
Processes to costs

Occasionally, helpful knowledge can be found covering narrow parts of the field and showing properties of materials or products that have had their functions related directly to costs. Such charts of properties related to functions and to costs provide a rather direct linkage between functions and costs. Although not listed above, some charts of relationships of functions to costs probably exist and more are likely to come, and they will constitute an invaluable part of the special knowledge serving the needs of value analysis.

The reader will do well to tie the process of bringing special knowledge to bear directly and efficiently upon a product to techniques 7, "use industry specialists to extend specialized knowledge"; 9, "utilize vendors' available functional products"; 10, "utilize and pay for vendors' skills and knowledge"; and 11, "utilize specialty processes." Often the special knowledge serves at best to identify the particular approach which is most likely to yield good results. Then suitable industry specialists must be brought into contact with a clearly defined function objective so that they, in turn, using their experience, can apply special knowledge, special materials, special products, and special processes with a degree of effectiveness which would be impossible for anyone less skilled in that particular field.

5-4. *Listing of Specialized Competence*

The special knowledge fund should also contain listings of specialists to be consulted, as the first step taken, after an approach to be explored has been indicated by application of the general special knowledge. Because of the vital importance of this part of the special knowledge fund, part of a listing that has served this purpose in actual practice is included. While the names and addresses of the persons to be contacted were included in the original listing, the transcription here shows only the activity involved. The tabulation is illustrative of the manner of developing sources of specialized competence on the products and functions being studied.

VALUE ANALYSIS SPECIAL KNOWLEDGE
SOURCES OF SPECIALIZED COMPETENCE

Item	*Source*[1]
Castings:	
Aluminum, bronze, brass sand	
Austenitic and stainless steel	
Carbon and alloy steel, sand cast	
Centrifugal castings, nonferrous	
Design and metallurgical assistance	

[1] Names and addresses of the sources listed in the original are deleted, as they were appropriate only to a particular work type.

Item	Source[1]

Die castings, nonferrous
Ductile iron
Gray iron, sand cast
Malleable iron sand castings
Pattern work
Permanent molding, nonferrous
Precision Castings:
    Investment
    Centrifugal
Shell molding, nonferrous
Chemistry and chemical engineering:
    Organic
    Physical and analytical
    Processes
Computational methods
Contracts
Cost accounting
Design and application engineering:
    Acoustics, vibration, and stress analysis
    Appearance design
    Engineering statistics
    Specialist applications
    Standards
    Technical data
    Technical systems
    Thermal systems
Electrical engineering laboratory investigations:
    Computer engineering
    Control systems engineering
Electronic engineering
Electronic data processing
Electron and radiation equipment engineering
Electron tubes
Equipment development:
    Coil design and manufacture
    Equipment engineering
    Equipment manufacturing
    Machinability
Information systems
Instrumentation
Insulation engineering
Laminated and insulating products:
    Mica products
    Varnished products
Magnetics and electromagnetic engineering
Manufacturing engineering:

Item	*Source*[1]
Manufacturing methods	
Plant engineering	
Plant layout	
Production control	
Purchasing factory equipment	
Purchasing ferrous materials	
Quality control	
Time standards	

Metallurgy and welding
Nucleonics and radiation
Office procedures analysis
Patents
Porcelain products
Printing and related work:
   Addressograph
   Binders
   Composition
   Electrotyping
   Letterpress printing
   Mimeograph
   Multigraph
   Offset printing
   Photoengraving
   Planograph
Product planning
Product service
Punching, tool and die
Purchasing
   Chemicals
   Fuels
   Ferrous and non-ferrous materials
   Research
Screw machine, cold heading, slotting, roll threading:
   All types of special
   Automatic, 0 to 3½ inches diameter
   Cold heading
   Hand, 0 to 17 inches diameter
   Screw-machined parts in any quantity
Semiconductor engineering
Specifications, Army and Navy
Tinsmith practice
Traffic knowledge
Training and education
Welded products
Woodworking

5-5. *Specific Product and Process Knowledge*

For the purpose of illustrating the types of resources on which data must be included and which must be available in some suitable form as special knowledge, the following abbreviated samples are presented. In each case there must be enough knowledge available to make a preliminary evaluation of the suitability of the material, the product, the modified product, or the process to effectively accomplish the type of function involved, together with a reasonable amount of comparative information concerning costs. In some of the lists offered here, only the item is named, while in others, somewhat more of the type of information required is provided.

MATERIALS:

Adhesives
Bonding
Coating
Glue-type
Hot melts
Rubber-base
Sealing
Synthetic-resin
Thermoplastic
Thermosetting
Vegetable-resin

For value analysis work, as for various other purposes, the usefulness of the data file on adhesives, as on many other items, is enhanced by a cross-reference listing indicating the applications for which a particular type is especially suitable, together with characteristics of the bonds obtained.

Asbestos
Cloth
Cord
Tape
Thread
Tubing
Yarn

Asphalt
Coverings
Products
Sheets

Ceramic
  Chemical-containing materials
  Extruded materials
  Guides
  Insulators
  Low-loss materials
  Metal-cutting tools
  Pressed materials
  Specialties

Fibers

Animal:
  Mohair
  Silk
  Wool
Mineral:
  Asbestos
  Metallic threads
  Tinsel
Trade-name:
  Vistex
  Vulcoid

Vegetable:
  Cotton
  Flax
  Hemp
  Jute
  Ramie
Synthetic:
  Nylon
  Orlon
  Rayon
  Spun glass

Glass
  Fabric
  Fibers
  Heat-resistant
  Insulation
  Shock-resistant
  Tapes

Paper
  Barrier
  Cohesive
  Electric-conducting
  Electric-shielding
  Fire-resistant
  Laminated
  Oil-resistant
  Water-resistant

Plastics

The rapidly developing and expanding spectrum of plastics material covering substantially all ranges of properties and prices is increasingly accomplishing functions reliably for the lowest cost. A clear understanding must be well in mind of the relative strengths and weaknesses, i.e., plus and minus properties, the relative costs, and also the limitations and opportunities of different fabricating methods of, say, at least twenty-five different plastic materials. This information can be obtained in different forms from the different companies providing the plastic products and materials. It is a "must" item in the value analysis special knowledge fund.

Aluminum

Special alloys for stamping, spinning, drawing, forming, shaping, brazing, welding, etc.

Special bonded material in which aluminum is bonded to various other metals

Special shapes for particular functions, extrusions, disks, etc.

Bonded Metals

A wide array of laminated, bonded, and overlaid materials including metals and nonmetallic materials; prebrazed and prewelded materials; and prefinished, preplated, preenameled, prepolished materials.

Metals, Embossed and Expanded

Available raw material with surface formed and deformed, textured, split and expanded, etc., to accomplish low-cost rigidity and/or appearance objectives.

While this listing is a highly abbreviated one, it should include enough to show the reader something of the proper penetration of information required in the special knowledge for value analysis.

PROCESSES—SPECIALTY:

Specialty processes are listed here although in some form the necessary standard and common processes must also be included and considered.

Assemblies, Welded-wire

Welded assemblies of wire-formed parts are successfully replacing sheet-metal assemblies because of savings in material and make-up of low-cost wire-formed parts.

Bonding, Roll

Joining sheets of aluminum or copper by first silk-screening a desired pattern on one sheet, then hot-rolling two sheets together, thus creating a permanent bond outside of the applied pattern and allowing the portion inside the pattern to then be expanded by hydraulic fluid pressure. Tooling cost is extremely low.

Casting, Centrifugal Special

A lost-wax process in which molds are spun after metal is poured to flow metal to all sections uniformly.

Casting, Continuous

A process for forming a wide range of copper-base alloys into the equivalent of long mill rods, tubes, and shapes ready for machining or other fabricating operations.

Casting, Die

Produces low-cost castings, in multiple cavity molds, primarily of zinc, aluminum, and brass. Castings are of good surface finish. Dimensions can be maintained to ±0.002 inch.

Casting, Die, Miniature

Parts, up to an ounce in weight, of zinc or nylon can be cast automatically at a very low cost. An acorn nut that was formerly made on a screw machine at a cost of $12.24 per thousand is now made by this process for $5.76 per thousand.

Casting, Frozen Mercury

A precision investment casting process similar to lost wax except that mercury is used instead of wax for making molds. Produces castings to close tolerances.

Casting, Lost-wax

A precision casting process that produces parts to close tolerances. For example, a valve handle that was sand-cast and machined for $1.10 could be produced by the lost-wax process with the price reduced to 70 cents.

Casting, Plaster-mold

Precision casting made to ±0.005-inch tolerances in materials of aluminum, brass, and bronze with plaster molds. Cost of tools is low. Piece price usually lies between that of permanent-mold and die castings.

Casting, Shell-molding

A relatively newly developed casting process that produces parts with good surface finishes and tolerances within $\frac{1}{32}$ inch. Cuts down considerably on machining time.

Casting, Small-lot

Produces small zinc die castings in short-quantity runs. Owing to redesign of die-casting equipment, tool cost is kept to a minimum without sacrifice of quality or workmanship.

Circuitry, Mechanized

Etched circuits can be produced by either silk-screen or photographic processes. The photo process gives better definition but costs more than the silk-screen process.

Plated circuits can be plated on both sides of a Textolite board or its equivalent and connected by plating through holes in the board.

Printed circuits can be produced by printing on a suitable plastic board.

Stamped circuits are made by die stamping the basic circuit connections out of a sheet of conducting material and attaching this circuit securely to a sheet of insulating material. The die construction is similar to a dinking die and is suitable for large quantities with costs often less than those for other processes.

Chromizing or Chrome Diffusing

A heat-treating process which transforms the surface of iron, steel, and most ferrous metals into a chromium-rich alloy to resist corrosion, heat oxidation, and abrasive wear. A low-cost substitution for some types of stainless steel.

Cleaning, Ultrasonic

Transmitting ultrasonic waves through cleaning solutions produces a violent action that literally blasts soil from intricate parts in a matter of seconds.

Connecting Wire, Solderless Wrapping

Developed by Western Electric and Bell Laboratories. Consists in wrapping wire around a rectangular terminal for electrical connections. Up to 40 per cent faster than soldering.

Extrusion, Impact

Drawn shapes or cans can be extruded from zinc, magnesium, and aluminum slugs at low cost. High tool costs limit this process to high-quantity runs.

Floturn

Cold-forming of metal blanks by applying pressure spirally with a roller over a mandrel. The blank diameter is exactly that of the finished part, but its thickness is greater. The machine flows the metal into the intended shape with dimensions held to ±0.002 inch.

Forging, Automatic Precision

Process for producing precision forgings in a fully automatic manner.

Forging, Cold-impact

Method of shaping high-strength aluminum alloys by direct compression. Can often produce in one operation parts which formerly required multiple machining or a number of smaller pieces.

Forging, Precision

Improved electrical upsetting and forging techniques that reduce costs over previously known forging methods.

Forming, Electro

An electroplating process that plates coatings of material on a formed matrix which is later removed to leave behind an intricate shape that it might have been impossible to produce by machining.

Forming, Hydro

Produces intricate and deep-drawn shapes by hydraulic pressure. Requires only a punch of low-cost material with a rubber pad as a die.

Forming, Roll

A process mainly for large quantities of low-cost parts with formed sides. For instance, a hinge could be roll-formed for 27 cents as compared with 37 cents by the former conventional method.

Forming, Stretch

Process of gripping a metal blank at its ends, applying a force sufficient to bring the material to its yield point, and then wrapping it around a die while it is held under this tension. After material has been formed around the die, the tension is increased and the material is permanently set.

Forming, Vacuum

Consists in clamping thermoplastic sheet in a frame, applying heat to soften the sheet, and then sucking the sheet over or into a mold by means of vacuum. When cool, the formed sheet is removed from the mold. Particularly useful for short runs since tool cost is low.

Grinding, Electrolytic

Removing stock by conventional grinding accompanied by electro-chemical decomposition of the work material. Applicable on metals where grinding wheels quickly glaze and refuse to cut.

Heading, Cold

Forcing wire into a die under pressure to shape parts that normally are produced on screw machines. Adaptable mainly to medium- and high-production quantities. Very much lower in cost where applicable.

Machining, Electrical-discharge

A series of discharges occurring at the rate of 20,000 to millions per second between the electrode and the workpiece remove stock accurately on extremely hard metals that are otherwise difficult to machine.

Lacing, Metal

With a patented punch and die that can be set up in conventional punch presses, sheet metals are joined together without rivets, welds, or solder. Metal is pushed downward from the top to become depressed sideways and make a permanent fastening wedge under the surface of the bottom sheet.

Metalizing, Vacuum

Metals and nonmetals can be coated with bright metallic finishes by evaporating the coating material in a vacuum and allowing the coating to condense on the objects to be finished.

Milling, Chemical Process

To remove stock from complex shapes and fragile parts, the metal to be removed is left exposed while the rest of the part is masked with a specially developed coating. The entire part is then submerged in an etching solution that removes the desired amount of metal to accuracies of 0.002 inch.

Molding, Small-lot

Process for producing small-lot plastic parts at a low piece price and a low mold cost.

Painting, Electrostatic Spray

An efficient, economical spray method of electrically applying paint to parts. Appreciable savings are often achieved in labor and material over other spray, dip, or flow-coat methods.

Polishing, Electro

The reverse of electroplating. Normally used to remove from 0.0003 to 0.001 inch of metal. Can provide savings in finishing wire forms and assemblies and on parts with tiny recesses or intricate designs. Often, burr removal and polishing, which normally require two separate operations, are performed simultaneously.

Powder-metal Process

Metal powders are formed in dies to desired shape, then hardened in baking ovens. Parts produced by this method are low in cost and close in tolerance.

Shaping, Cold

Billets of mild steel are formed by 3,000-ton presses into cylindrical shapes. Parts are made to close tolerances and with very smooth surfaces.

Shaping, Hot Extruded

Heated billets of metal are fed through dies set up in horizontal presses to produce many types of shapes. Extrusion dies cost approximately $300 to $500 depending on the complexity of the part.

Shaping, Small Parts Drawn on Eyelet Machines

Very low cost. Adaptable for high-quantity runs in view of high tool charges. Highly automatic.

Soldering, Ultrasonic or Fluxless

Special soldering iron sets up vibrations which remove tough oxide film from surfaces with resultant improved tinning and better joint properties. Used commercially, especially in England, on aluminum and its alloys.

Spinning, Automatic Metal

Automatic spinning, without expensive tooling, can produce parts which ordinarily take several drawing operations on draw presses.

Stamping, Chemical Etched

Intricate brass and aluminum sheet-metal parts, up to 0.020 inch thick, are produced by chemical etching without resorting to tools. Cost is approximately 3 cents per square inch.

Stamping, Multislide

Low-cost stampings are produced on a multiple head that eliminates secondary operations for forming, tapping, reaming, counterboring, and countersinking. Minimum quantity is 100,000 parts.

Stamping, Small-lot

Process for producing small-quantity stampings at low cost with low tooling cost.

Stamping, Squirt

Produces unusual stampings on conventional punch presses from developed lengths of bar stock.

Stitching, Metal

A low-cost method of fastening materials together. Without prepunched holes, wire is pierced through the materials and formed over on the bottom side.

Swaging, Bar

Long tapers are produced on bars at low cost in special swaging machines. Tool cost is low. Piece prices by this method are considerably lower than parts machined on screw machines or centerless grinders.

Thread Rolling and Form Rolling

Low-cost method of threading round parts by feeding parts between two thread dies that move back and forth, forming the thread instead of cutting it. Knurling, grooving, and undercutting can also be done by special dies in the same manner. Cold-heading suppliers are fully equipped to perform this work.

Welding, Cold

Joining of two sheets of metal or wires by pressure without need of flux, solder, or heat.

Welding, Tip

Welding of wire joints without need of solder or flux.

The fund of special knowledge required must also include information on specialty products and specialty materials of which the following are typical examples.

PRODUCTS—SPECIALTY:

Bumpers, Rubber

One-piece rubber parts with molded-in holding grooves that eliminate the need for additional fastening provisions.

Cans, Standard Drawn and Formed

Standard drawn and formed enclosures are available, with no extra tool cost, in more than 3,000 stock sizes, both round and rectangular. They are made from stock 0.019 to 0.025 inch thick and in sizes from $\frac{7}{8}$ inch in diameter by $1\frac{1}{16}$ inch long to $6 \times 7 \times 7$ inches.

Fasteners, Special

A great variety of special fasteners, including self-tapping screws for steel and plastic materials, screws with preassembled lock washers, plastic rivets, nuts with preassembled lock washers, terminals, and precision-stamped gears.

Junction Boxes and Covers, Standard Aluminum

Over 500 different-size deep-drawn aluminum junction boxes and covers up to $17 \times 19 \times 7$ inches deep. Secondary operations on these boxes and covers are performed.

Pins, Roll

Rolled spring dowel pins that can be used in place of solid straight and tapered pins for one-half the cost with the elimination of hole reaming.

Spacers, Rolled

Rolled split bushings and spacer tubes from flat stock. Holes, slots, and cutouts are punched out before forming, thereby eliminating more costly machining operations after forming.

Terminal Blocks

Standard, molded, low-cost terminal blocks for appliances and other applications eliminate mold charges.

Terminals, Small

Solderless terminals for wire sizes 22 to 0. These terminals are supplied as individual terminals or on reels in strip form that can be attached to terminals automatically by machines which the producers also furnish. These producers also manufacture solderless terminals for special applications, such as relay tabs and plugs and receptacles. A push-on terminal recently developed is replacing the conventional terminal that is fastened with a screw.

Terminals, Tubular

Swaged from strip stock for use in place of more expensive, solid screw-machined terminals.

Tool, Wire-wrap

A tool for the wire-wrap method of making solderless electrical connections. The wire is automatically wrapped with a power tool so tightly around the terminal that it meets the exacting requirements of a permanent electrical and mechanical connection.

MATERIALS—SPECIALTY:

Adhesive and Tapes

Electrical tapes with paper, plastic, glass, cotton, and acetate backings. A variety of pressure-sensitive tapes and adhesives.

Gaskets, Flow-on

Liquid-rubber material, flowed on with a gun, to replace die-cut and molded-rubber gaskets.

Insulating Products, Plain and Laminated

All types of conventional varnished cloth including silicone and other treated glass cloth. Mica and Mica-Mat tapes, sheets, tubes, and special shapes; also laminated sheets and tubes.

Materials, Electrical-contact

Thermometals, electrical contacts, precious metals, bimetallic products, and special alloys.

Metals, Rigidized

Sheet metal with rolled-in design patterns for rigidizing to yield increased strength and permit the use of thinner-gauge materials.

Nylon and Teflon

Nylon and Teflon slab, rod, strip, tubing, tape, and powders.

Paper, Fireproof Treated

Low-cost impregnated paper to replace more expensive asbestos paper and sheet for uses such as catching paint drippings.

Plastics, Reinforced

Glass-reinforced plastic giving added strength to plastic parts.

Rust Inhibitor, VPI

Chemical which is a slowly vaporizing corrosion inhibitor that preserves the surface of metal by forming a protective atmosphere. It is replacing grease and other protective coatings that take longer to apply and remove.

Rust Inhibitor, VPI Paper

Packaging material treated with vapor-phase inhibitor.

Shims, Laminated

Laminated material that peels off in 0.002-inch thicknesses. This material is stamped out to make shims that eliminate the grinding of solid shim material.

Steels, Coated

Electroplated with either zinc, copper, nickel, brass, or chromium or hot-dip-coated with lead alloy, tin, or lacquer.

Strip and Sheet, Prepainted

Prepainted steel supplied in coils ranging in width from $7/32$ inch to 30 inches and in thickness from 0.006 to 0.040 inch. Color coatings and lacquers in all shades on one or both sides are available in all types of synthetic enamels, as well as in chemical finishes such as acid and weatherproof materials.

Achieving value by generating appropriate alternatives is a task of preparation, study, and comparison. In this work it is obvious that relative costs are of the utmost importance. Therefore, included in the special knowledge of value analysis will be a large amount of accumulated relative-cost data to guide in the selection of materials, processes, and approaches which must be penetrated deeply in order to find the combination of ideas which reliably accomplish the function at lowered cost.

Securing maximum value is a difficult matter because the "basic rules" change during the act; that is, the actual costs of material and of processes change and so do the relative costs. However, the change in relative costs, which is of vital importance in making comparisons and in selecting alternatives that bring the best value, is far less than the change in actual costs. Inflation factors often increase all costs, be they of steel, aluminum, copper, brass, or other material. Hence it is valuable in this work to prepare and accumulate special tables and charts of relative costs as efficient direction indicators in preliminary examinations for the selection of alternative materials, products, and processes. Such tables are useful general guides which provide suggestions for possibilities to be the bases of subsequent specific examinations.

Tables 5-1 to 5-8, providing relative-cost data, are examples of this class of special knowledge.

Table 5-1. Machine Speeds*

Machine	Operations per minute	Average per 1,000
Punch press, high-speed auto., 4 tons...............	250–400	$ 0.25
Cold header, ⅛-in. stock...........................	100–500	0.35
Punch press, high-speed auto., 15 tons..............	150–550	0.40–0.28
Punch press, high-speed auto., 25 tons..............	125–200	0.50
Cold header, ¼-in. stock..........................	90–450	0.60
4-slide machine, light............................	75–175	0.60
Punch press, 60 tons..............................	75–150	0.65
Cold header, heavy 1-in. stock.....................	80–400	0.75
4-slide machine, heavy............................	50–125	0.75
Punch press, hand feed (blanking), 75 tons..........	50–125	0.75
Punch press, hand feed (blanking), 300 tons.........	40–80	1.25
Thread roller....................................	40–80	1.25
Screw-head slotter...............................	30–60	1.50
Automatic wire cutter and stripper.................	30–60	1.50
Dial tapper......................................	30–50	1.80
Punch press, forming, slide feed....................	30–40	2.25
Punch press, forming, hand feed....................	15–30	3.00
Tapping machine, foot-operated....................	15–25	3.75
Tubular riveting machine..........................	8–15	5.50
Resistance welding machine........................	5–10	10.00
Centerless grinding machine.......................	2–8	12.00
Molding machine, thermoplastic....................	1–4	25.00
Brazing machine..................................	1–2	40.00
Molding machine, thermosetting....................	½–1	100.00

* These are average figures and are based upon one operator and one machine.

Table 5-2. Operation Speeds

Operation	Operations per minute	Average shop cost per 1,000
Take micrometer reading	5–8	$12.00
Use GO and NOGO snap gauge	10–15	6.00
Stamp part with hammer	15–20	5.00
Stamp part with rubber stamp	20–30	3.00
Drill small hole, drill press	4–8	15.00
Pierce small hole, punch	20–30	3.00
Wrap part in tissue and seal in carton	2–5	25.00
Position part in "egg-crate" carton	10–15	6.00
Pick up and position part in fixture	15–30	4.00
Pick up and drop part in fixture	30–50	2.00
Pick up, start, and hand-drive small screw	3–6	20.00
Pick up, start, and air-drive small screw	10–12	7.00
Power-drive small screw, hopper feed	10–20	4.00
Rivet with high-speed hammer 2 parts	4–8	15.00
Resistance-weld 2 parts	5–10	10.00
Tubular-rivet 2 parts	8–15	5.00
Cut off small tubing, screw machine	5–10	10.00
Cut off small tubing, abrasive wheel	30–60	1.50
Count parts visibly	60–120	0.75
Sort handful of parts 2 stacks	60–100	1.00
Deburr small screw-machine parts	7–12	10.00
Polish head of chrome-plated screw	5–12	15.00
Draw arc and hand-weld 1-in. pass	3–6	20.00
Ream hole, drill press	2–10	20.00

Table 5-3. Steel: Miscellaneous Forms
(Relative Costs: hot-rolled 0.20 carbon = 1.00)

Name	Bar	Relative price		Plate
		Sheet	Strip	
Hot-rolled, 0.20 carbon	1.00	0.95	0.94	
Hot-rolled, medium steel	1.00			
Cold-drawn	1.37			
Bar, cold-drawn; sheet, cold-rolled, 0.20 carbon	1.37	1.10		
Cold-drawn, sulfurized carbon	1.50			
Cold-drawn, screw stock	1.52			
Cold-drawn, 0.4 to 0.8 carbon	1.37			
Galvanized sheet steel (10 gauge)	....	1.30		
Enameling sheet steel	....	1.16		
Aluminum deoxidizing strip, cold-rolled	....	....	1.35	
Ingot iron strip, cold-rolled	....	....	1.35	
Plate, structural quality, under 1½ in. thick	....	....	....	0.85
Plate, welding quality, over 1½ in. thick	....	....	....	1.06
Plate, copper bearing	....	....	....	0.95
Plate, boiler, flange quality	....	....	....	0.92
Plate, 0.35 to 0.45 carbon, under 1½-in.-thick silicon, killed	....	....	....	0.99
Plate, chrome-silicon, flange quality, under 1½ in. thick	....	....	....	1.60
Plate, carbon-silicon, flange quality, under 1½ in. thick	....	....	....	1.04

Table 5-4. Stainless Steel

(Relative costs with steel = 1.00; base price including chemical extras only, 1960)

Name	Bar and rod	Relative price	
		Sheet	Strip, cold-rolled
13% chrome, no nickel, magnetic...............	7.80		
Free machining...............................	7.80		
High chrome, decorative, magnetic.............	6.70	7.02	7.00
Turbine quality, magnetic.....................	6.70		
18-8, nonmagnetic...........................	8.80	9.30	9.20
18-8, low-carbon, nonmagnetic................	10.00		
18-8, free machining, nonmagnetic.............	9.00		
27% chrome, heat resisting, magnetic...........	8.60	10.80	
18-10 titanium stabilized, nonmagnetic..........	10.00	10.40	10.30
18-10 columbian stabilized, nonmagnetic........	10.70	13.00	12.70
25-12 heat resisting, nonmagnetic..............	11.90	13.20	13.00
25-20 heat resisting, nonmagnetic..............	15.90	16.20	15.90
18-12 Ni-Cr-Mo, heat resisting................	12.60		

Table 5-5. Brass and Bronze Rod

(Relative costs with steel = 1.00; base price as of 1960 does not include extras)

Name	Relative price
Yellow brass (free cutting)....................	5.40
Yellow brass (leaded, high)....................	5.40
Yellow brass (semifree cutting)................	5.40
Forging rod (drawn).........................	7.20
Muntz metal................................	7.25
Naval brass.................................	7.30
Yellow brass (high)..........................	7.50
Low brass..................................	8.00
Red brass..................................	8.15
Commercial bronze..........................	8.35
Everdur....................................	9.25
Cupronickel, 15%...........................	11.85
Nickel silver, 18%...........................	10.60
Phosphor bronze, grade B (leaded).............	11.70
Phosphor bronze, grade A.....................	11.75
Phosphor bronze, grade C (8% tin)............	12.20
Phosphor bronze, grade D (10% tin)...........	12.70
Beryllium copper (Berylco 25S)...............	25.00

Table 5-6. Brass and Bronze Sheet

(Relative costs with steel = 1.00; base price as of 1960 does not include extras)

Name	Relative price
Muntz metal, ½ in. thick and over	8.40
Naval brass, ½ in. thick and over	8.66
Yellow brass (65–35)	7.95
Yellow brass (high)	7.95
Yellow brass (2.5% lead)	7.95
Yellow brass (clock)	7.95
Extra quality brass (70–30)	7.95
Low brass	8.45
Red brass	8.60
Commercial bronze	8.85
Muntz metal, less than ½ in. thick	8.40
Cartridge bronze (low), 95–5 gilding metal	9.00
Manganese bronze, ½ in. thick and over	9.25
Naval brass, less than ½ in. thick	8.70
Admiralty, less than ½ in. thick	9.00
Everdur	9.90
Manganese, less than ½ in. thick	9.25
Nickel silver	11.10
Phosphor bronze, grade E (1% tin)	11.32
Ambraloy (aluminum bronze)	11.30
Phosphor bronze, grade A (4% tin)	12.30
Phosphor bronze, grade C (8% tin)	12.70
Phosphor bronze, grade D (10% tin)	13.20
Trodoloy (Berylco 10)	25.90
Beryllium copper (Berylco 25S)	29.10

Table 5-7. Brass and Bronze Wire

(Relative costs with steel = 1.00; base price as of 1960 does not include extras)

Name	Relative price
Yellow brass	6.35
Yellow brass (high)	6.35
Commercial bronze	7.00
Everdur (3% silicon)	7.75
Everdur (silicon-manganese)	7.75
Phosphor bronze, grade A (5% tin)	8.45
Phosphor bronze, grade C (8% tin)	10.10
Beryllium bronze (Berylco 25S)	23.00

Table 5-8. Copper

(Relative costs with steel = 1.00; base price as of 1960 does not include extras)

Name	Relative price	
	Bar and rod	Sheet and strip
Hot-rolled rods, tough pitch.............................	8.05	
Hot-rolled rods, tough pitch (hot forging).................	9.55	
Hot-rolled rods, tough pitch (cold forging)................	9.55	
Drawn rods, tough pitch.................................	8.20	
Drawn rods, tough pitch (bus bars)......................	9.55	
Hot-rolled rods, tough pitch (switch blades)..............	9.55	
Commutator copper (scalped)..........................	8.55	
Plain extruded copper sections.........................	8.75	
Commutator copper (high silver bearing, 25 to 30 oz.)......	9.05	
Strip tough pitch, rolls.................................	....	8.89
Sheet and plate, hot-rolled, tough pitch..................	....	9.00
Sheet and plate, cold-worked, tough pitch................	....	9.00
Strip, silver bearing (10 to 15 oz. per ton)................	....	9.30
Spring and brush copper................................	....	8.79

CHAPTER 6   *Decision Environment Required*

By now, the reader will be well aware that two separate types of work must be done well in the important task of eliminating substantial amounts of cost which do not contribute in any way to the customer's use or satisfaction.

First, identification of unnecessary cost through the generation of value alternatives

Second, decision making to effect implementation of the work on appropriate value alternatives and bring its benefits into the product

The value analysis techniques and special knowledge serve for the execution of the first phase, but the dollar payoff comes only with appropriate actions in the second phase. It is deemed both desirable and necessary, therefore, that the reader of this text attain an understanding of the problems that almost always prevail in the decision-making area.

6-1. *Common Behavior Pattern*

The matter of securing good value alternatives is a straightforward proposition. Qualified and value-trained people can be hired and assigned to the task, and given the proper working tools, they will invariably produce good alternatives. The matter of implementing this work is very much more difficult because the people who must do the implementing are normally already in place and are operating according to plans and schedules based on established thinking and practice. This means that they must be won over to accept different thoughts, different types of ideas, and different technologies, all of which may seem to conflict with their endeavor to maintain established reputation of success in their field of operation. Besides, they may have had unfortunate prior experiences with poorly conceived or incompletely developed attempts to lower cost and hence may be wary of efforts in that direction.

149

An organization for the generation of good value alternatives can normally be set up and made to function well within a period of a year. In contrast, it is well to figure that it may take several years to effect sufficient changes in the thinking of the decision makers to approach the same efficiency in the implementation as that attained in the development of good alternatives.

The following observations along this line may be helpful:

People are accustomed to liking certain things.

They are also accustomed to disliking certain things.

Men are accustomed to holding certain beliefs about their associates and expecting certain things from them.

Any organization may be likened to a network of piping. All the valves in the system have, by experience, belief, habit, and tradition, been set in a certain manner. As long as the flow is entirely according to this accustomed pattern, all actions are smooth and few frustrations are created. However, if more value alternatives are to be implemented, actions must be taken which differ from the habitual. Familiar "do it our way" patterns must be disturbed. Some valves in the system must be further opened, some further closed. This causes a complete readjustment of the flow in the system. The change from that which was expected is apt to be resisted at every turn.

Only with a realistic recognition of these actions and interactions in the decision environment will the value consultant and value engineer be able to understand and take a mature viewpoint toward the long delays and the multitudinous objections which are commonly raised prior to the implementation of good value alternatives.

Now, with this recognition of the situation, thought may well be directed to the questions: What can be done about it? and What are the first steps to take for improvement in this decision environment?

Unless the reader stops here to make a searching study of himself, he will be inclined to discount the relevance of this chapter. By analyzing himself, however, he will find that he fits into the same type of pattern. To be useful, this particular discussion must be extremely realistic and must deal with situations as they are, not as they appear on organization charts or in reports or in statements made by people operating in the outlined environment.

6-2. *Elimination of Risk of Personal Loss*

A series of research studies brought forth the surprising information that most decisions are made on a basis of avoiding or minimizing personal losses such as reduction of authority, demotion, or dismissal. This finding seemed so improbable and so startling that it caused the writer to think back through several of his most difficult decision-making experiences, especially a considerable number which he knew were wrong but which "had" to be made in a certain way. Surprisingly, every one of these decisions was made to avoid or minimize personal loss. Again it is suggested that the reader stop to reflect on and analyze some of his own decision experience before proceeding on to the following pages.

A few examples of situations in which the danger of suffering personal loss occurs may further illustrate the point in question.

A purchasing agent may for years have purchased a product from one supplier, even though this supplier may not have kept pace with either technical progress or value innovation. A decision by the purchasing agent to change over to what seems to be a better product at a lower price brings immediate danger of personal loss.

The engineer who traditionally used a certain type of assembly for accomplishing a certain function and has decided to change to the use of what he believes to be a simpler, more reliable, and certainly much more economical assembly is certainly taking a chance of personal loss.

As for the manufacturing manager, he is apt to be operating with machines of certain types, with people of certain experience, with buildings of certain area, and with patterns of so-called "overhead liquidation" accruing when chips fall from the machines. For him to decide on a value alternative which might temporarily use a fraction of the machines, a fraction of the people, and a fraction of the building and which might provide little "liquidation" places him in a position of immediate personal loss.

Any business manager knows that there are few things that rate as "sure." However, a thing which has been done over and over in the past is more sure than something new. Therefore, any different decision runs the chance of bringing personal loss to the decision maker.

Experience has shown that merely securing good value alternatives—even before implementation—may bring personal loss to engineering people, manufacturing people, purchasing people, in fact everyone connected with the present mode of doing the job. This is especially true if the particular value alternative appears to be so straightforward that important people in the management and decision-making area see at a glance that it will probably work.

The normal pattern in any decision-making area is to "play" progressive in speech and writing and to have great plans for big new things, for big changes, etc. This minimizes the chances for personal loss. If the higher levels of management did not hear and read such pronouncements, they would become concerned and might think in terms of making changes that bring about personal loss. When it comes to making decisions and taking actions, that is something different. Here most people concerned with making decisions "stick to the channel," rationalizing each decision on the basis of some nearly related data or experience. In this manner, they again minimize the chances of personal loss. For very much the same reason, there is often a very strong and very understandable resistance on the part of management to the establishment, in any organization, of a really competent value group which could effectively produce good value alternatives.

Anyone who wishes to become expert in the area of identifying unnecessary cost and stimulating corrective action may well follow a two-step approach:

1. Recognize this behavior pattern as *the* big problem.

2. Take every step possible to minimize the personal loss which comes, or may come, to those in the decision area supporting changes.

An estimate of where the fountainhead, or source, of this personal-loss obstruction lies indicates this general situation:

> Managers and bosses........... 90%
> Peers........................ 10%

This clearly shows the problem to be that of creating the required action environment, i.e., decreasing the personal-loss risk. To decrease it effectively, work must be done on changing the attitudes, pronouncements, and actions of managers and bosses. The crux of the problem is:

What are their real beliefs?

What are their pronouncements?

What are their actions?

A further point to be borne in mind is that in the average run of cases in which the results of good value-improvement work identify value alternatives which will bring very much lower costs, reactions are invariably uncomplimentary to those responsible for the present practice.

For instance, in a case cited in an earlier example, a value alternative developed by the use of value analysis techniques showed that the functions of a spacer stud costing 8 cents could be provided for eight-tenths of a cent. The manager said, "What do we have on our methods engineering staff, men or boys?" Did the men who first accomplished this job suffer personal loss? Surely.

In another case, after the use of value analysis techniques provided a value alternative at $2\frac{1}{2}$ cents which reliably accomplished the total function of a $15\frac{1}{2}$-cent item made on a special installation of $30,000 worth of automatic equipment, the manager said, "Why didn't you think of doing it this way before we spent the $30,000 for tooling?" Did the men who previously worked on that job suffer personal loss? Certainly.

Quite normally, when, as a result of the use of value techniques, an effective alternative is brought into view which will reliably accomplish the entire function for a small fraction of the cost, the comment is made, "That was done wrong in the first place!" Do the men who previously worked on the item suffer personal loss? Most certainly.

It is coming into indelibly clear focus that in the matter of achieving a much higher degree of value, i.e., faster implementation of more good value alternatives, the personal loss to the men in the environment must be reduced or eliminated and that action must start at the top.

One example of the type of communication which is necessary with top men and bosses at their present stage of recognition of this problem may be recounted here.

Steel J bolts, threaded on one end, were used in large quantities for a holding function. They cost $11\frac{1}{2}$ cents each, $92,000 per year. Use of the value techniques produced an interchangeable alternative which accomplished the total function with the same reliability at a cost of $1\frac{1}{2}$ cents each or $12,000 per year, a saving of $80,000 per year in purchase cost. As already indicated, the important question always is how to convey this type of information to a manager or a boss in a way that will allow him to see the merit of the value system that produced the suggestion rather than to follow the normal pattern of depreciating the men who previously worked on the job. In this case, it was handled by the following dialogue:

"Mr. Smith, would you like to see what your men are accomplishing by the use of these value analysis techniques?"

"I certainly would."

"You use large quantities of this J bolt in this application [showing him the product using it]. Now, if you had the assignment of removing large amounts of cost from this without in the slightest reducing its quality or safety factor, how would you go about it?"

"Is it made of steel?"

"Yes."

"A piece of standard steel with a hook on one end and a thread on the other. How can you make it any simpler?"

"That's right, Mr. Smith, that's where your men started. Now let's see what they produced using the value analysis techniques. This part [showing the value alternative] accomplishes the total function with the same reliability, but instead of costing $11\frac{1}{2}$ cents, this costs $1\frac{1}{2}$ cents."

Mr. Smith, startled, said, "How much difference did that make in our yearly cost?"

"Eighty thousand dollars per year reduction in purchase cost."

And now, for his final comment, "How many men do we now have doing this type of work?"

Did this mean that men in the organization suffered personal loss? Of course not, because the manager was put in the same position as they were in before the answer was provided.

What managers believe is extremely important in that it governs what they say, and what they say controls the extent of personal loss to men who face situations and effect changes. Experienced men in industry know that changes invariably involve risk. The manner in which management handles cases which "temporarily go wrong" as a result of changes for the improvement of value is a positive indication of what beliefs they hold about value and what importance they place on removing unnecessary cost and meeting other assumed commitments, such as those pertaining to performance and shipment. Management's reaction in these circumstances determines the amount of personal loss which individuals in the decision environment must risk if they make decisions that involve change for the purpose of implementing good value alternatives.

Instructions from the boss to "keep it working but get the cost out," "keep the daily shipments on schedule but get the cost out," or any similarly worded operating "dogma" clearly indicate that management inwardly believes the elimination of unnecessary cost to be very much secondary in relation to the over-all benefit to the business. They signal that to embark on a change for the purpose of substantial elimination of unnecessary cost is to choose a course of great personal risk.

In general, today's management and managers are sufficiently well accustomed to technological advancement to realize and inwardly feel or believe that they must make sacrifices, effect changes, and take risks to secure essential performance improvement in their products. To date, however, they have not been long enough subjected to the hard economic pressure which results from the maturing of products, coupled with the growing resourcefulness of a widening number of competitors, to develop the same sense of urgency and necessity in matters relating to the elimination of unnecessary cost.

Persons choosing value work as a career will be wise to investigate and determine, before accepting any assignment, whether there are enough positive factors in the particular decision environment into which they will feed their value alternatives to make their work rewarding to the company and, in the long run, to themselves.

Finally, management people or value consultation specialists who want to delve deeper into these normal human reactions which delay and minify the realization of dollar benefits from good value engineering work will find valuable guidance by studying some good psychological literature on the subject of human behavior in situations involving change (see references listed in the Appendix).

CHAPTER 7   *Effect on Other Work in the Business*

A number of very vital interrelationships come into play in the effective use of value analysis techniques. Some of the most important of these are the relationship of value analysis to:

Accounting	Management
Appearance design	Purchasing
Cost reduction	Quality control
Engineering	Sales
Manufacturing	

In the simplest language, the objective of value analysis and value engineering is to develop practical value alternatives to the end that all decision making will achieve an improved degree of value in the final product or process.

7-1. *Accounting*

In the same simple terms—perhaps too simple for the accountant— the principal objectives of accounting activity are twofold.

1. Accumulate suitable after-the-fact figures so that period-end profit and loss accounting will be proper both for tax purposes and for business-owners' purposes.

2. Suitably apportion costs and incomes to guide before-the-fact decision making.

Value analysis bears no relationship to the first objective but a very significant relationship to the second. More general acceptance of this fact is needed.

It is only rarely that the situation is assessed as it was by an accounting manager who said: "As in engineering, where a product developed for a particular purpose can be made to accomplish that purpose efficiently and well, so it is in accounting. Systems can be developed to accomplish particular purposes. The serious problem, however, is that accounting systems often are used either as they are or in some amended form for other than the originally intended purposes and then are not as effective. Give us a clear understanding of an exact purpose, give us time and resources, and we can develop an efficient system which will accomplish that purpose."

As in the physical sciences, where men often endeavor to accomplish several purposes with the same product and seldom accomplish divergent ones efficiently, so it often is with accounting systems.

In the past, as an analogy, the horse was employed to pull the plow and then also to pull the buggy. If he was heavy enough for an efficient draft job, he was far too slow and inefficient with the buggy. Conversely, if he was light enough and fast enough to be an efficient buggy horse, then he was far too weak and inefficient as a draft horse. In four respects this use scheme bears a striking resemblance in its accomplishment to the accounting systems commonly in use.

1. A horse suitable for the draft job is used also on the buggy. The owner rationalizes by saying, and by learning to believe, that "he is also pretty good on the buggy."

2. A horse suitable for the buggy job is used also in the field. Again, compromises are accepted, but the owner gets used to the level of performance of the buggy horse in the field. He rationalizes for himself that "the horse is also a pretty good field horse."

3. A compromise horse is used. Though the horse is not capable of the heavy loads in the field or of fast work on the buggy, the owner gets accustomed to its degree of performance in both respects and rationalizes, "He is a good buggy horse and also a good draft horse."

4. Two different horses are used. The importance of the draft work and the importance of the buggy work cause the owner to acquire two distinct types of horses. He now gets efficient draft work and efficient buggy work, but he has two horses to own and to feed. From a businessman's point of view, he must decide whether the increased efficiency justifies the extra feed.

Although, as the accounting manager stated, accounting systems can probably be developed to efficiently accomplish almost any purpose, there is quite naturally and properly a great reluctance on the part of management to provide more than one basic system. Since tax and earnings accounting are considered absolutely vital, compromises are usually made and inefficiency is allowed in the second area, which covers useful and meaningful cost data for making before-the-fact decisions. Usually modifications, sometimes at great expense, are made in the tax and earnings accounting systems, and the over-all system then is considered "pretty good" and is used extensively in decision making. In effect, those interested in costs for decision making usually find that they must use the "draft horse" or attempt to work with a modification.

As emphasized in section 3-2, the quality of value alternatives and the quality of the resultant decision making, which affects the degree of value in the product, are very deeply affected by the degree of meaningfulness of the costs with respect to the specific purpose of making a proper selection of the engineering, manufacturing, and other alternatives to accomplish the functions the customer desires.

Decisions affecting value can be no better than the information which enters into the comparisons, and this information cannot be better than the meaningfulness of the cost figures derived from accounting. When a better degree of value is required, the payoff to the company of meaningful costs created for the purpose of comparing value alternatives will become very large.

The use of effective value analysis is both troublesome and rewarding to the accounting activity. It is troublesome because:

Meaningful costs are required. To interpret costs meaningfully, analysts must inquire into and learn how they are determined.

It may show that much of the detailed work of breaking down costs by parts and assemblies does not really make a contribution but provides misleading information instead. If so, accounting must face up to the shortcomings of traditionally done accounting work and cost compiling.

It may show that many of the costs traditionally used do not precisely reveal how the business is affected when individual decisions are made one by one.

It may become necessary for accounting and cost people to learn and develop some very new practices, procedures, and systems to convert one system to another.

The rewarding aspects are:

Accounting work can now make real additional contributions to earnings.

Accounting will face real challenges in providing meaningful information for the necessary decision making.

Satisfaction will be derived from seeing that the work of accounting is put to good use and forms the basis of decision making that results in better decisions and improved earnings.

Two of the important classes of decisions that we are concerned with here are:

Make-versus-make decisions
Make-versus-buy decisions

At first glance, it may appear to be of vital importance to learn how the business is really affected only in the case of make versus buy. However, further thought will show that this is not at all true. The class of make-versus-make decisions may involve hundreds of different alternatives, some of which will be tabulated here. The costs may very well vary by a factor of 10 to 1 between different methods for individual items or individual functional assemblies. The lack of meaningfulness of the costs can easily lead to support of decisions which cause the product to contain so much unnecessary cost that orders are lost or perhaps the total business is lost.

Some of the kinds of make-versus-make alternatives that may be involved are as follows:

Casting versus stamping
Wire form versus sheet metal
One part versus several parts
One type of machine versus another type of machine
One shift versus another shift
Varying degrees of automation

Totally in-plant parts versus partly in-plant parts and partly purchased parts or assembly (the border line or "gray" area between a make-versus-make and a make-versus-buy decision)

Make as needed versus make periodically and hold in inventory

It is readily seen that although no decisions to make versus buy are involved in these cases, wide ranges of applicable costs are controlled by the decisions made on the basis of the costs provided by the accounting activity for the decision making.

In make-or-buy decisions—or, more correctly stated, in the area of determining at which stage in the cycle from the rawest form of raw material to the finished product is it advantageous for the factory to bring the material into the plant and perform the necessary operations on it—it is both exceedingly difficult to develop and exceedingly vital to have meaningful cost information. It is a relatively easy matter to make make-or-buy decisions pertaining to large groups of activities, but to be realistic in operating a business, even where over-all looks are taken periodically, important decisions must of necessity be made one by one. Unless the over-all decision arrived at is one in which decisions made one by one provide for the right value, the cost information used is inadequate and unsatisfactory.

While at first glance it would seem simple to determine how the business would be affected by making a part, this cannot be done by merely determining the material used, the labor required, the indirect expenses in the form of maintenance and liquidation of machines and equipment employed, and the amount of consumed supplies. Buildings are involved which might, or might not, exist regardless of the decision on a particular item. The entire supervisory and management staff of the organization will probably exist regardless of the decision on the item, and the same amount of space may be required regardless of the decision; likewise, the same amount of maintenance may be required. The question of determining precisely how the business will be affected if a particular decision is made to buy rather than to make is a most difficult one.

Often, with traditional systems of accounting, it is more straightforward to determine how the business will be affected by a change from buy to make if the change is comprehensive enough so that new buildings and new machines will be required. In this case, definite costs can be assigned as an increase to be computed in the decision-making formula. The sticky problem results when serious consideration is given to taking the decision in the opposite direction, i.e., from make to buy, because now many facilities already on hand and already being paid for in various accounts may not be needed.

A further reason for the need of particularly objective and meaningful comparative costs in this particular connection is that make-or-buy decisions lie in the emotional area. A strong emotional pull toward decisions to "do it ourselves" usually exists. Often, this pull is so strong that neither the accounting specialist nor anyone else is requested to develop really meaningful alternatives which could lead to decisions contrary to the do-it-ourselves practice.

Finally, it should also be noted that the techniques of value analysis apply to any action which costs money. Each activity of the accounting unit can be analyzed by the use of these techniques to determine precisely what function is accomplished by each act, by each piece of paper, by each file, by each person each minute of the day. Such evaluation by accounting people, who have first learned to use the value analysis techniques and then applied them to their accounting practice, has brought important yields.

7-2. *Appearance Design*

Those not engaged in value work often believe that decisions prompted by value analysis techniques will tend to decrease the appearance and attractiveness of a product. Not precisely understanding the value analysis techniques or approach, they expect that the procedure is to eliminate all except the use functions. Nothing could be further from the truth. Value analysis techniques in the very basic approach recognize two classes of functions, namely, those functions which cause the product to work and those functions which cause the product to sell.

The latter class is comprised mainly of features of appearance and convenience. More often than not, the application of value analysis techniques results in an improvement in the appearance of the product by opening up opportunity for effective work in the appearance-design activity.

One of the phases of the study of a product consists in determining precisely what, from the viewpoint of appropriate volume of sales at appropriate prices, constitutes the major areas of opportunity. These opportunities may fall in one or more of three categories:

Improved performance
Improved appearance and/or features
Lower cost

With the factors of appropriate performance and appropriate cost under control, attention is then sharply focused on the areas of improved appearance and features in order to build up the appropriate sales volume.

Value analysis studies have shown that great opportunity exists in the appearance-design area. Technical people, however, who are expert in development of performance, often do not realize the magnitude of the contribution which can be made by those especially skilled and trained in appearance design. In many cases, they make decisions affecting the appearance as "best they can." This usually results in added cost and only a moderate degree of appearance improvement. Because of such experience, there is a rather widespread belief among technical people that improved appearance requires increased cost. This is seldom the case.

Being specifically oriented toward identifying the problem and developing better solutions to it, the value analysis techniques promote the use of specialized skills and knowledge in all fields, including that of appearance design. With appearance-design aptitude brought to bear on design problems very much better appearance at substantially lower cost usually results.

Case Study

THE RED POINTER AND RED INK

On an appliance knob, a strip of bright metal containing a red pointer was mounted. Its function was to snap on over the screw which held the knob, thus concealing the screw and providing the appearance which the customer wished.

A value audit of the product showed that $20,000 was spent each year on the production of 1 million. This stylist was apprised of it and asked for guiding suggestions which were followed in developing alternatives. A polished stainless-steel part was one alternative which would accomplish the function as well, providing the customer liked it. There were, of course, other alternatives.

The industrial stylist asked, "Why does the red pointer increase the cost so much?" The answer was that it caused the small part to become a "name plate," which imposed certain costs and restrictions on its manufacture and procurement. Some of the other alternatives, such as the polished stainless steel, were merely small stampings not using name plate technology and not limited to the sources of supply who provide name plates.

The stylist promptly issued instructions to take out the red pointer and use polished stainless steel. He said that the red arrow was not good, that it caused the product to look more like a toy and less the mature, reliable product that it was, that he never had liked the red color in it very well but had never had another alternative in view. The change was made, both improving

BEFORE   AFTER

FIG. 7-1. The pointer.

the customer appearance value of the product and eliminating $20,000 of unnecessary cost.

The application of value analysis techniques to a product contributes materially to the separation of the work functions from the sell functions and brings appearance design directly into focus to gain from management the emphasis and support that it deserves.

7-3. *Cost-reduction Activities*

Where emphasis is put, accomplishments result.

Traditionally, performance-oriented work is a scheduled, measured, and integrated activity in the business. Planned resources are spent, and planned results are normally achieved. The work is taken in stride by the business. Thus, in the absence of temporary performance problems, suitable performance of the product is the result of long-term and regular activities.

As for value, the situation is almost directly the opposite. It is everyone's job. How a good degree of value is obtained is not too well known, nor is the degree of value obtained readily measurable. Each person involved does as well as he knows how. The normal measurement of the suitability of value work is based on an appraisal or a guess of how well it is done as compared with how competition does it.

Since performance work is basically "right-hand" work and value work is traditionally "left-hand" work, it is normal that costs often become too high. Short-range activities of a fire-fighting nature must then be established and must be given enough emphasis to prevent results that are intolerable.

Often, in a particular business, the extent of this problem can be predicted, so it is planned well in advance to impose, by a number of expediencies, a certain amount of cost-reduction effort, together with the resultant measurable reports throughout each regular period of a year.

The work involved competes with the regular work of most technical men who believe their principal job is one of accomplishing other objectives—usually performance objectives, new-product objectives, or similar ends. Quite commonly, the manager or boss is more oriented toward, and more comfortable with, performance work, and so his best supervising effort goes in the direction of helping and measuring his subordinates on the performance parts of their jobs. To him, cost-reduction work then becomes an added or "thrust-in" burden which he must, to some extent, do something about.

In these circumstances, a certain amount of pressure may be necessary to compete with the motivation of a man for the regular phases of his job, and he is often told that it is intended that he shall spend part of his time, perhaps one-half day a week, on the cost-reduction activity. In order to strengthen the pressure which will cause him to do this, he is given a budget of savings which he is expected to accomplish in a certain period.

Cost-reduction work, as a rule, is after-the-fact work. The tooling has been provided and the product has been standardized; changes spell deviation. In many cases, replacement parts must be continuously stocked, and when changes are made, other items must be added to the catalogue. Likewise, drawings must be changed. Indeed, these and many other deterrents to good cost-reduction work often diminish substantially the valuable results of the activity.

Nonetheless, what is known as cost reduction is a vital activity. As most businesses are organized, they could not long endure without it. A first step, when instituting a value analysis program, is to make sure that those who are working on cost reduction continue to do at least as much of it as they have been doing. A great deal of effective cost-reduction activity will be necessary until, for a planned and integrated activity, professional skills, techniques, and knowledge are provided to the business so that value work can be taken in stride, the same as performance-oriented work is.

As a business begins to apply value analysis techniques to cost reduction, two changes will be observed:

The results per man-hour of cost-reduction work will be greatly increased.

More satisfaction will be derived from the work because it will be seen to be effectively done with the achievement of a larger yield.

Cost Reduction versus Value Analysis

In contrast, value analysis is a long-range planned activity. It has set objectives, and it operates to always keep the costs right.

Similarly, just as long-range integrated performance work uses good tools, long-range integrated value work uses good tools to accomplish the set objectives.

Suitable value work is done in the product-conception stage, in the engineering-design stage, in the manufacturing-engineering stage, in the purchasing stage, and in the production stage.

By doing this work on a planned basis as the product "grows" and is developed, it becomes practicable to take many actions not possible in after-the-fact cost-reduction work, which is not a part of the normal pattern and which is hampered by problems of existing tooling, standardization, servicing, replacement, etc.

The reader must not, however, overlook the fact that the value analysis techniques are often also used on products in the after-the-fact stage, especially when the particular industry has progressed to the point where substantial redesign is imminent or when a competitive degree of value work has not been done during the earlier product stages.

Case Study

Increased Dollar Yield per Man-hour for Cost-reduction Work

When fabricated, 2½ cents worth of steel in this back plate became 10½ cents of cost. The part was in a high-volume appliance. With a quantity of 1 million, each penny becomes $10,000. Therefore, each penny of un-necessary cost *is* important. The function of the back plate was evaluated at considerably less than 10½ cents. Cost analysis and value analysis study showed that far too much of this cost was for the operations of suitably smoothing and deburring the top edge of the plate. Investigation was made of

Fig. 7-2. Back plate.

alternative materials, products, and processes which would accomplish the needed functions. It was found that adding ½ cent per pound to the cost of the steel, which ensured providing it with a mill edge, completely eliminated the burring and smoothing expense. The result was an identical part from a use and appearance viewpoint—probably a somewhat neater part— with cost reduced from 10½ cents to 4½ cents. This study was motivated by the cost-reduction coordinator and netted him a $60,000 credit to his budget.

7-4. *Engineering*

The enormity of the engineering activity in most organizations is largely underestimated. Greatly oversimplified, it may be said that the engineering function has two responsibilities:

Design and development of new products
Constant reduction in cost of existing products

A somewhat closer view will show the complexity of the responsibility normally carried by engineering. While in years past its job was deemed satisfactorily done if the product performed its functions reliably, in more recent times a great many complicating requirements have been included in the engineer's responsibility. Some of these—aside from determining a way to accomplish a function and providing a design which will do it—are:

Design to size
Design to weight
Design to special conditions of vibration, temperature, corrosive environments, etc.
Design to appearance
Design to cost
Design to new manufacturing processes
Design to time schedules
Design to utilize new materials

A realistic appraisal shows that the engineer must keep in mind so many factors that he usually has to be satisfied with compromises in some areas of his responsibility. Quite naturally, the areas in which he can prove his attainments readily by tests are the ones that get his best attention. In other areas, such as that of value, where definite measurements are largely nonexistent, he must often, under the pressure of time schedules and other commitments, consider that he has "done well enough" and jell up his designs.

It is in the areas affecting cost that value analysis has an intimate relationship to engineering and can contribute greatly to the value content of technical work. The relationship of value analysis to engineering may well be compared to the relationship of, say, metallurgy or heat transfer to engineering. In these two fields, information vital to engineering decision making is recognized to exist, and the engineer is accustomed to drawing on these techniques, and the knowledge therein, before he makes his decisions. As the metallurgists act to assist the engineer in identifying appropriate metals for use in accomplishing a specified function, so the value analyst acts to provide the engineer with information which will allow him to identify unnecessary costs.

The engineer must draw his conclusions and make his decisions based on the best facts he can lay his hands on. The value analyst must be prepared to provide more facts about value alternatives for the engineer to use at the point and time of engineering decisions.

It may help the reader to review here some of the types of situations which every experienced engineer has faced and which have often been the cause of unnecessary costs in designs.

Frequently, costs are lacking. In theory, the engineer might be said to have cost figures to use in choosing his alternatives. In actual practice, however, very many vital decisions must be made with exceedingly poor cost estimates, if indeed cost estimates are at all available. It is not unusual to find an engineering manager saying, "I had no reasonable idea of what the costs would be until after the first production run." *A part of the kit of tools of the value analyst will serve to provide useful and meaningful costs at the time of decision.*

Commonly, in any particular plant, there is considerable pressure and habit directed at designing for the machines already owned. The engineer knows that the machines will make suitable parts, and especially if he is short of time, he might be open to criticism if he produced a design that could not be made on the local equipment. In consequence, he takes the normal way out and designs for the available equipment. One of the functions of the value analyst is to search out the very best process for a functional part or assembly, regardless of what the process may be or where the equipment may be located, and to determine what the cost of the found alternative will be. Again, the engineer is provided with sound value information at the time of his decision making.

Some applicable methods of manufacture are unknown to the particular manufacturing and engineering people in any one location at some time or another. It is again the task of the value analyst to reach out and cause the corresponding value alternatives to be developed and brought into focus for the engineer's decision.

Certain materials are thought to be unsuitable. Every person tends to draw upon his experience and his knowledge, thinking that it is applicable when it is not. As a result, excellent value alternatives are not considered. The search techniques in the value analysis kit of tools, combined with the special knowledge of value analysis, must be applied to develop objective information for the engineer to use in his decisions. The same is true when certain methods and processes are thought to be unsuitable. Objective information will show that they are suitable and represent good alternatives. Every human being accumulates a certain number of misconceptions as he proceeds in his business career. The use of the value analysis techniques illuminates whole families of misconceptions with fact and brings out into the open good value alternatives which otherwise would be rejected without even being considered.

Wide ranges of functional products can be furnished by specialty suppliers to be used, either as they are or with some modification, to accomplish the needed function. Once again, the search techniques and the special knowledge of value analysis bring much more of this sort of information into clear view for the engineer's consideration in his decision making.

The field of new materials is expanding so rapidly that it provides a wide area of opportunity for the value analyst to search out and identify new applicable materials for the engineer's functions and then to bring them to his attention with complete, appropriate costs.

One of today's normal methods of securing business in many industries consists in providing an engineering service. The engineers of suppliers are anxious to become acquainted with needed functions and to endeavor to adapt their products, materials, or processes to them. Value analysis includes action to search out such supplier engineering competence, to clearly convey to capable representatives the functional problems in question, and to bring back their solutions for the responsible engineer's decision.

Engineers working on a design often realize that more time and resources would provide better value in their solutions, but at the same time, they may be hard pressed by a management to end their work and make the product as it stands. Utilization of the special knowledge and techniques of value analysis helps to bring useful alternatives into view within time periods allowable.

Any individual can use only those ideas which he is able to think of at the specific time. The value analyst, by application of his techniques, can often assist the engineer in thinking up more applicable value ideas.

Experience indicates that it is not an unusual thing for engineers to find themselves bogged down in clerical work. Taking a leaf out of value analysis teachings and proceeding to analyze the function of such clerical activity have, on numerous occasions, helped the engineer to rid himself of much clerical effort and have thus enabled him to proceed with his creative work faster.

One extensive area in which value analysis can be of great importance to the engineer may be well identified as the "warm-blood" area. After a person has been confronted with a situation, studied it, collected information on it, thought it through, and reached a decision, this decision becomes his "warm blood." Psychological studies show that it is very difficult for him to start again with the same problem and not be pulled into the same preformed channels of thinking. Value analysis can assist him greatly in such situations by bringing up new objective alternatives for his consideration and decision making.

It is well to recognize again that the engineer has one of the most difficult of all jobs to perform. He must first search for and develop his own evidence. He must then be the judge and make his decision on his own evidence. Experience shows that when more and better evidence is developed through value analysis, decision making by engineers results in very much improved value.

Case Study

CAN WE SCRAP THE SCRAP?

In order to secure advantageous operating characteristics, it was necessary to provide a silicon-steel transformer core of a specific configuration with relation to the coils which went on it. As the steel laminations were stamped to make this core, 42 per cent of the steel became scrap while the remaining 58 per cent was used in the product. It appeared that, without sacrificing efficiency or operating characteristics, this was the way to do it.

A value consultant brought into contact with the job went to the silicon-steel specialist and also to the transformer specialist in a large research organization and confronted them with the problem. It just didn't seem right to him to live with the enormous amount of unworking cost involved in throwing away 42 per cent of the silicon steel. The silicon-steel specialist brought forth a change which resulted in reducing the scrap from 42 per cent to 25 per cent by working out a new stamping pattern. Two months later, after careful study and test, changes were put into effect which eliminated 5 cents apiece of the cost on 3 million transformers per year, a difference of $150,000.

Then two interesting things occurred. The engineers were startled and intrigued that this could be done, and both the transformer-circuit specialist and the silicon-steel specialist became intrigued by the problem. In about a year, another suggested improvement was made and tested. This involved changes both in the silicon-steel core and in the coils. Improved performance was found to be provided without adding to the coil cost, and the silicon-steel loss was reduced to 5 per cent.

In conclusion, the relationship of value analysis to engineering is one of generating greatly expanded information for the use of engineers and of identifying value alternatives for the engineer's inclusion in his decision making. It is little wonder that the first vice-president of engineering of a well-known company to examine the operation of these techniques stated, "Value analysis is the best method yet found to help engineers remove unnecessary costs from their products."

7-5. *Manufacturing*

Basically, the job of manufacturing is to use machines, processes, and people to change the form of material to conform to the designs of engineers.

The basic function of value analysis is to identify each element of function provided by each element of cost.

Accordingly, the consultation provided by the value analyst to manufacturing will start always with a clear identification of the contribution to function furnished by each activity in manufacturing which adds cost. Creative study of the increments of function and of the increment of cost brings expanded information into the decision-making area and makes practicable a still further elimination of unnecessary cost.

For example, more information is provided by observations of rather difficult or time-consuming operations throughout manufacturing.

What contribution is made by the hardened steel?

What contribution is made by having holes slightly different instead of the same size?

What contribution is made by heat-treatment between operations?

What contribution is made by a tapered instead of a straight screw?

What contribution is made by an operation that is causing quality difficulties?

The functions and contributions required of the process and the related difficulties having been brought into view, the search techniques of value analysis, together with the special knowledge, elicit alternatives for the responsible manufacturing man to use in his decision making and in his discussions with the engineers.

Studies of manufacturing work often show that unprofitable items are being produced. The reason for this lies in the nonexistence of clearly crystallized and developed alternatives. When information of that character is developed, unprofitable work may be removed from the factory.

Case Study

Did the Vendor Contribute?

No operation should be performed by manufacturing people unless it contributes to the enterprise; in fact, if many are performed which do not contribute, the vitality of the business is sapped. This case reports one study to determine the realities of manufacturing contribution.

In one phase of value work on an assembly of a few hundred parts, quotations were obtained from appropriate vendors on machine parts which were actually being made in the plant. The quotations showed that, on a considerable number of the specialized parts, vendors' prices were lower than the comparable in-plant manufacturing cost, which consisted of labor, material, and overhead.

In this particular plant, it was the custom for the manager of manufacturing engineering to make make-or-buy decisions. He was considerably challenged by these lower competitive costs and arranged for a study of his own manufacturing operations on the items in question. In all but one of a dozen cases, he was able to lower his costs comparably, and hence he allowed only the one part to be placed with a supplier. This was protested by the purchasing people who had been instrumental in helping select the vendors who provided the lower quotations. As a result, the case was resolved in the higher manager's office. There, after the facts were developed, the question was asked: What is the right action for us to take in cases of this type? It was quickly decided and accepted that the right action was, whenever suppliers had made contributions, to compensate them in some suitable form.

The manufacturing engineer, however, felt that the suppliers had not contributed. "They didn't show us how to speed up our machines, how to use different types of cutting tools, how to plan some of the parts more effectively. All of this we did ourselves."

The manager's response was, "Whenever anyone comes here and takes any action that causes us to eliminate substantial amounts of unnecessary costs from our products, he has made a contribution regardless of all other circumstances." Again he raised a question: What is the appropriate action to take in this case?

After discussing the issues involved, he instructed that at least one-third of the jobs on which suppliers had developed effective bids and made constructive quotations should be awarded to them regardless of other factors and that they should continue to enjoy the business for approximately a year, even though the factory now had improved its own processing to meet the lower costs.

Good value work will help rid manufacturing areas of "busy work" which does not contribute so that their efforts may be used on operations which make important contributions to the business.

Often manufacturing work proceeds along rather habitual lines involving the particular products being made on orders placed with the factory for quantities according to specific schedules. More complete information on expected quantity requirements, inventory-carrying costs, types of tooling for the resultant volume, and applicable specialized vendor knowledge often allows the manufacturing decision makers to eliminate important amounts of unnecessary cost.

Whenever a change is to be made, there is much work to be done in connection with obtaining the new and complete information, analyzing and evaluating it, and persuading those involved that the path to better value lies in a different direction. In all these activities, the value analysis tools and special knowledge are very helpful to manufacturing.

Case Study

MANUFACTURE FOR PROFIT

A few hundred fiber washers, ⅛ inch thick and 1½ inches in diameter, were needed. They were simply made by purchasing fiber rod 1½ inches in diameter, drilling the center hole, and cutting them off like wafers. This required no special tooling and was easy to accomplish in any machine shop. The cost was 16 cents each. As the product involved became successful and the quantities increased to many thousand per year, the washers continued to be made by the same process. Subsequently, the function was evaluated at much less than 16 cents. In fact, a value alternative proved that functional washers could be made from sheet instead of from rod at a total cost of 3½ cents. After the existing stock of rod was used up, sheet was ordered, a standard punch set was purchased, and a punch press put into action to replace the cutoff machine. These manufacturing changes reduced the cost from 16 cents to 3½ cents. The manufacturing operation on the item changed from a liability and a drain on the business to a contributor. *The use of the evaluation techniques of value analysis often provides good answers which, after they are developed, seem extremely obvious but which, before development, were not in clear view.*

Misunderstanding is often eliminated by the application of value analysis tools. Too often costly specifications are continued, and in effect, needless and costly operations are performed which do not, if the whole story were known, add in the slightest to value. In one instance a stamped steel bracket was carefully "sized" in an expensive operation so that it would fit perfectly into a mating part. Study to ascertain precisely the value that came from the mating operation showed that a lead mallet was always used at assembly and so, of course, the sizing operation made no contribution whatsoever to value.

The process of associating precisely the contribution to function of each addition to cost identifies the area in which the relationship of value analysis to manufacturing allows manufacturing men to make different decisions that help solve their problems, speed production along, prevent quality problems, and lower costs.

7-6. *Management*

Basically, the objectives of management with relation to the business are to provide the proper organization, including facilities, and to make the proper decisions to operate on a profitable basis. If not profitable, all the tragedies of bankruptcy will soon occur.

The method is to use the resources of capital, men, materials, equipment, and time to make and sell products (or services) as skillfully as competitors do. Competition is the measure. The need is for answers as good as, or a little better than, competition in order for the business to endure.

Case Study

THE CONTACTS THAT WERE LOST

Large benefits to management result from the new information which they can now have as a result of knowing the value of the various functions in the products they manufacture. Often normally undiscovered opportunities to increase these values will result.

In the design of new products or in major redesigns, accumulated experience is studied, new information believed to be applicable is searched, and models are prepared for test. In the case of electrical equipment, certain types are also sent to the Underwriters' Laboratories for its inspection and test. The value audit of a product which had been in production two years indicated that it contained considerable "waste," that is, cost which made no contribution to life, safety factor, or use of the product. The contacts used cost $26,000 per year more than seemed appropriate, and an investigation was made. It was found that during the design work reasonable and appropriate contacts had been developed by test, and they had been selected. However, it was also found that, during the assembly process for preparation of samples to be sent to the Underwriters', something had gone wrong and the supply of the appropriate contacts had been exhausted. In order to avoid delay at that time, the engineer had furnished another, more expensive contact to the assemblers. This had solved the assembly problems and the samples had been made and sent to Underwriters' Laboratories where they had received approval. Two years later, with this information in hand, the appropriate contacts were submitted to the Underwriters', and of course, approval came forth with the result that the unnecessary, noncontributing cost was eliminated. *Searches often disclose the unexpected.*

The work of a business is twofold: to provide something which the public wants and to provide it for low-enough cost. The business will succeed or fail according to the effectiveness with which management makes decisions in these two areas.

The relationship of value analysis to management, of course, falls in the second category. In the past, there have been severe organizational shortcomings. High among them is the fact that most important responsibilities can be effectively delegated and the degree of their accomplishment measured so as to be known. For example, the president or general manager delegates:

To his engineering head responsibility for performance and design quality

To his manufacturing head responsibility for production quality and shipments to a predetermined schedule

To his industrial designers, or the engineering head, responsibility for competitive appearance and features

To the manager of inventory control responsibility for keeping. inventory within certain established ranges

To each of these men, that which is delegated is the prime job. Success or failure depends upon accomplishment in the assigned area.

When it comes to value, this is everyone's business. Each party is told to coordinate and cooperate with the others to secure good value. Attainment of good value is a "second job" with unclear delegation and indefinite evaluation.

Experienced managers have often said that one of their major problems is that they have had little choice, no matter how much they were in need of lower costs, but to have the same people reexamine their work of the past. The result has been that a very negative, unrewarding, and inefficient job has been done.

With the advent of value analysis techniques, this vital problem of management is being corrected. The manager may now arrange for a suitable number of competent men to learn how to handle value. He may delegate directly to them responsibility for achieving certain value objectives. This becomes their job and they succeed or fail according to their performance on this one objective. Accordingly, the magnitude of results is of a different order.

The best managers agree that where management places emphasis, there they secure results. This they are enabled to do with the help of the value analysis suggestion sheet written in managers' language. The reader will recall that the suggestion sheet is a clear-cut presentation of unveiled solutions uncluttered by supporting data which are needed only by the engineer or other on-the-job decision maker. With the value information oriented to specifics, the manager may now apply effective emphasis to achieve the degree of value results which he feels the business needs.

Another important way in which the use of value analysis techniques can greatly assist the manager is in identifying, and helping to compensate for, the costly disadvantages of honest errors. In any field of activity, responsible people accumulate honest wrong impressions and, accordingly, make entire patterns of decisions incurring more costs than necessary. Experience has shown that the costs in such instances can often be from two to five times as high as is necessary to reliably accomplish the desired functions.

In this respect, any manager can do much good by having his subordinates know he understands that a portion of their decisions will be in error and that they will not be criticized for what is a normal occurrence. He must also recognize that the same is true for a percentage of his own decisions, and since these may vitally affect the earnings position of his company, he would do well to use value analysis techniques to illuminate wrong beliefs with objective value data, so that decisions in the future may be more in harmony with best alternatives.

An important phase of the relationship of value analysis to management can be emphasized by the question: What is a most important responsibility of management to value analysis? In Chapter 6, the importance of the decision-making environment, which is largely under the control of the manager, was discussed. As a prime requisite, a manager, to enhance his earnings results, must provide an environment in which men can make decisions to obtain better value without the risk of personal loss. Full recognition and proper implementation of this situation by the manager can more than double the rate at which good value alternatives that deviate from past practice are put into use to retain product reliability and quality and to provide increased earnings.

7-7. *Purchasing*

A significant part of the responsibility of the value analyst, after the functions required have been determined, is to locate in the vendor market the particular product, process, or know-how which will bring the best answer at the lowest price. Therefore, close and extensive relationships must exist between purchasing and value analysis.

Fortunately for both operations, effective value analysis greatly improves the grade and degree of purchasing work, and efficient execution of certain purchasing activities greatly improves the degree and amount of value analysis accomplishment.

Case Study

IT'S PATENTED

A large quantity of special metal dials were being purchased. They cost 90 cents each, which seemed high, but purchasing had been able to get no other bids.

A value consultant studied the functions. They were found to be very simple, certainly not worth 90 cents.

Discussions were arranged with the supplier, whose attention was called to the large increase in the quantities purchased and to the simple function of the dial, as well as to the fact that cost analysis showed it was not worth 90 cents.

When the chips were down during the negotiation, he acknowledged these statements but said, "The dial is patented." It was such a simple product, however, that the patentability of it seemed very much in question. The patent attorney was consulted, and when he got in touch with the patent people of the supplier company, he received information on what was patented. It proved to be only an extremely minor detail which was relatively unimportant in the use to which the dial was being put. The result was that the supplier proposed a price of 40 cents instead of 90 cents. He stated that, although a quotation of 30 cents might be expected, he felt that his pioneering work in the field of dials had been important and that even though the precise item he had patented was of little value, it seemed reasonable to him to receive a 10-cent payment for it. This was a well-founded contention.

The matter was concluded by deciding to continue buying the dials from him, but for 40 cents rather than 90 cents. This resulted in saving a large amount of the cost of the military product involved. *Investigation of questionable patent situations, as well as of any other situation which might add cost, is a part of value analysis.*

To those using the value analysis techniques, purchasing can supply valuable information about specialty-vendor knowledge and precise data regarding individual companies' personnel, products, or processes. The following value analysis techniques can be most efficiently used only with continuous purchasing support:

Use industry specialists to extend specialized knowledge.

Utilize vendor's available functional products.

Utilize and pay for vendor's skill and knowledge.

Utilize specialty processes.

Utilize applicable standards.

Purchasing men, situated as they are at the point of transfer of the company's money for materials, products, and services, often have reason to suspect that good value is not being obtained on particular items. In such circumstances, their invitations to value consultants to study the items, combined with their suggestions as to where to turn and how to obtain efficient work, almost always prove highly profitable.

The inducement to such action by purchasing men lies in the added job satisfaction—over and above the day's pay—derived from feeling that extra contributions are being made to improve company earnings. Basically, purchasing personnel are dedicated to getting their money's worth. In the atmosphere of competition, however, they must also be constantly aware of the fact that their expenditures have a bearing on the profit picture. They can ill afford to let this point be overshadowed in the execution of the diverse, and often laborious, aspects of their responsibilities, such as ensuring that needed materials and supplies of satisfactory quality are obtained on time and that emergencies of supply, of transportation, etc., are resolved promptly.

The work of obtaining full value for expenditures, which is in keeping with the attainment of higher earnings, can be inestimably enhanced by the effective use of value analysis techniques by competent persons trained and skilled in applying them. As functions are studied and further clarified, value alternatives come to light. Discussions with technical people crystallize the alternatives that are practical, usable, and acceptable from the technical viewpoint. This allows purchasing people to buy a material or a product which may be entirely different from that originally intended but which is obtainable at very much lower cost and still is functionally useful. The result is satisfaction in a job well done.

Case Study

VALUE ANALYSIS OF ASSEMBLY PURCHASED COMPLETE

In developing a new product, a control regulator was needed. It consisted of about 1 cubic foot of electrical and mechanical equipment. Its function was to control speed, load, fuel, etc., in response to inputs from an operator and a machine. A responsible vendor quoted a price of approximately $5,000 each on the basis of supplying the few hundred needed regulators. Included in his services would be adjusting some of the final details of the design, finishing a few minor tests, making sure that design details were such that assembly would be facilitated, etc.; thus the vendor did make small important adjustments on the drawings.

After a few years, it became apparent that the complete product on which this assembly was used was facing severe competition in the industrial market from other means of accomplishing the job and that economic considerations, i.e., cost, would be governing the obtainable volume. Hence it became necessary to identify and remove sufficient unnecessary cost to retain a place in the market. In the meantime, the production cost of the assembly had been reduced by experience and important modifications to $3,000. What could be done?

The vendor said that he had gone through all parts of his operation and had taken out all costs he could without lowering quality. His quotation for the future, even anticipating increased volume, stood at $2,500. When asked what help he would like from value analysis people, he stated that although he felt the details of the costs of his individual parts and subassemblies were confidential and should not be revealed to his customer, value engineers would be welcome to observe the manufacturing process and make suggestions. His viewpoint was accepted as being very correct. It has been found throughout value analysis that, in a competitive economic atmosphere, the end product— its quality, reliability, functions, and cost—is the important thing and that the details of how a supplier arrives at it must be his, as must the responsibility for providing in the product ideas and technology capable of meeting the competitive conditions.

In the case under discussion, the value engineer spent a few days studying the manufacture of the parts, of the assembly, and of the subassemblies as well as the various operations in the supplier's plant. On returning to his desk with a full understanding of the way costs are built up in the use of various processes, he made up a sheet for each of the parts and each of the important subassemblies, with estimates of the costs based on the processes he had seen being used. This gave him the information he needed to provide positive suggestions to the vendor on steps that might be taken to lower the costs even more. Further he was now in a position to advise the vendor on approximately what costs he felt appropriate for many of the individual parts and individual subassemblies, and these costs the vendor could then use for comparison with his own costs. The tabulation below includes two items: first, the cost which the value engineer estimated after reviewing the supplier's manufacturing processes; second, the cost which he considered appropriate and which was based on positive suggestions made to the vendor. The latter cost is designated "value."

Item	Estimated present cost	Value
Spur gear	$ 15.00	$ 5.85
Gear	20.00	7.25
Sleeve	105.00	90.00
Side plate	2.00	0.00
Block	4.00	0.00
Shield	5.80	1.80
Gasket	1.00	0.05
Gasket	4.00	0.15
Adjusting sleeve	4.00	1.50
Spring	1.30	0.31
Pin	3.00	0.75
Special screw	1.00	0.10
Shoulder bolt	3.10	0.10
Spring retainer	3.50	0.05
Cartridge pump	137.00	89.00

It should be noted that, in making these suggestions, the value consultant brought into play the various value analysis techniques such as utilizing vendors' functional products, buying standard products and modifying them slightly, using specialized vendors, and reevaluating tolerances which make no contribution to performance.

After study and implementation of the alternatives, the vendor was able to make a new quotation of $1,800, and the redesigned equipment retained its capability to accomplish the total function with reliability. His costs had been decreased sufficiently so that his company was still provided with its proper earnings.

The use of sound value practices together with very much better value knowledge benefits both the user and the seller.

It should be observed at this point that full recognition of certain basic premises is necessary for the effective interplay of the relationships in question. These premises are:

1. *The value analyst will not do the buyer's job.* Unless the value analyst has a complete prior understanding with the buyer, the interest that he takes in vendors and his communications with them will be questioned. As the buyer sees it, this is his corner of the ball diamond, and now the value analyst is on it. Quite naturally he wonders: "What is he doing in there? What is the effect going to be on my job? How will the efficiency and effectiveness of my work be affected? In the past I have enjoyed contacts even with the technical people of the vendors and have progressively learned from them. Will the value analyst's work now reverse this trend and steadily weaken me in the area?"

These and allied questions will interfere with the buyer's performance, and it is imperative for him to know that the value analyst will not do his job and also just what the value analyst will do. With a precise understanding of the relationship of value analysis to his job, the buyer will recognize that it will extend his range, increase his competence, promote his growth, and enhance his contributions to the company's earnings. The value analyst will not be making decisions which were formerly the buyer's, but he will be providing more information for the buyer to work on so that he can make more rewarding decisions.

2. *The buyer must be kept advised.* If the buyer, as well as the company, is to benefit from the value analyst's activities, the buyer must be protected from any embarrassment that could result. Therefore, he must be a party to whatever work is being done in his area. This does not mean that he personally needs to expend time sitting in on all discussions. It does mean, however, that the value analyst will let him know what is going on and will give him the opportunity to take part, to the extent he wishes, in discussions leading to later purchases. It is very common for technical people to work with competent vendors on projects involving considerable complication and to arrive thoughtlessly at the answers to the various problems so that the purchasing decision is in reality being made step by step by others than the buyers. This is contrary to the philosophy of good management under which a specific person is assigned responsibility for each major activity, such as engineering, manufacturing, sales, purchasing. Thus management expects the purchasing manager and his organization to be responsible for properly purchasing any particular product. When, during the cooperative development of a purchasing decision, the purchasing people are not properly advised of the steps along the way, but are told only of the final answer, they become, in effect, rubber-stamp manipulators who blindly place orders and abdicate their responsibility to make sure that their purchases represent value. If they refuse to follow the decision and open the project to bidders who have not had time either to learn all of the intricacies of the job or to make substantial financial and tech-

nical contributions to its development, their action may result in injury to the competent vendor who originally worked with the technical people as well as harm to their company. The product thus selected will probably not be up to standards when it arrives from the new vendor; and the result will be additional injury to the purchasing department, which becomes subject to criticism by management, and, in the final analysis, to the customer, who may not receive on time the product he had a right to expect.

A few simple ground rules and a reasonable amount of mutual understanding provide for a very rewarding cooperation between purchasing people and value consultants. For anyone who expects to be using value analysis techniques, it will be profitable to examine some of the purchasing practices which would be affected, adversely or favorably, by his work. The following extracts are offered from a set of guides which have stood the test of usage.

PURCHASING PRACTICES PERTINENT TO THE PROPER RELATIONSHIP BETWEEN VALUE ANALYSIS, THE PURCHASING FUNCTION, AND THE PURCHASING MAN

These statements and purchasing practices are guides to be used with intelligence and with consideration of the other fellow and his job.

1. *Sources of Supply*

The purchasing department will select sources of supply. They will endeavor to do so in the best interests of the company and with a view to creating and maintaining good vendor relationships. *If vendors are asked to bid, they must know that the source has not already been decided.*

Strong and enduring relationships with tested suppliers are to be maintained. To do this, frankness and fair dealing, with maintenance of quality, delivery, and fair price, will have a great weight. It is the intention of the company to conduct purchasing so that suppliers will value business sufficiently to make every effort to meet legitimate competition.

a. Buyers will buy from sources with good reputation and sufficient financial standing to meet the job requirements.

b. The best bid on the combined bases of price, quality, and service will be accepted.

2. *Commitments*

a. The purchasing department conducts and concludes all negotiations affecting purchaser, selection of vendor, prices, terms, delivery, adjustments, etc.

b. Commitments and orders, to be valid, are to be stated by a letter, a purchase order, or a contract which sets forth appropriate details and which is signed by the purchasing agents or by a person duly authorized to sign in his stead.

c. Negotiations leading up to, or apt to conclude in, contract arrangements should not be undertaken without the knowledge and authorization of the interested buyer in the purchasing department.

d. No one who is not a member of the purchasing department should commit himself to any vendor on preference for any product or source of supply for any product or give any information regarding competitive performance, final approval, or price.

3. *Vendor Relations*

The purchasing department, realizing that good vendor relations is a company asset, must be alert to promote a program of equity and friendship with sources of supply.

a. Salesmen will be received in the purchasing department and in other departments after arrangements have been made by the purchasing department.

b. In addition, the purchasing department will arrange interviews between vendor representatives and company production, engineering, research, and maintenance personnel when it appears to be to the advantage of the company or when the buyer is in doubt as to the merits of the proposal or when such an interview has been requested by an appropriate employee of another department.

c. All suppliers' representatives are to have a complete hearing for their sales arguments the first time they call. Subsequent policy will depend on the particular circumstances. Courtesy and prompt reception of salesmen are part of the code; if the interview is to be denied, there should be a prompt acknowledgment of the call, together with a reason for not granting the interview. A buyer, or any other company person, is not required to put his time absolutely and indiscriminately at the disposal of any and all comers, however frequent at whatever time, or on what mission they may be calling. Some matters are not appropriate to the department's needs or are not timely at the moment the salesman elects to press them. The buyer must necessarily be the judge, but he is not relieved of his obligation of courtesy.

d. The purchasing department will handle all correspondence with suppliers except when technical details make it desirable to secure technical or other assistance.

e. Requests for prices, trial lots, etc., should be made by the purchasing department.

f. When a free sample is accepted for test, an obligation is assumed by the company to make a fair trial and to inform the vendor of the outcome of the test. However, as a preferred practice, the company may *buy* sample lots, thus incurring no obligation but establishing the interest of the company in completing the trial and making a fair evaluation.

g. In fairness to all concerned, prices and other specific information received from vendors are considered confidential. The quotations of one supplier may not be divulged to another, and such information should not be circulated indiscriminately within the company.

h. Buyers should be reasonable in requesting supplier's technicians to call, unless volume of business justifies such expense. Information can ordinarily be obtained by letter, telephone, or telegraph.

4. *Interdepartment relations*

The success of the purchasing department depends on the kind of job it does in procuring materials, equipment, facilities, ideas, and supplies. The most effective functioning of the purchasing department is possible only when other departments perform well their functions of engineering, planning, receiving, testing, and storing. Therefore, intelligent, constant, and harmonious contact between purchasing and other departments relative to their needs and the procurement of their needs is a "must."

a. The purchasing department has the duty and authority to ask reconsideration of specifications or quantity of material if, in the opinion of a buyer, it appears that the interests of the company may be better served. However, the final determination of quality and quantity are the prerogative of the engineering and requisitioning departments.

   (1) Purchasing specifications, while written by engineering, should be checked by the purchasing department before being issued to be sure material is obtainable and practical.

   (2) It is desirable that the drawings for new-purchase parts be submitted to purchasing, as much in advance of the required date as possible, to allow purchasing to develop the best possible source of supply.

b. Buyers must be alert to pass on to potentially interested individuals information derived from salesmen's interviews and direct mail or other advertisements and deemed useful. In a similar manner, members of other departments are expected to reciprocate by drawing items deemed to be of value to the attention of the purchasing department. If the purchasing department does not have a record of, or experience with, the items, suitable inquiry will be made by its personnel.

7-8. *Quality Control*

While value analysis is not as directly related to quality control as it is to purchasing or engineering, one specific relationship exists with extensive opportunity for mutually beneficial activity. Before dealing with it, it will be well to identify two important areas of possible misconception about the relationship of value analysis to quality control.

These two misconceptions, which are entirely too general, are:

1. "The function of value analysis is to identify and cause to be removed all costs which provide extra safety, extra quality, and extra life beyond the minimum needs. It is the aim of value analysis to remove all of the quality which can be eliminated without having the product fall apart in its customary use."

This statement is totally false in every degree of its implication. The use of the value analysis techniques identifies unnecessary cost, i.e., cost which does *not* add to safety, to performance, to life, or to the appearance desired by the customer and which, in fact, adds nothing whatsoever to the product under any condition.

2. "Lower cost means lower quality." This common belief, which is often inherited from early childhood and which normally persists to control vital decisions, is also entirely false. Cost and quality have no direct relationship. Indeed, it frequently occurs that the highest cost gives the lowest quality. The reader will add greatly to his value competence if, at this point, he frees himself of any remaining tie to his childhood experience of buying small oranges for 25 cents a dozen and larger ones for 50 cents a dozen.

The reason for the existence of any product is that it accomplishes a certain function or a certain group of functions. Good quality comes with the selection of good answers to the question of how to use materials, processes, parts, and human efforts to accomplish these functions. Poor quality results from having poor answers to the question. It is as simple as that. Cost is not part of quality determination.

Now, to introduce cost in its proper perspective:

Good-quality products result whenever the answers chosen are good answers, whether they be high-cost answers or low-cost answers.

Poor-quality products result whenever the answers selected are unreliable answers, whether they be high in cost or low in cost.

Case Study

Lower Costs May Mean Doing It the Right Way

Precision gear sleeves, about 2 inches in diameter and 5 inches long, were used on a precision product with expanding volume. They were manufactured in the plant at a cost of $15.75 each. Extensive inspection was required, as this was both a high-temperature and a high-speed gear on which even minute imperfections had to be eliminated.

As the volume increased faster than the production facilities for manufacture, it became necessary to locate another source. Considerable purchasing effort produced a source which made suitable gears. However, the cost was $17 each.

During this search for suppliers, a specialist who had achieved considerable success in some of the branches of the gear field had also been located, and he had quoted a price of $6. But the consequences of the failure of the job were great, and thus a feeling prevailed that, "He is so new in this business that he doesn't know what he is up against, and to do business with him will bring trouble."

Nevertheless, after the $17 supplier was located, discussions proceeded in an orderly fashion with the one who had quoted $6. A tool maker and an inspector from the factory visited this vendor and brought back word that his facilities, processes, and equipment were excellent. The buyer then revisited the supplier and went through each detail of the drawings and specifications, encircling in red the tolerances, requirements, and specifications which it was feared the vendor might have overlooked. The vendor advised that, in each case, he had noted the requirements and had expected to make the sleeves according to the specifications. He did, however, sense that concern was caused by the lowness of his quotation, and so he increased his price to $6.75 to provide a contingent amount for any possible unforeseen factor for which he had not planned.

A production order was then placed with him subject to the strict limitation of individual-lot release. Thereafter, when the first ten were released and arrived at the plant, they were found to be the smoothest and best gears of this type which had ever been seen. Still, a normal cautiousness and concern existed. The inspector said, "I doubt that these were built on the production facilities the vendor expects to use. Every one is perfect. They seem to have been built on gauge machines instead."

After being assured that the ten gears were built on the equipment which was put in place for the production order, a release of one hundred was issued. These hundred were also of the same hitherto unexperienced high quality. This was followed by a release of a thousand, also of the same high grade.

Two interesting results followed. First, the inspection department, after days of making inspections and never finding any flaws, began to feel that inspection was superfluous, a simple checking routine was established which eliminated 95 per cent of the inspection of the gears from this supplier. Second, inspection personnel started putting strong pressure on the procurement department and on the factory to discontinue buying from the $17 supplier and also to discontinue in-plant manufacture of the item so that the extensive inspection required on gears received from these two sources could be permanently and totally discontinued.

The outcome was that the $17 supplier was dropped. But, in order to have a second source of supply for the vital part should a serious problem of any nature end production temporarily in the plant of the $6.75 supplier, 25 per cent in-plant production was continued.

Scores of cases of this type prove to the experienced that good quality is the result of "doing it the right way." So is good value.

As stated repeatedly in the foregoing discussions, the operation of value analysis is to identify the functions clearly and then to search out and develop, by using value analysis techniques and special knowledge, good answers for the lowest cost. No quality reduction is involved. However, if quality problems are present at the start of the value study, quality improvement will result.

With the factual situation in clear focus, it will be recognized that value analysis and quality control have joint opportunities. Value analysis techniques can have an important impact on the solving of quality problems, and in turn, the quality control activity is an important means of identifying the areas in which contributions can be made by the use of value techniques. Whenever quality problems exist, it means that the functions involved are not being secured in a suitable manner. This provides a clear start for the effective application of value analysis.

7-9. *Sales*

It will be found that beneficial relationships exist between value analysis and sales work. Products in general may be divided into three classes:

Existing products
New products
Products adapted to customers' special requirements

With regard to existing products, the sales department must provide to customers the performance features and attractiveness they want at competitive prices. Often, costs in comparison to competition are too high, and the sales department is unable to sell until lower costs are established. Lowering of costs by the required amount is invited and supported by the use of value analysis techniques in important areas of the product.

In the development of new products, it is incumbent upon the sales department to determine what functions, or what combinations of functions, the customer desires and, further, to determine at about what market price these functions can be sold. It is at once apparent that the sales department is here dealing in functions and costs, which are the stock in trade of value analysis. The opportunity exists for value consultants to apply the special techniques and the special knowledge toward the development of value alternatives which will provide a sound basis for investment, planning, advertising, staffing, etc., to provide the new products.

In connection with customers' special requirements, the value analysis techniques are tools for studying with them precisely what their needs are. With a clear understanding of the function, or functions, a customer needs, sales people are enabled, by providing the precise new functional components required, to effectively adapt their products to accomplish most economically the full need of the customer.

Viewing the relationship from the opposite end, it will be seen that sales provides to value consultants important areas of opportunity. With regard to established products, they know precisely where to work to meet the company's emergencies. In connection with new products, they know the considerations which should receive top priority in the new product line and can make contributions that will have long-standing high value. As for special products, they have the extra opportunity of using their techniques to help secure specific additional orders.

CHAPTER 8 *Effective Organization for Value Work*

Appropriate organization for the attainment of the best benefits of value analysis will be discussed first from a viewpoint of the over-all business, second from the viewpoint of the interrelations among the men performing the work, and third from the viewpoint of the relationship between the men doing the work and the management of the business.

Performance orientation having been of maximum importance in the industrial development of the United States, normal management people have learned quite precisely how to effectively accomplish performance-oriented assignments. In these endeavors, value has been recognized to be important to the extent that each person has given thought to value and has constantly taken certain actions with reference to value. It has been expected that such actions will normally be taken in addition to carrying out the performance-oriented assignment.

This means that getting value has been and is generally considered by most managers to be somewhat similar to breathing. As the individual takes his bath, has his breakfast, and drives his car to work, he just continues breathing, and he does a reasonable job of it at all times without paying much special attention to it. Care is taken by the employer that air is provided for breathing, and care is taken by the employee that nothing obstructs his ability to breathe. Otherwise, each continues the especially identified activities for which he has acquired certain training or skill.

Similarly, normal management believes that value is everyone's business, whether his specific assignment is to design the product, to handle its drafting, to engineer its tooling, to lay out the factory, or to do anything else. Periodically, emphasis is placed upon the importance of achieving value, i.e., periodic drives are made, during which men are relieved of other work in order to place more emphasis, for a time, on value. It is expected that an acceptable degree of value will be achieved in the product by this "everyone-does-it" approach.

184

That method of handling value is, in fact, satisfactory as long as everyone else uses the same method. In the final analysis, the only real measure of value is a comparison, on the basis of functions provided versus cost, with the same functions and costs of competition.

However, when competition takes a different approach and provides better value, the traditional system is no longer satisfactory. The situation parallels that which has taken place in accounting practice through a certain development in the past few decades. Not long ago, it was normal practice to expect the bookkeeping and accounting staff of a company to be sufficiently informed to prepare any necessary reports for income taxes or any other purpose. As the years went by and tax matters assumed more importance, it was recognized that the amount of tax experience and knowledge a good accountant could have in addition to keeping up with his other fields of endeavor differed widely from the penetration of knowledge required by a tax specialist—a man who dealt with tax matters every day of the year. This caused a change in thinking. It became recognized that the well-informed general accountant could not possibly know enough about tax matters to identify even a reasonable amount of unnecessary taxes and that the extra expense to the company of making it "everybody's business" to know all the intricacies of tax matters was prohibitive. The management situation and the management attitude changed. It became standard practice to expect from regular accountants a basic understanding of tax law and practice but to utilize tax specialists and consultants, specially trained and experienced in income tax practice, to identify important amounts of unnecessary tax at the proper time and to the proper extent.

Likewise, in a number of the fields of performance engineering, it is well recognized that it would be both inefficient from a viewpoint of cost and ineffective from a viewpoint of performance to undertake to teach every engineer all of the knowledge necessary to advance design work in areas where, for example, extra-high-temperature metals are required or high efficiency of heat transfer is needed. Hence, specialists who have a depth of penetration of knowledge and experience in those areas are called in at the right time and to the right extent in order to provide information which will bring better decisions and achieve better performance.

Thus industry is learning that there is a vast difference between the everyone-does-it result and the result which is achieved by specially trained men using an appropriate set of techniques and a specialized universe of knowledge. And so managements of competitive businesses—businesses in which value is important—are learning that it is efficient to provide value consultation to aid their decision makers at the right times and to the right extent.

It is not the intention in this chapter to suggest that the use of value techniques is exclusively a matter for full-time specialists. That would be like taking the stand that all sections on tax accounting should be removed from textbooks on general accounting. It is rather the intent to point out clearly that while much can be gained in achieving good value by everyday use of certain of the value analysis techniques large amounts of unnecessary cost will still be unidentified. Further, if value really is important to the business, the benefits from value activities must be enhanced by the use of specialized skill and knowledge.

Obviously, the prevailing philosophy of management and the size and scope of the particular business will determine the appropriate provision for value analysis effort. Hence the discussion which follows merely outlines basic patterns that should help to orient the reader.

8-1. *Smallest and Smaller Businesses*

It is useful to understand clearly that while in the smaller businesses organization is not a problem, the lack of large expenditures of the hardware and process type obscures opportunity. To accomplish important results, a clear focus on the fundamentals of all business—even the smallest business—is necessary.

1. What is money spent for?
2. What precisely is the performance or service or benefit which is to come to the business as a result of the expenditure?
3. What is the value of that performance or service or benefit?
4. What are the alternative ways of securing the same performance or service or benefit and what are the associated costs?
5. The value then becomes the lowest-cost alternative which will reliably accomplish it.
6. Regardless of the size of business, the number and status of individuals involved, the type of business, and the type of alternative, whenever change is involved there will be resistance at every step.
7. Typical of the nonproduct type of expense, i.e., items for which money is spent, are the following:

Paper work: Precisely what necessary function or service does each item of expenditure serve? What are the alternatives and their costs?

People's time: Precisely what necessary function or service does each item of expenditure serve? What are the alternatives and their costs?

Maintenance: Precisely what necessary function or service does each item of expenditure buy? What are the alternatives and their costs?

In businesses of below $200,000 sales per year, the owner or manager will benefit his business very profitably by securing training in value techniques.

In businesses of $200,000 to $2 million, one competent and dependable man from among the top three is usually given training in value techniques. This man will himself evaluate functions, services, and benefits secured in important expenditure areas. He will promote suitable group work and action in appropriate areas. He will constantly teach the functional approach and lead activities which bring benefits from it.

Depending upon the size and nature of the business and the emphasis at the time, he will devote more or less of his attention to this responsibility and activity.

8-2. *One-man Setup*

Businesses with $2 million or more of annual sales will start with one or more carefully selected and trained value consultants.

The selection of personnel for the one-man setup is most important. This man must rank high in competence, must have a proven record of high accomplishment, must be respected by his peers and management alike. His background must be exceedingly broad. The qualifications set forth in Chapter 9 are a *must* for him.

Even so, it must be recognized by management that, since he will be constantly calling for change, his will be a most frustrating job. Experience shows that when one good man works in an atmosphere of frustration long enough, he often decides that it is not worth it and asks for reassignment to more traditional work which will make him more acceptable to his associates.

Real attention must be given by management to this new work until it becomes understood by, integrated into, and accepted by, every phase of the business.

8-3. *Two-man Setup*

Two men can provide a much more satisfactory penetration of the necessary knowledge and experience. Combined in the two should be skill in engineering ideas, in manufacturing methods and processes, and in the very extensive field of using vendor and specialty-vendor competence. While the two men work together, they do not work as an interlaced team. Rather, they work as consultants to each other on any particular job. In every instance, each project or activity is the responsibility of one of the two. That individual, in turn, to the right extent and at the right time, consults with the other man on the job. One of the two may be the senior man and carry certain responsibility for assigning work to the other. Care must be taken, however, that neither of the two works as an assistant to the other but rather that each accepts responsibility for a particular activity in the plant and consults with the other as needed.

8-4. *Three-man Setup*

Normally and practically, three men constitute the smallest efficient operating unit for wide-range value work. It is then usually possible to have the necessary penetration in the three required areas of skill named above. The three men again act as individual value consultants, each taking responsibility for particular value work and calling on the others as consultants to improve the degree of accomplishment. Again, one man may be a senior member who organizes and assigns work to the others, or else the three may report to one and the same manager who, in that case, must have a real grasp of value work, its problems, and its opportunities, and must be capable of performing the management function skillfully. Three men often aid one another during the creative phases of their work studies, and having enough in common, they do not readily become frustrated and discouraged.

8-5. *Four or More Consultants*

As the business begins to see the benefit of the activity, additional value consultants will be added. This will provide more penetration in the three identified areas, and besides, additional abilities will be secured. For example, with groups of four persons or more, an individual who has special abilities in teaching and communicating will be very valuable in that education is an important part of the work of value consultants and specialists, as further outlined in Chapter 10.

With four or more individuals assigned to the value work, it will be of definite advantage to have the managerial functions delegated to one of them. He, then, will be the one to:

Set objectives

Establish plans and programs

Provide for proper staffing of the group, augmented by provisions for continued development and growth in the individuals' competence

Motivate appropriate actions

Support each specialist in his work with other segments of the business

Administer work assignments, schedules, compensation, facilities, etc.

8-6. *Structuring*

In setting up a specific value work activity, first attention must be given to how this work fits into the over-all organization of the business. The objectives to keep in mind here are:

Accomplishing the value work in the most efficient manner

Securing the fullest support of the effort

Constantly improving the competence in execution

Coming continuously into prompt contact with those vital areas of the business in which the best contributions can be made

As will be even more clearly understood after studying Chapter 10, value work begins in the sales function of the business and continues into, and through, design engineering, manufacturing engineering, purchasing, and production. It is important to note that here sales is at the beginning instead of the end of the series. This is so because it is normally the responsibility of the sales department to determine what products and functions the customer wants. Hence the product cycle starts, in effect, with the sales activity.

Since specific actions must be taken in each of these areas in the development of the product, it follows that certain benefits are secured and certain risks must be accepted if the activity is made to report to any one of them.

Unlike the tax consultant who will clearly report to the accounting manager or the high-temperature-metals consultant who will clearly report to the engineering manager because the respective contributions of these specialists fall within specific functions, the value specialist's point of reporting in the organization is not precisely defined since his contributions go into all areas.

The benefits of having the reporting point in the sales area are that the value consultants, through close contact with sales and marketing-planning people, get to know early in the cycle the functions desired and the approximate price for which the functions will probably sell on the market. Thus they become especially well conditioned to study these functions, evaluate them, establish value alternatives, and help carry on proper value activities throughout the business for maximum contributions to the excellence of the final product. On the other hand, as the reader will readily see, a drawback exists in that the value specialist's work will suffer because these people are so far removed from a depth of knowledge of such things as who the specialty vendors are and where specialized skills are available from vendors.

Similarly, if the reporting point is engineering, the value personnel are likely to be too closely identified with the engineering phase of the product cycle. Although they will bring great benefits by clearly identifying and evaluating functions and by providing value alternatives, experience shows that they tend to become more and more like engineers. Their penetration of knowledge in the vendor field and of specialized products and specialized skills, especially outside the company, becomes arrested to the detriment of their competence as value consultants.

Further, if the materials procurement or the purchasing area is the reporting point, great benefits derive because the value specialists are in constant and normal contact with the almost unbelievable supply of functional products, functional ideas, and specialized skills which the vendor area has to offer. However, they are now isolated in some degree from what is going on in sales, in engineering, and, to an extent, in manufacturing, and much care must be taken to avoid losing a balance in competence and developing skill only in the vendor field.

When the reporting point lies in any of these segments of the business, it has been found necessary to provide periodic and arbitrary pressure, measurement, emphasis, and motivation to make sure that both a balanced activity and a balanced growth in all necessary areas continue.

Effective long-range organization for proper value is most likely to result when the activity is structured into the area of the business which is accountable for earnings and profits.

The direct and full purpose of all value work is to improve earnings and profits by making it possible both to sell adequate volume in competition and to have costs lie sufficiently below the selling price. Therefore, understanding, emphasis, and support flow normally from a management area which is accountable for earnings.

A well-organized business will have definite plans reaching at least five years ahead and will be implementing those plans. Some of these will involve new products or improved performance of existing ones, others will involve expanded manufacturing capacities, and still others will involve increased ability for sales. The first plan is the primary responsibility of the engineering department, the second that of the manufacturing department, the third that of the sales department. To the extent that there are definite plans for identifying and minimizing unnecessary costs to provide increased earnings and definite implementation of these plans by a suitable number of people with direct skills in the area of increasing earnings, this important objective is likely to be secured.

8-7. *Integration of Research and Development with Emphasis on Military Contracts*

A top challenge to everyone engaged in work on products for the military agencies is making research and development work yield products of required performance in sufficient quantities. This is a difficult task, but it is also a fascinating opportunity promising very high rewards.

It is the purpose of the following discussion to help the reader recognize his opportunities to make contributions toward significant advances in dealing with this problem.

Some very pertinent questions here are:

To what extent does the present output of research and development result in products which can be economically manufactured in the large quantities needed for the available expenditure?

Can this extent be drastically improved?

If so, what are some of the steps to take in going about the task?

Will not the research and development period be prolonged?

For the moment, research and development work, which has as its objective the important job of producing lower costs for weapons which already have satisfactory performance capabilities, will be bypassed. Instead, consideration will be given to the greater challenge of applying value engineering techniques to research and development work concerned with providing weapons of new capabilities desirable from new technologies and to doing so in a minimum of time.

Decision Criteria—Performance and Time

The matter of securing better problem solutions depends, first of all, upon providing a clear and exact view of the problems. In research and development work, two factors are commonly given overwhelming and overpowering status and emphasis: performance and time.

Decision Criteria—Performance, Time and Cost

In order to meet the challenge of providing adequate new weapons, three factors must receive equivalent emphasis: performance, time, and cost (quantity capability).

Understanding the Research and Development Problem

Certain basic factors seem to decree the creation of designs and specifications which are suited to single- or small-lot manufacture.

In making test samples in lots of one or two, processes which will produce such samples at minimum time and cost, with minimum tooling, and with minimum search into outside special production technology are quite naturally used. For example, weldments, sand castings, specially made machine parts, and the like are often unquestionably best for quickly constructing experimental models, but they are often decidedly the worst solutions for economical production later. It is natural that this fact tends to be overlooked by the people whose prime obligation is to get their mental creations into hardware, to test them against natural law, and to press harder into the fringe of human knowledge as quickly as possible. Technical people in this type of activity do not at any time intentionally use a material or process which is more costly than another which they feel confident will accomplish the function as well. As they press their objective of expanding performance capabilities, they turn in each case to the most economical combinations coming within their sphere of knowledge and confidence. And when a design is tested and proven, they feel that it represents, in general, the lowest reasonably achievable cost and that performance results would be retarded if they were to accept the additional design criterion of cost.

Two factors make the problem even more complex.

First, at this stage of the development, with a design proven and tested, time has usually run out, so the only acceptable procedure seems to be to go into the market to buy, however fantastically costly this may be, these "near breadboard" designs with all their complexity, with all the design experience based upon the single or small quantities made during development, and with attendant loss of reliability in operation.

Second, manufacturing engineers delegated the job of producing the design-in quantities are extremely reluctant to change even small details of a proven design for the purpose of making large reductions in cost. Their only safe course is to make it like the proven design and specifications and to perhaps limit suggestions to only relatively minor deviations. This plan is extensively followed.

On the foregoing bases, it appears that to bleed in the skills of quantity manufacture by searching out the best technology, materials, processes, and manufacturing procedures during the reseach and development stage would prolong development and that by doing so just prior to his first production order, the contractor would subject his organization to delays, uncertainties, and possible losses which it is beyond the realm of reason for him to accept.

Unless a new approach is found, all of the above considerations make it appear that in critical military work it is necessary to continue to force through the research and development on a *time* and *performance* basis, to proceed to buy the first production lot or two, and then, perhaps with established experience and with some of the particular weapons on hand, to go after the job of applying the value techniques in order to provide simpler, more reliable weapons for, say, one-half to one-third the cost.

This will be at a time when drawings and specifications are complete, spare parts lists have been prepared, spare parts are in stock, all of the tooling has been paid for, and instruction books have been written and when, not unlikely, the weapon is obsolete.

The obvious conclusion from this review of the situation is that it behooves government and industry to provide a better answer.

Research and Development Problem Solution

In essence, the problem is how to add work to accomplish the new objective of attaining better cost value and, at the same time, promote the established objectives with respect to performance and time.

One good type of organization for this purpose is shown in Figure 8-1. Competence in value technology is injected to work along with other needed competence at all stages of the research and development.

The value engineering techniques being specifically developed out of day-to-day encounters with constant roadblocks represent means for breaking through these roadblocks, whether they be against better costs or better performance. Actually, experience has shown that as much as 25 per cent can be cut from expected research and development time when challenging cost objectives have been added to previous performance-time objectives and when value technology has been brought into play along with the cost objective.

Commonly in research and development work, 95 to 98 per cent of the product falls in areas of known technology, and 90 per cent or more of the product cost is ascribable to the provision of known functions.

Fig. 8-1. Practical organization for securing both value objectives and performance-time objectives.

Often it is desired to provide these functions in the new product in a manner which makes them simpler, more reliable, smaller in size, or lower in weight, i.e., with qualities which are the normal direct result of the use of the value technology.

Better Research and Development Answers Sooner

Illustrations by the score are to be found in military work areas. Study of some of them will provide the reader with guidance in establishing the use of value technology in his research and development activities.

An example, documented by the Navy in a film available for showing to qualified groups, is the Bureau of Ships' application of after-the-fact value engineering to a procurement of 1,000 landing craft.

One included item was a 200-gallon gasoline tank which was completely drawn and specified to require very costly metal, much custom welding, and other cost-consuming factors. It was quoted at $520 each, $520,000 for the lot.

As the value technology was applied, the function of reliably containing 200 gallons of gasoline was evaluated at approximately $50. The result was that four 55-gallon steel drums, treated for gasoline and other environmental conditions, were used at a cost of $80 each or $80,000 for the whole procurement. (See example 4, section 3-4, for a more complete discussion of this case.)

In retrospect, it can be seen that if the value technology had been available and had been used during original research and development on the product, it would have been totally unnecessary to design and draw up the tank and to prepare specifications on the welding, testing, etc. Instead, standard steel drums treated with available environmental finishes would have been specified, probably on one 8×11-inch page, with no design work and no drawing preparation. Engineering time would have been conserved and devoted to the acceleration of other research and development work on the craft, with the end result of shortening the time for the total project.

It follows that better solutions are attainable sooner by:

1. Utilizing the value techniques to overcome stoppers against either improved performance objectives or improved cost objectives.

2. Expanding the technological competence addressed to both the performance aspects and the value aspects of the product throughout the development by drawing upon the huge supply of top-grade knowledge, technology, and creativity which exists in diverse government and industrial circles. Organizing for the task of bringing good alternative solutions into clear focus in a minimum of time and with the utilization of best know-how wherever it exists is a part of executing sound value engineering.

In these ways, the research and development process for better means of accomplishing functions becomes substantially one of blending together the twin needs of extending the range of performance on the one hand and lowering the cost on the other. Technology oriented toward the performance field will be utilized to the fullest, while at the same time, equal competence in people trained in the techniques for accomplishing functions at lowest cost will be working hand in hand to produce more reliable, lower cost (higher quantity) research and development work in less time.

It would be gross oversimplification to contend that the suggested change in approach is an easy one to bring about. The conflict with past human concepts, thoughts, behavior, and procedure is too great. However, it seems indisputable that the day is here when the technologies for obtaining very much better cost must take their place beside the technologies for obtaining better performance. Only in this way will each weapon have quantity capabilities as well as performance capabilities.

CHAPTER 9 · *Essential Make-up, Qualifications, and Training for Value Analysts and Engineers*

9-1. *Qualifications*

Successful accomplishment of some types of work requires logic and experience. Examples are the work of the plumber and the electrician. Other types of work require logic and experience supplemented by the development of certain skills. Examples are the work of the surgeon, the typist, the telegraph operator, and others. Then there are types of work whose successful accomplishment depends on experience and extreme creativity. Examples are certain types of art and some types of music production.

Probably most other types of work activity fall in the range between these extremes.

As wider experience is gained, the specific qualifications for the relatively new vocation of value specialist or consultant will become more clear, more tangible, and more reliable. The indications of experience to date are that for the successful accomplishment of value work, the requirements are logic, experience, and great creativity, plus the development of certain mental skills such as ability to:

Make rapid and effective searches
Recall
Sort out useful information from what is not useful
Put together new, different, and useful combinations of ideas, materials, products, and processes to accomplish functions
Promptly select those combinations which are most apt to be good ones

All these abilities and skills, it will be seen, have a close tie-in with creativity and thus actually become the means through which creativity operates. It will also be noted that the special information and knowl-

195

edge of value analysis operate directly to support the development and use of this skill.

9-2. *Traits, Characteristics, and Experience*

The necessary traits, characteristics, and experience, as spelled out and defined below, constitute essential qualifications for men engaged in value work.

Knowledge. A practical understanding of the properties of materials and their uses and of manufacturing processes, their potentialities, and their limitations is needed.

Imagination. A good practical creative imagination commonly includes ability to retain extensive amounts of information concerning ideas for approaches and solutions to product problems, types of materials, properties of materials, processes, costs, and so forth, all arranged in a suitable order so that differing combinations may be creatively brought together and examined for applicability to problems at hand.

High Degree of Initiative. In value work, there are no definite beginning and ending points, and specific instructions on how and where to proceed are usually nonexistent. Further, this type of work is not well enough comprehended by general management for a rate at which it should be accomplished to be spelled out. For these reasons, it is essential that men in value work have a high degree of initiative, which must include what might be called self-drive, so that work activities will be started and carried through to completion with little if any supervision.

Self-organization. Initiative and drive are not enough; work must be effectively organized. Because of the lack of precedent and the lack of knowledge of organization for value work, conventional management supervision provides no experience for effectively instituting and executing the work. Therefore, the individual doing the work requires the ability to organize his activity effectively, as well as enough initiative to carry it out.

Personality. The work requires a mature, stable personality which is not easily discouraged. The entire field of activity in value work comes within the area of change. The amount of opposition to change usually prevailing cannot be conceived by anyone who has not attempted to operate in this area. The individual doing value work will be confronted with negative attitudes and delays of all sorts, with belittlement, and even with ridicule. The basic nature of anything new and the inherent attitude of the people with whom he will be dealing decree this. As Charles Kettering said, "The consensus of any group of people concerning something new in their field is always wrong." Or, as Thomas Edison said in 1926, "It requires about seven years for the average individual to accept a new proven solution to a problem." Because of this very exhausting aspect of value work, it is strongly recommended that it be performed by two or more persons working together. Each can then have an emotional environment of support, at least part of the time, which helps him feel that his work is a satisfactory and worthwhile endeavor.

Cooperative Attitude. A desire to work with others and a general knowledge of how to do it are other requirements, since the work is largely an endeavor based on working with others. It begins with acquiring an understanding of the job and proceeds by developing information which is often not available in ready form but which must be obtained if good value alternatives are to be produced. Knowledge concerning desired functions and methods for accomplishing them must be collected. Significant information must be communicated to competent commercial and technical people, and their wholehearted support (often with quotations) must be enlisted in expanding the area of knowledge in the direction of their skills through the preparation of value alternatives. In many instances, the work includes the difficult assignment of getting information without giving offense.

Experience. All indications to date suggest that some five years of industrial experience in engineering, in manufacturing, or in special procurement dealing with particular specifications, opportunities, arrangements, and negotiations between buyer and seller (or equivalent experience) is essential. It seems also that actual experience in working with the normal situations that affect the development of value alternatives is required. These situations involve decisions between varying ways of accomplishing a function, between varying sources of supply, between differing systems of make versus buy, etc. Without experience along this line, there is a lack of background for efficient and effective search of possible combinations and for presentation of new and good value alternatives.

Belief in the Importance of Value. Starting with certain native inclinations and modified by childhood and business experience, any person develops interest in certain lines and disinterest in others. In essentially all cases, human beings are interested in food, although in some cases of unusually unfortunate environments, even loss of interest in food is developed by people. Some individuals are interested in flying, while others vow that they will resist it to the death. Similarly, some people develop an interest in providing new products through the development of new functions which their ingenuity can translate into a practical product. Other individuals develop an interest in making products more economical so that distribution may be widened with resultant benefits, not only to the company involved in selling the products, but to mankind in general, through more universal use. At the present stage of experience with value work, it appears that there exist marked degrees of difference in the beliefs of various individuals in the importance of low cost—or its equivalent, high value—in the general sense. Experience has shown that men who have strong belief in the importance of value are much more likely to be sufficiently motivated to develop the initiative, self-drive, and enthusiasm necessary to accomplish their work well. Such strong belief also seems to be an important factor in creating emotional stability in this very frustrating type of work. Hence the conclusion that "belief in the importance of value" is a significant trait.

9-3. *Training*

Some of the knowledge which must be acquired and some of the new skills which must be developed are:

How to use each technique
When to apply each technique
How to use each phase of the job plan effectively
How to expect and to overcome the "stoppers" or roadblocks that are sure to come
How to successfully search out new information and new good answers for what is needed
How to acquire enough special knowledge so that it can be used efficiently and can be expanded to continue to be valuable

The necessity for good training and the problems which have been experienced in providing it are the reasons for the following discussion.

What is the necessary length of the training? Experience alone can provide the answer, for it is not definitely known and will depend upon the background, perceptiveness, and ability of the learner and also upon the degree of effectiveness with which he is expected to go about his work.

The procedure in the past has been to provide alternating periods of training and on-the-job work. An average pattern might be about as follows:

Three weeks of training followed by six months of on-the-job value work
Another three weeks of training of a more advanced nature, often including aiding in the teaching of beginners
Six months' additional on-the-job value work
Finally, a three weeks' more advanced training period, again with some part in helping to teach those less advanced

A general conclusion is that with this year of alternating between on-the-job work and periods of training, men who have the proper characteristics, qualifications, and traits for the type of work involved can acquire a sufficient degree of knowledge and skill to be considered competent to start on a career of work as value consultants.

It is significant to understand that training is mandatory because value work is based on the use of different sets of techniques in a special way and on the use of special knowledge. Without suitable training, the quality of the value work will degrade the profession for those compe. tent qualified people who can accomplish results of the highest order.

It is hoped that, with the appearance of texts like this one, good train, ing will become increasingly available.

Six sources providing at least the first stage of training are:

University of California, Los Angeles
405 Hilgard Avenue
Los Angeles 24, California

Industrial Education Institute
221 Columbus Avenue
Boston 16, Massachusetts

Northeastern University
360 Huntington Avenue
Boston 15, Massachusetts

Value Programs for Industry
425 State Street
Schenectady, New York

Value Analysis, Inc.
141 North Broadway
Schenectady, New York

Value Engineering, Inc.
53 State Street, Room 1013
Boston 9, Massachusetts

CHAPTER 10 *Work Content for the Value Analyst, Engineer, and Consultant*

In this chapter, as throughout the book, the names value analyst, specialist, engineer, and consultant are considered synonymous. Not unlikely, as the profession grows, differentiated meanings will develop for these four terms.

The principal work content falls into four basic classes:

Integration
Value appraisal and product evaluation
Value consultation
Value training

A suitable proportion of work from each of these classes must be achieved in each of the product-cycle stages, beginning in sales and progressing through engineering, manufacturing engineering, purchasing, and production.

10-1. *Integration*

It is normal human nature to discredit that which we do not understand. Thus, if a new entity appears in the industrial or other business setup, it will be subject to suspicion, doubt, discredit, and disfavor by all who do not understand it. It is self-evident, therefore, that what comes first is to integrate the work into the activities of every individual in the work area. Each person must know what the work of this new activity is; how it will be done; how it will affect him; in what respects it will make his work more difficult or simpler; what benefits that he has been getting he will now have to divide with value personnel; that this activity is not the boss's "pet" brought in under disguise for a period of time and later to be changed into something that will affect him badly.

The responsibility for answering all these questions before they have had time to arise to any significant extent becomes the first part of the work content of newly established value consultants.

Experience proves that it is a safe rule to devote as much as half of the entire resources for a period of many months to correctly accomplish this part of the work. Obviously, as understanding grows, the time devoted to it diminishes. However, with new situations continually developing and new people often coming in, care must be taken not to overlook this part of the work even in a going operation. It must be clearly understood that the purpose of the value consultants is to assist each individual who makes decisions affecting value to have at hand more information at the time of decision making so that he will make better decisions. Unless this is well known and unless working understandings are developed which include all of the relations, the results of the value activity will be greatly diminished.

10-2. *Value Appraisal and Product Evaluation*

This is after-the-fact value work. It consists in starting with the product, or process, in its present form, studying its functions intensely, applying the value analysis techniques and special knowledge, and producing improved value alternatives which are then presented, in suitable form, to the decision-making people involved. This is probably the part of the activity which is best known and which is most apt to be overdone.

It is very important to periodically provide a value appraisal for typical products of a particular area. This not only brings possibilities for greatly improved value of the specific item but also serves as a measurement of the degree of value work which is being effectuated on other, unstudied products. Results in this class of value analysis activity are limited in that it represents after-the-fact work. Often the outcome is embarrassing to the people who had to make operating decisions at an earlier stage, perhaps when they had important performance problems to solve and were possibly short of time and help. Work in this area brings much antagonism unless it is handled with extreme care. Besides, changes here are more costly and often more slowly made because drawings have been made, instruction books have been printed, replacement parts have been standardized, etc.

Nevertheless, sight must not be lost of the tremendous benefit to increased earnings which may come from doing a proper amount of work in this direction.

As one engineering manager said, "When a product is designed, the entire field is at risk, and lacking time to make minute studies of every detail, all decisions must be made on the safe side even though it is well known that some of them are locking into the product considerable excess cost." After the product is in operation and has proved itself, work can then proceed on studying these various phases of the product one at a time. Unnecessary cost should be identified and should be made subject to removal as promptly as practicable.

Experience has shown that much more satisfactory results are accomplished if value consultants study products of this class on the invitation of whichever department—sales, engineering, manufacturing, or purchasing—is involved in the later decision making. When thus invited in, their findings are sought and do not come as an embarrassment to the original decision makers.

10-3. *Value Consultation*

It is, of course, normally very much more desirable, and in actuality very practical, to provide value alternatives before the fact. This results from consultation, a direct parallel to the work performed by the tax consultant. Sales, engineering, manufacturing, or other people, faced with a product to design and produce or with a manufacturing system to develop or with a function to evaluate, quite naturally invite value consultants to make their contributions.

The process starts, then, by learning thoroughly the functions needed. This can be done almost as well from a drawing or specification as from a model. Next the consultants proceed to apply the value analysis techniques and special knowledge to establish the values of these functions and provide tangible information on value alternatives. The information thus derived is used by the decision makers in their original decisions so that the product will have the intended performance or features and will offer a better degree of value as well. As value people have worked successfully along this line in an operation, they have been accepted, and more and more of their time has been requested for before-the-fact consultation work.

10-4. *Value Training*

An important segment of the work content lies in constantly training substantially all individuals in the business to recognize and use certain of the value analysis concepts and techniques which they need and can take in stride in their daily work. In some cases, it is also desirable to provide training which will provide for replacements in the full-time professional value work.

Experience has proved that many of the value analysis techniques are useful not only for the purpose of helping sales, engineering, manufacturing, and purchasing people to secure better value while they execute their other essential assignments, but also, in many cases, for enabling these people to better accomplish their basic assignments.

The value analysis techniques are means for recognizing what is basic in the product, i.e., what the required functions are. They are also means for efficiently developing alternative answers which often will provide better quality, increased performance, lighter weight, improved appearance, and other added values to the product in addition to lower cost.

As a consequence, it is obviously desirable to establish courses to provide basic value analysis training to substantially all design engineers, draftsmen, manufacturing engineers, methods experts, production leaders, materials specialists, buyers, and others whose decisions affect the value of the product.

From practice it has appeared that training of people throughout the business environment will produce about half of the gain which can be accomplished by the effective use of the value analysis techniques and special knowledge. These people then take the work in stride, and it improves their value on the job. It also improves their yield to the company as well as their own job satisfaction. It is therefore important that value consultants recognize this area of responsibility and opportunity and effectively organize appropriate training.

As to the amount of training, this will vary with the individual, the individual's work, and the prevailing situation. Between forty and eighty hours of combined training and "do-it" work for each of these people is likely to result in substantial accomplishment. One afternoon of training each week for ten to twenty weeks is a good plan.

The training should consist of indoctrination in the value analysis techniques and in the special knowledge, concurrent with the study of actual products from an area which provides opportunity for the application of the techniques. It will include suitable contact with experts from outside the specific area whose knowledge penetration is of vital concern to the trainees in providing better answers to the projects under study. It will also include dealing with representatives of vendors of available specialty functional products to make the learners realize that large numbers of functions can be readily accomplished by using what already exists on the market, usually at the most economical cost.

It is apparent that when others in the business environment have had this basic training the task of integration is practically completed. In consequence, the consultants will be called upon to make their contribution to value at the right time, before decisions are made, and much more challenging value objectives for the business can be reached in a straightforward manner.

10-5. *Application to Various Business Activities*

Sales. INTEGRATION. Make sure that each salesman, each sales engineer, and each development engineer working in sales is fully advised on what the value consultant's work is and how he will work with them.

VALUE APPRAISAL AND PRODUCT EVALUATION. The first indication that a product has become comparatively overpriced often comes from experiences in the sales department. When this happens, the sales people are in a position either to turn the product over to the value consultants for value study and appraisal or to initiate action which will result in this being done by the design engineers or by other proper decision-making personnel.

CONSULTATION. With reference to both new products and existing products, sales people are directly oriented toward providing the desired function to their customers at competitive prices. On the invitation of sales people, the value consultant proceeds to study the functions involved. He applies the value analysis techniques to develop values for the functions, value alternatives, and alternative courses so that the sales people may make, or promote, decisions which will meet their objectives.

VALUE TRAINING. In order that sales people may bring the benefits of many of the value techniques into their daily work, a liberal number of them need value training. They will be benefited by increased abilities to identify the functions which the customers really want and to help provide the customer with what he really wants at the most reasonable cost. They will recognize these benefits and will want to be included in suitable value training programs.

Engineering. INTEGRATION. The availability of value consultants in a business lengthens the reach of all engineers as far as value is concerned. Before this contribution can be made, engineering people must know that the value consultant, starting out with the functions desired, will be capable of developing tangible value alternatives, thus saving them time and aiding them in their decisions. They must also know in what respects the value consultant needs their assistance in order to bring benefit to the common enterprise.

VALUE APPRAISAL. The engineering activity is faced with continual demands for lower costs of existing products. Alerted to the effectiveness of the value analysis techniques as used by the value consultant, the engineering people will invite the consultants to study the existing work and provide practical value alternatives for their decision. The same thing occurs in many instances when quality problems arise; the value consultant then will seek to provide value alternatives from which one may be chosen to yield a lower cost and also to eliminate the quality problem.

VALUE CONSULTATION. Perhaps one of the greatest opportunities for contribution by the value consultant comes when he is invited by the design engineers to acquire an understanding of their new products, to study the functions which are to be designed into them, and to present value alternatives for engineering decision. On new products, design engineers often have other objectives, besides function, which can be promoted by the use of the value techniques. Objectives such as smaller size, lighter weight, increased reliability, and better appearance are automatically furthered as the value consultant develops alternatives for reliably accomplishing the function. From these alternatives, the engineer can then choose the one which most nearly achieves his major objectives.

EDUCATION. Engineers, designers, and draftsmen—in fact all personnel in an engineering department—are busy at the basic tasks of determining the best ways to accomplish functions and of suitably drawing up the solutions and specifying them. Day-to-day use of some of the value analysis techniques will allow them to attain a much higher degree of value in their work, and in addition, it will often help them to reach other objectives more efficiently and economically. An effective training program for these people is of great significance.

Manufacturing. INTEGRATION. Basically, all manufacturing people are engaged in some part of the activity of endeavoring to manufacture and ship reliable high-grade products economically. This involves the choice of machines and processes, the development of methods, and the planning of patterns by which manufacturing operations will be performed and manufacturing costs will be expended on the product. Whether the product will be made or purchased is of great significance to them. Likewise, the alternative methods of purchasing materials at various stages of completion and the economies and costs involved are of great interest and must affect their decision making when high value is a prime objective. It is thus apparent that the manufacturing people must be at once advised of the work which is to be done by the value consultant and of the method he will use in doing it. They will also need to learn how their particular activity integrates with the consultant's activity and what responsibilities and opportunities they have in making his value work effective. Finally, they will want to know when to call on the value consultant for information that he can prepare for them for better decision making.

VALUE APPRAISAL AND PRODUCT EVALUATION. Normally, little of this type of work is done for manufacturing people, although in many cases, they are manufacturing functional components in certain ways and will request value studies to determine alternative means by which they may provide all functions desired by the engineers and still simplify their own manufacturing.

The reader must be cautioned here to note that it is not intended that value consultants should know more about manufacturing than the manufacturing people. They do not act as consultants to the manufacturing people on manufacturing methods or processes unless these are of such a highly specialized nature that the value consultant is in a better position than others in the organization to determine the sources of the required specialized knowledge.

CONSULTATION. A part of the stock in trade of the value consultant is knowledge of where to turn to find specialized knowledge of great depth. Therefore, he attends special exhibits and special shows where he can learn of the sources of such knowledge. From these sources, he will be able to derive specialized manufacturing knowledge or functional product knowledge of special interest in manufacturing considerations. For that reason, manufacturing people will, on occasion, call on the consultant for studies and suggestions.

VALUE TRAINING. It is no doubt now readily understood that men in manufacturing who are making decisions on processes, shapes, exact arrangements, and similar factors which will commit costs and which are needed to provide the functions expected by the engineers can derive large benefits from having a basic understanding of the use of the value analysis techniques. Accordingly, such men should be included in suitable training programs.

Purchasing. INTEGRATION. An important part of the contribution of the value consultant is to bring into the sales, engineering, and manufacturing areas new information concerning specialty functional products and specialized skills which vendors can provide if they are searched out and found at the right times. It is clear that unless purchasing people understand the exact nature of the work of the value consultant they will look askance at his contact with vendors and will rightly fear complications in connection with future purchases. Establishment of complete understanding and integration on the basis of practical working relationships is a vital first step.

VALUE APPRAISAL AND PRODUCT EVALUATION. Purchasing people often buy functional products or material which is made into functional products. They are at the point of transfer of the company's cash, and they are, by tradition, very much concerned about protecting this cash and bringing equivalent value to the company. Experience has shown that they continually ask for and want product evaluation work, the results of which may be intended to influence decisions made by the home-plant engineers or specification writers, in the vendor's plants, or by themselves. Good product evaluation work brings great benefits to purchasing people. Caution should be taken, of course, that when the decisions to be made by purchasing involve engineering, manufacturing, or sales people, these individuals are brought into the picture early so that they will have the same desire to have the product evaluation made. Only in this manner is embarrassment avoided and results accelerated. As for items which will have a bearing on decisions to be made by the vendors and vendors' technical people, each is a case unto itself. Competent purchasing people, faced with alternatives involving vendors' decisions, normally know how to carry out negotiations advantageous to both the buyer and the seller.

CONSULTATION. In relation to the purchasing activity, product evaluation and consultation become substantially one and the same activity because purchasing will call in assistance at any rate before they make the purchases.

VALUE TRAINING. It has been found that when buyers are made acquainted with the techniques and with the use of the techniques and the special knowledge several important results occur. First, buyers develop the practice of thinking in terms of buying a function or functions, and their minds are directed into very profitable channels in a high percentage of cases. Second, they recognize the high value to the company derivable from specialized vendors to whom they have ready access. They become more willing to make searches. They learn how to search better for any type of specialized competence which will make contributions to the company's products. They learn also the great importance of providing for proper communication between the company's technical people and the vendor's technical people. They become catalysts to bring the right competence outside the company into immediate contact with the proper competence within the company. Increased benefits result for both performance programs and value programs.

10-6. *Indoctrination of Management*

Allied to the training of the "doers," along the lines discussed in the foregoing paragraphs, is the matter of indoctrinating management. A full comprehension by management at all levels of the aims and workings of value analysis is a prerequisite to the attainment of the fullest measure of benefit from coordinated value activity. It falls within the scope of the work content of the value consultant to arrange and conduct indoctrination sessions as the conditions may warrant. Well-proportioned attention to this phase of cultivation invariably brings substantial "payoff" both to the company and to the individual.

CHAPTER 11   *Motivation, Measurement, and Tests*

11-1. *Motivation*

Achievement of significant objectives in any activity requires motivation in some form or another. What constitutes appropriate motivation in the area of substantially decreased cost, and thus increased value, will be discussed next.

Motivation will be considered in the four categories of:

The business
Managers
Value consultants and others using value analysis techniques
Decision makers

The Business. No business has sufficient competent personnel to pursue all desirable objectives with high emphasis. The general situation in business may be likened to that faced by a baseball team, which has only nine men to cover the entire field. Depending on the score, the pitcher, the batter, and the phase of the game, these men will be placed somewhat differently and will play under instructions to put emphasis on particular activities. Much the same occurs in business. The organization must possess an appropriate amount of competence, or else it will fail. But the men who make up this competence must vary their activities to meet the greatest pressures and thus produce results in those areas in which action is most needed. To motivate a business to organize for high value content in its products, a "force of necessity" is normally required. It must be vital to the business to accomplish value objectives in addition to performance objectives, shipment objectives, and other goals.

A corresponding force is often created by a forward-planning management which, when it sees a threatening situation developing, proceeds to generate emphasis for effective actions to prepare the business to meet the situation when, perhaps years hence, the time arrives.

In the absence of either of these two forces, motivation is usually inadequate to cause steps to be taken to establish and execute a program which will provide for leadership in value.

Managers. Experience has shown that motivation in four forms provides satisfactory results.

NECESSITY. This may be the necessity imposed by the immediate situation or the necessity created by forward planning by the top management of a business. Either of these forces makes it vital to efficiently identify unnecessary costs, and they dispel all doubt about the importance to the business of assigning sufficient resources to accomplish significant results in the area of value.

BOSS PRESSURE. This force must, of necessity, be clearly promoted by the managers' superiors so that there can be no question in managers' minds as to whether they should strive for significant progress in the value area or merely continue to give attention to the traditional areas to which they have been accustomed. Each manager must know that, to an important extent, he will be measured and appraised according to his accomplishment, i.e., the accomplishment of the group he manages, in this activity.

MINIMUM-PERSONAL-LOSS ENVIRONMENT. The creation of an environment for *minimum personal loss* is a third form of motivating force. Taking different actions in order to achieve a very much improved degree of value means doing things differently and hence brings about the ever-present risk of personal loss. To the extent that the chances of personal loss due to value action are not eliminated from the manager-boss relationship and the manager environment, important negative motivation exists. It is therefore imperative, in creating a maximum of positive motivation, to give much attention to reducing the personal-loss factor.

COMPANY RECOGNITION OF ACCOMPLISHMENTS. Managers have traditionally been recognized for their accomplishments in areas other than that of product value. They need to be assured that, as a reward for their efforts and for the risks they take in the value area, they will receive appropriate recognition for accomplishments.

Value Consultants and Others Using Value Analysis Techniques. In developing reasonable motivation for people who are doing value work, five important methods should be kept in mind.

EMPHASIS. Enough emphasis must be placed by management on the importance of high-grade value work so that the endeavor and the time of the men engaged in it are not constantly encroached upon by ever-demanding performance problems, delivery problems, etc. That management does indeed place as much emphasis on good value as on these other, more short-range factors in the business needs underscoring.

SUPPORT. Good value work is not accomplished without a great amount of "doing." This means men going places, studying new things, encountering problems, and being misunderstood by their coworkers in other company activities. The extent to which their new type of work gets support from management in these situations adds a very significant plus or minus factor to the motivation of the "doers."

STATUS. Anyone engaged in value work requires a status corresponding to that of others in the organization whose work is better known and hence receives more consideration from management. The man must be able to go home at the end of the day and say proudly, and with conviction, "I am in the value activity." Again, the degree to which management provides appropriate status for the people doing this new type of work accounts for a significant plus or minus factor in motivation.

FAIR MEASUREMENT. Fair methods of measurement of performance must be established. Traditional methods of measurement, which do not fit but which are familiar to others in the environment, must not be improperly used. If the man does a good job in his work of identifying unnecessary cost, will managers say, "Good work, Joe"? Or, if he does a poor job, will the managers be able to say, "I think you can do better, Joe"? Fair effective measurement is a strong motivator.

RECOGNITION. Proper and appropriate recognition before their peers in relation to the effectiveness of the work of value consultants becomes a vital plus factor in motivation.

Decision Makers. Each decision maker has specific measured responsibilities; for instance, he may sell the product, design the product, manufacture certain quantities of specification-grade product, provide metered quantities of materials of appropriate grade to the factory, or reach certain inventory-investment objectives.

EMPHASIS. In all cases, emphasis is very real and measurement is very direct. If these people are to invest important segments of their time in working out value alternatives, "debugging" them, testing them, and taking the necessary chances which always come with any change, they must interpret the emphasis on these tasks to mean that accomplishment therein is as important a part of their work as the measured part.

MINIMUM-PERSONAL-LOSS ENVIRONMENT. The reader was alerted in an earlier chapter to the importance of eliminating the personal-loss factor if decisions to produce better value are to be expected. Experience would indicate that the motivation to produce effective results in the improvement of value by decision makers is affected by extremely large plus or minus factors according to the effectiveness with which management handles this phase.

MEASUREMENT OF ACTION AND LACK OF ACTION. Nearly every phase of human nature promotes a negative decision on the part of the decision maker. If the value alternative can be rather promptly ruled out on plausible grounds, the decision maker is then at liberty to return to his major measured field of activity without having suffered personal loss. To provide reasonable motivation for action, measurements are needed which will clearly highlight lack of action. As soon as a fair and supportable measurement of lack of action is provided and accepted, the personal-loss factor is increased by negative rather than positive actions and significant increases in motivation result.

UNDERSTANDING OF FAILURES. In normal activity, success does not result 100 per cent of the time. In some of the projects of studying value alternatives, making models, testing, developing new vendors, and proving new processes, results will be found to be negative. Meanwhile, an important amount of time and of money may have been spent upon the project. It is never known before this work is done whether the result will be an important accomplishment or not. It is important, therefore, that management clearly show itself ready to stand back of, support, and understand the effort when it judges alternatives that had a fair trial but did not work out.

RECOGNITION OF SUCCESSES. The earnings position of the company will be greatly benefited from time to time by specific activities in the area of value improvement. Important motivation will be provided and future results will be greatly enhanced if clear recognition of successes is given.

11-2. *Measurement*

Measurement of Organizations. The following Value Analysis Organization Study and Measurement Guide illustrates a good approach to the important problem of measuring organizations. It is meant not only to cover measurement questions but also to contain some of the significant answers for the indoctrination of management people who are performing the study and measurement.

VALUE ANALYSIS ORGANIZATION STUDY AND MEASUREMENT GUIDE
(*Mark on scale of 5, 4, 3, 2, 1: 5 indicates highest merit, 1 lowest*)

Areas of study:

1. How well is value analysis understood?
2. How well is the value analysis organization suited to the business involved?
3. How correctly is the value analysis operation set up?
4. How effectively are the value analysts operating?
5. Do miscellaneous factors aid the value analysis operation?

1. *How Well Is Value Analysis Understood?*

How well is it understood by:
Top management?
Intermediate management?

Engineers?

Manufacturing and methods staffs?

Buyers?

Value analysis is a creative study of every item of cost in every part or material. It considers other possible materials, newer processes, abilities of specialized suppliers, and possibilities for engineering re-evaluation. It focuses engineering, manufacturing, and purchasing attention on one objective—equivalent performance for lower cost.

Is value analysis well understood to comprise special techniques and special knowledge, not to be just a substitute for cost reduction, by:

Management?

Engineers?

Manufacturing people?

It is not a substitute for present engineering, manufacturing, and purchasing cost-reduction work; it is a supplement. It improves the effectiveness of the work being done in those areas and, in addition, fills a blind spot. It is accomplished by carefully selected, trained full-time specialists using established techniques and following an established plan which results in eliminating all types of unnecessary costs not normally identified and eliminated by other methods.

2. *How Well Is the Value Analysis Organization Suited to the Business Involved?*

Does it include the proper number of specialists?

Do they work full time?

Normally, value analysis specialists return from $10 to $25 to the manager for each dollar they cost.

How well are value analysts qualified by ability, experience, and training?

Do they have (rate each man and average):

a. Engineering or methods and planning experience supported by a general understanding of the properties of materials and their uses?

b. A good creative imagination?

c. Enough initiative, self-organization, and self-drive to start and complete their projects with little if any supervision?

d. A feeling of the importance of value?

e. A mature, stable personality not easily discouraged?

f. The desire to work and deal with others and general knowledge of how to do it?

Have they had sufficient instruction in value analysis techniques?

How well has each learned:

a. To develop the *complete* facts?

b. To use a businessman's judgment?

c. To think and act creatively?

d. To use and bring in help from others?

e. To provide himself with special information?

How well is the value ability developed in each man?

As other skills are developed, we believe value ability can be developed. Value analysis training aims at that objective. Experience and proper action further develop it.

3. How Correctly Is the Value Analysis Operation Set Up?

Do the analysts work individually, with one man responsible for one project, instead of by committees?

Do they avoid all discussions or meetings involving more than a total of three at the table at one time?

> Value analysis is not committee work. It is conducted by one man intensively following a project; he may discuss particular phases with others, one or two at a time at most.

Are the value analysts expected to constantly crystallize their suggestions in the value analysis suggestion sheets?

Are the suggestion sheets clear, concise, definite, and tangible, and are they drawn in executive language?

If the value analysts report to materials management, have they established a working relationship based on 100 per cent understanding, confidence, and cooperation with engineering and manufacturing?

If they report to engineering or to manufacturing engineering, have they established a working relationship based on 100 per cent understanding, confidence, and cooperation with the purchasing department and every buyer in it?

Do they report high enough in the organization for their critical problems to be immediately known by sufficiently high authority to at once receive effective action?

To what extent is the business getting a fresh look into each job? (Men with years of experience in the area, who have gone over the same work several times, rate a 1.)

> Surprisingly, men who have long worked on a project are often the least capable of eliminating further large quantities of unnecessary cost by value analysis techniques. To eliminate large quantities of unnecessary cost, such men should usually be assigned other work and "new blood" brought into the job.

4. How Effectively Are the Value Analysts Operating?

How effectively have the value analysts developed "function" thinking? Is all of their thought on function?

> Value analysts relate costs to the function or service or operation purchased by that cost. They question each specific item of cost to determine what function it really buys. For example: What is it? What does it cost per year? What does it do? What else would do the job and what would that cost? Then, each dollar of cost which does not clearly buy definite function is strongly questioned. Function is simply defined as something that makes the product work better or sell better.

Do they actually get *all* of the available facts before starting work?
  Drawings and specifications that are available
  Planning cards when they exist

All costs when they exist

Samples of parts when they exist

Assembly in which parts go when such information exists

When starting a job, do they always learn the basic engineering?

Do they always learn the basic manufacturing?

Have they learned to listen and to make absolutely no suggestions at this stage?

Do they avoid going back to engineering and others and making incomplete suggestions?

Are they using the value analysis job plan in all its phases?

Orientation phase

Information phase

Speculative phase

Analytical phase

Program-planning phase

Program-execution phase

Value analysis work follows the value analysis job plan in which the analyst intensively seeks out, adapts, evaluates, and applies.

Do the value analysts "blast" in attempting to initiate long-term gain or large-percentage gain of at least 50 to 90 per cent cost reduction in fields of:

Engineering?

Manufacturing methods?

Purchasing?

Do they also strive for reductions of 50 per cent down to 10 per cent?

Value analysts both blast and refine. A portion of their time is invested in searching for means of accomplishing the same job for one-tenth or one-fifth or one-half of the cost. The remainder of their study consists of effort to refine, with reductions more nearly in the area of 40, 30, or 20 per cent. It is often easier to remove 50 per cent of the cost than 10 per cent.

Does the managers' representative promptly refer suggestion sheets to the proper managers for their assignment?

Do about 80 per cent of suggestions develop into substantial savings?

Do the analysts get right out into the vendors' plants to learn?

Does this activity take analysts out into other plants about one day on the average in each two weeks?

Have any deterring factors which would retard results been avoided, such as the necessity to ask permission of someone who does not understand the details of the need?

Do the analysts use all means of immediate and effective action such as:

Immediate personal contact through trips or planned conferences?

Telephone?

Telegraph?

In searching for methods of value improvement, does the analyst have free reign to initiate studies which take him into the area of:

Engineering?

Manufacturing?

Make-it or buy-it?

Proper ordering quantities?

Better inventory control?

All others?

> All have a bearing on value. The analyst is free to develop facts in any and all areas.

Does management select about half of the analyst's projects?

Do the value analysts normally select about half of their own projects?

> Value analysts should have the initiative to ferret out and identify cases of poor value. They accordingly select 50 per cent of their own jobs and normally handle, in the remainder of their time, jobs referred to them by management. An important reason for this is that, unless they do, shocking cases of poor value which could be readily corrected continue year after year because management in the particular area involved happens to be overlooking them.

Do value analysts regularly consult others—specialists in engineering, in methods, in procurement—in preplanned interviews of one or two hours' duration?

Do the managers assign the suggestion sheets to their appropriate subordinates, supervise them, and secure progress reports on them exactly as they do with other job assignments?

> It is recognized that the managers will supervise their own men and that the men will report back *only* to their own bosses on the status of accomplishment or lack of it.

Do value analysts do no *policing?*

> Value analysts develop and crystallize the facts; prepare them in executive language on the suggestion sheet, one item to one page; submit them to the person designated by the managers; and do absolutely no policing. They will assist further in any case when requested by the manager or his appointee to develop specific additional facts.

Do they avoid *all* follow-up to see what was accomplished by their suggestion sheet?

> Value analysts make no savings claims. Their suggestions materialize as savings in either the engineering, manufacturing methods, or purchasing areas. There is no flag waving. There are no claims of big dollar totals to alienate the various functional groups.

Do the value analysts avoid *all* savings reports, issuing only day-to-day suggestion sheets?

> The only report issued by the value analysts are the day-to-day, item-by-item suggestion sheets which show the possibilities on the various individual items.

Is it well understood that the value analysts make no decisions?

> Value analysts make no decisions but develop facts for management decisions; accordingly, while they are a large factor in such matters as "make-it or buy-it," they develop the facts and management decides.

Are the men provided with suitable physical and clerical assistance so that they can invest their time effectively at their highest potential?

Adequate and suitable space for interviews, for study, etc.

Clerical assistance

Stenographic assistance

5. *Do Miscellaneous Factors Aid the Value Analysis Operation?*

Are all buyers trained in the value analysis techniques that pertain to buying?

Have the value analysts arranged for equipping themselves with the specific information they will constantly need to do their job well?

Has the value analysis group assumed a position of real leadership in the department by constantly increasing the knowledge, understanding, and use of value skills through regularly planned courses or study groups?

Are the habits and attitudes which allow significant value improvement in the department progressively improving?

In management

In engineering

In manufacturing methods

In purchasing

Value analysis requires serious thought, hard study, and immediate action. In cases of doubt, it is necessary to err on the side of doing something rather than on the side of stable conservatism. Value analysis performs as an engineering and a manufacturing tool and reaches out of the company into the limitless supply of technical information.

Have the analysts learned how to work with and through the buyers, the engineers, and the manufacturing methods men, never around them?

Do they always, in the long pull, strengthen each in his own field?

Do others always cooperate fully with the analyst?

In management

In engineering

In manufacturing methods

In purchasing

The job of value analysts is to get today's and tomorrow's materials, ideas, methods, and processes into use today. If they operate properly, they will use all of the resources in the entire country in this program.

Measurement of Value Work. Each of the four types of work comprising the value analyst's work should be measured separately, and in general, measurement should be both of the amount done and of the amount not done. The four types of work, the reader will recall, are integration, value appraisal, consultation, and training.

INTEGRATION. The manager to whom value consultants or analysts report should set up with them listings of all persons in the organization who have certain important information about the plans of operation of the value analysts. In large organizations, these lists may best show the name of the activity rather than the name of the individual, together with the number of people involved in each case. At the end of report periods, which might each be ninety days, the work done and the work still to be done should be shown in order to provide the various men or the various groups of men with proper understanding. The quality of the understanding which is being secured by typical men of the various groups indoctrinated should be evaluated. On this basis, replanning to provide the additional understanding can be done.

VALUE APPRAISAL. Wrong measurement is a worse deterrent than no measurement to the establishment of any sound activity. It often happened in earlier value work that a traditional form of measurement, which provided definitely deceptive results, had been used. More recently, the shortcomings of this type of measurement are being realized, and it is being ended. It is definitely incorrect to measure value consultants or value analysts, who use the value analysis techniques and special knowledge for the purpose of identifying unnecessary cost, by the amount of savings which result from their value alternatives. The reader will be quick to recognize that savings are the result of good value alternatives plus effective decisions and actions by entirely different people. First, the value men act to provide value alternatives, then the decision makers act to either implement the suggestions or not implement them. True, the tangible benefit to the business is the result of the actions of these two groups in series, namely, the decrease in cost and the added earnings which actually result. However, it is fallacious to use this outcome as an indication of the quality of the value alternatives or of the effectiveness of the work of the value consultants. Changes in the value group based on such measurements may bring disaster to the business.

When the nature of the personnel in the decision group and the degree of their motivation are such that good action normally results, very poor value alternatives indeed may seem to produce large improvements in earnings. A management that gives credence to such measurements would be inclined to believe that they had indeed learned the proper type and operation for value personnel and would take action accordingly. Exactly the opposite is true; the decision group is so effective that with a very small input it produces large results.

In businesses hardest pressed for good results in value work, experience has shown that the controlling practices of the decision makers are the reverse of the above. Now, even though the effectiveness of the value group in producing value alternatives is very high indeed, very little if anything "comes out" in the increased earnings column. A management judging by this result would be inclined to decide that its value group was inefficient or improperly staffed or organized and would tend to make changes which would destroy any possibility of improving the situation.

It should be very clear that the quality of value alternatives must be measured as such and that, as time progresses, business must learn also to measure the quality, as such, of the decision makers in matters affecting value. Only then can an enlightened management make appropriate decisions and take appropriate action to restore and enhance the value of its products.

An important measurement, then, in value appraisal will be based on an evaluation of the alternatives covered by the suggestion sheets, which, as the reader will recall, constitute the output of value consultants. This must be an objective evaluation of the likelihood that the suggestion will prove practical and of the probable amount of reduction in cost which will be accomplished. Care should be taken in making these evaluations that men who have vested interests, i.e., who will later have the responsibility for either taking action to implement the alternatives or taking action to kill them, are excluded from the evaluation team. A suitable amount of product evaluation should be planned in discussions by the value consultants and the manager to whom they report. In this planning, the various products and product lines should be brought into view, discussed briefly, and either bypassed or scheduled for study. Measurement then follows the system of matching results with plans. Plans will, of course, be constantly subject to change to take into account new information learned from the results of the studies.

CONSULTATION. Important guidance on consultation is obtained from a clear review of both the consultation which has been done during the measurement period and the consultation which has not been done. In other words, these questions should be raised:

On what jobs was consultation done?

On what jobs was consultation not done?

For what men, or groups of men, was consultation done?

For what men, or groups of men, was consultation not done?

A progressive study of this type for each of a few report periods provides vital information to show where more consultation is required and also where more integration knowledge and understanding must be provided to men in other work areas.

Reports of consultation work should contain memorandum statements of activities involved in consultation, such as, "assisted engineer Smith by locating for him a double-range thermocouple of smaller size, greater accuracy, and lower cost than the product previously used."

The report will show the number of times the consultants were invited into each area and the activities resulting.

TRAINING. In regard to training, it is again most significant to have clear-cut information showing what training has been done and what training has not been done. Plans will be prepared to include all the people who should have training, either by name or, in large organizations, by groups and numbers in each group. A suitable rate will be established, and a suitable schedule for training will be prepared. This, then, will allow measuring the actual training against the plan. When desirable, the plan should be adjusted at each measurement period to account for changes in emphasis, shifts in business, or new information of diverse types.

11-3. *Tests*

It is important to know whether the men being taught are learning. If the men are not learning, the trainer is not teaching. For this purpose, tests should be provided to ascertain whether those purported to be receiving training are indeed learning the fundamentals which they will require to effectively carry out their value work.

Periodically, perhaps once each year, a study should be made of the value analysis work content in each of the main areas of the business, such as sales, engineering, manufacturing, purchasing, and management. In studying each area, it is important to examine separately the actions on the four different types of work; for example:

Has suitable integration been completed? If not, what is the status and what plans should now be made?

Is the appropriate amount of product evaluation work being done for these people?

Is the appropriate amount of value consultation work being done for these people?

Are the appropriate numbers of personnel being properly instructed in training classes?

Such a separate study of the four types of value work in each area of the business often brings larger than anticipated benefits. It may show that a tendency has developed for value consultants to work quite efficiently on a few of the work elements, or in some of the needed areas, and to be working very superficially otherwise. With this knowledge at hand, emphasis can be placed where it belongs to the end that a more balanced and profitable program can be reestablished.

Measurement of Men. It is desirable, if not necessary, to have a test which can be given to the value consultant or value analyst to show, in reality, how well he is really doing in the work situations which make up the four types of value analysis work. To the writer's knowledge, no such comprehensive test exists today. Some work has been started on the preparation of such a test, and it is expected that tests will become available before too long.

It should be well recognized that in the testing and selection of men, the qualifications required are governed to an important extent by the number of people in the particular value group. For example, if one man has outstanding abilities as a teacher, plus the other essential knowledge and traits, so that he does indeed teach the subject matter, he need not have similarly high excellence in product evaluation or in value consultation. Conversely, if competence is provided to take care of teaching work, then others in that particular value analysis group may do an outstanding job in product evaluation, consultation, and integration without, in fact, having professional-grade skills in teaching, and there will be balanced competence for the over-all operation.

It has been found that great care should be taken to guard against assuming that technical people who are highly competent in searching out and generating sound value alternatives are also capable of communicating and teaching. This is not necessarily true. High-grade and skilled value analysts may entirely fail at the task of teaching and training.

While a dearth of over-all tests exists at the present time, the reader will find, by reexamining the chapter on qualifications for value work, that there are important opportunities for using available tests to help in the selection of men. For example, such essential qualifications as creativity, emotional stability, and technical knowledge have been sufficiently well established so that measurements and tests exist for these traits and qualifications.

Appendix

QUESTIONS

The following questions have been formulated and are presented as means of helping the reader crystallize his understanding and interpretation of the material in this book.

For convenience to the user, the questions are arranged in groups and numbered to correspond to the parts of the text.

Experience in lecturing on value analysis has proved that students benefit immeasurably from writing down in their own terms considered answers to these questions. It is suggested, therefore, that the questions be given careful attention.

Chapter 1

1-1. To what extent does any activity, such as industrial engineering, work simplification, manufacturing methods, or cost reduction, properly qualify as value analysis or value engineering?

1-2. Name ten matured products on which advances in value engineering control the success of the business venture more than do advances in performance engineering.

Name ten products which are still in the stage of rapidly developing performance capabilities.

Name five products which are at present in the growth stage, i.e., progressively changing from the research and development phase with the emphasis on performance engineering to the maturity stage with principal importance attached to value engineering.

State ten reasons why it is important to identify and remove unnecessary cost. Describe five of the reasons fully.

1-3. Write five sentences each using the word *value,* with that word having a different meaning in each case.

Describe the understanding you have of *use value* and of *esteem value.*

Is use value of importance in all products? Explain.

Is esteem value of importance in all products? Explain.

How is the appropriate ratio of use value to esteem value determined for any particular product or process?

Who normally makes the decisions concerning use value, and on what basis are they made?

Who normally makes the decisions concerning esteem value, and on what basis are they made?

What is meant by a manufacturer's statement about his own product when it says:

"Value of this product is satisfactory"

221

"Value of this product is unsatisfactory"

Name and explain five ways of determining whether value (appropriateness of cost) is suitable.

In common usage, how many kinds of values would you say that a clock has? What are they? Use each in a sentence. Repeat the same question for an automobile, a home, a necktie, earrings, a nail.

Name five products which you consider poor value and state why.

Name five products which you consider good value and state why.

1-4. Considering that there are five areas in a business which might have an important effect on value, describe some of the actions, both beneficial to value and injurious to it, which may be taken in:

Sales
Engineering
Manufacturing
Purchasing
Management

What is the principal action which each of the above activities must take with regard to value if a good degree of value is to be achieved? Describe.

Describe the effect on value of each of the following:

Lack of information
Lack of the best ideas
Temporary circumstances
Misunderstanding and wrong information
Attitudes previously accumulated under a variety of experiences
Habits of doing certain things in certain ways

1-5. Basically, what does a customer really want when he buys a product? What did you want when you bought your latest pair of shoes?

List, in order of importance, what you really wanted, or will want, in selecting a refrigerator.

Name twenty items in which the function most desired is a use (work) function.

Name twenty items in which the function most desired is an esteem (sell) function.

List ten items in an automobile which were put there by its designer and manufacturer to cause it to work.

List ten items in an automobile which were incorporated in it to cause it to sell.

Name five products which you have purchased within the past year predominantly for the purpose of accomplishing a use.

Name five products which you have purchased within the past year predominantly for the purpose of conforming to a custom, providing appearance, providing interest, etc.

Look around the room and note and write down the names of five items and their basic functions.

Indicate the approximate dollar value of each, and describe why you associate that dollar value with each item.

Name ten items which you have bought or seen priced, and state the approximate dollar value of each.

Name ten items, products, or types of products for which you have no reasonable idea whatsoever of the dollar value. These should be examples in which you have no experience to use for useful comparisons.

Attempt to evaluate, i.e., place a dollar value on, each of the latter group of items. Explain two or three of the difficulties you find in attempting to do this and also two or three actions you would take if it were necessary for you to evaluate them.

State five reasons why it is especially desirable to include in the original design the design concept and the manufacturing and engineering alternatives which will bring maximum value.

Give and describe ten reasons why this maximum value can never be totally accomplished in the original design.

Describe five actions which may be taken to get more of the better value concepts included in the original design.

List the functions for which a customer might purchase a hammer, a hat, a door for his home, an autopilot for his airplane.

Describe the sources to which you would go for information concerning the required functions involved in:

Tuning circuits in radios
Electrical contacts in home thermostats
Bearings on turret lathes
Transformers for fluorescent lighting fixtures

Describe two approaches that might be taken to secure more information so that more economical and reliable value alternatives can be established in each of the following situations:

Extremely high temperature use of metal
High-speed use of cutting tools
An extraordinarily shaped nail
Extensive crimping and welding of wire
Lubricants used at extremely high temperature
Plastics used in a corrosive atmosphere
Glass used under conditions of physical shock and vibration
Use of an electric motor submerged in water

1-6. From the designer's viewpoint, list and suitably describe the work function or functions of the following products:

Pencil	Automobile door
Spoon	Hinge on door
Liquidizer	Automobile seat
Automobile tire	

List the sell function or functions of the same items.

List the functions of both an axe handle and an axe head.

Examine the relationship between the axe handle and axe head, and list the functions which each has specifically in relation to the other.

Describe the function which a screw driver has specifically in relation to the details of the head of a screw.

Describe the functions of the following items with specific relationship to the associated items listed:

Door to house	Lock to door
Hinge to house	Knob to lock
Door to hinge	Knob to hand

State some of the items with which you might compare the following in order to gain a general idea of the value of the item:

Eightpenny nail
$\%_{32} \times 1$-inch steel screw
Green kitchen clock
¼-horsepower electric motor
20-inch reel-type gasoline lawn mower
75-watt electric light bulb

Explain the difficulty which results from trying to evaluate:

The right wing of a 707 jet airliner
The top ten stories of the Empire State Building
The electrical system of an automobile

Select five items in the normal home, and in each case list:

What the item is
What it does
Approximately what it costs (its value)
What else would do the job
What the alternative would cost

Make a similar list for three items from the office, factory or other location in which you work.

Chapter 2

2-1. Write down the detailed steps in the simple procedure of leaving the kitchen, going to the grocery store, getting a bottle of milk, bringing it home, and putting it in the refrigerator.

Write down the essential steps in the procedure for action required when a tire becomes deflated in driving along the road.

Note the inferior results and the increased frustration of omitting any step of the procedure.

Select the step in each of the foregoing procedures which could be omitted with the least consequence, and describe the ill effects, minimized results, or increased efforts caused by omitting just this one step.

2-2. List what you believe to be the top characteristics wanted by a customer when he buys the following:

Shoes	Axe
Motorcycle	Television set
Fountain pen	

State some of the differences in the top characteristics desired by the customer in a radio set for use in each of the following places:

Home	Airplane
Tractor	Submarine

Study a simple part, such as a hinge, with which you are closely familiar, and determine how you may provide all its functions reliably in the end product at very much lower cost. List and describe all the types of information which you will need before starting the study.

Assume that you are buying an electric switch to go into a product being manufactured. Study the situation to reliably provide all of the functions of the switch at a much lower cost. List and describe the types of information you will need before starting the study.

Sketch a dozen shapes for the operating handle on a toggle switch, and suggest a dozen materials which might be used for it. Also, suggest a dozen processes which might be used in fabricating the material for the handle.

In each of the three examples above, select the alternatives which you believe are likely to be the poorest solutions, either because they fail to accomplish the use function reliably or to yield the esteem or appearance function effectively or because they are likely to be the most costly. In each case, describe your beliefs about the situation.

Then select, in each of the three examples, the alternative which you believe to be the most economical, and describe its probable reliability in accomplishing the use function and its acceptability for accomplishing the appearance function. In each case, state the direction in which the thinking and development should be directed in order to overcome, without significantly increasing the cost, objections which you may have noted.

Describe three types of information sources in the United States to which you might go for more details and more technical and cost guidance in developing the best alternatives for each of the three items you have chosen.

Divide the electric refrigerator into approximately ten "functional areas." For example, one functional area may be "enclosure," a second "insulation." Describe each sufficiently to communicate your ideas.

Divide the automobile into approximately five functional areas, and again describe each sufficiently to communicate your ideas.

Divide a ¼-horsepower electric motor into at least a dozen functional components or groups of components.

Divide an electric clock into its two most important functional areas. Now subdivide each of the functional areas of the clock into two or three subfunctional areas. Finally, subdivide each of the resulting subfunctional areas into two or three sub-subfunctional areas.

As an aid in formulating an idea of the number of sources in the United States from which more information may be secured about various materials, products, or processes, list the manufacturers which you believe offer the desired types of services on:

Ball bearings	Electric motors
Screw-machined parts	Electric switches
Plastic parts	Molded rubber parts
Castings	Metal containers

In your study of the process by which the handle for an existing toggle switch is made, you collected its costs and other necessary information and, presumably, have valuable alternatives to report. Prepare a suggestion sheet written in "managers' language" which will set forth the pertinent information. Use sketches and provide typical information which will produce a meaningful and typical suggestion sheet.

In addition to the suggestion sheet you have prepared, you have collected supporting data which will be submitted to an engineer for his study and consideration. Identify by name and description the pieces of paper which you believe would be useful attachments of supporting data and, in general, what each would contain in order to allow the engineer to efficiently make his studies, accompanied by tests and modifications if necessary, in order to economically utilize the suggestions to bring benefits to the product.

Chapter 3

3-1. Write down five typical statements given to you at a store as justification for a price which you believe is too high. Note the "generality" nature of the statements.

Assuming that you were merchandising a product, for example, wrist watches, at $15 each and that you decided to increase the selling price to $20 each in order to provide better earnings, list five statements (generalities) of the type which you would expect to hear your employees using in making sales at the increased customer cost.

Describe the steps you would take in order to get away from the generality into workable "specifics" in the case of each of the following statements:

Underwriters' requires this type of construction.

This construction is necessary to meet the high-pressure code.

This type of flange is necessary in order to meet safety requirements.

This is the only type of casting approved for high-pressure fluids.

We have tried every other possible means; this is the only way to accomplish the function.

We must maintain interchangeability for ten years.

The customer is happy with this; why should we change it?

The Smith Company is the only reliable supplier for that class of product.

Experience has shown that rubberlike materials will not stand the corrosive atmosphere present.

In an assumed case, a small crankshaft machined from a forging cost $5.50. The same crankshaft machined from a casting would have an over-all cost of $2.50. The statement and belief which caused the continuance of the $3 difference was, "Forgings make better crankshafts than castings."

Write down and describe all the steps which you would deem it necessary to take, including the questions you would ask, to make sure that you were receiving reliable performance from the crankshaft at the lowest over-all cost.

3-2. Describe five purposes for which a cost system in a business might be developed.

Identify at least twelve different types of costs which are in somewhat common usage, and describe what, in general, each means to you.

As a value analyst or a value engineer, you are advised that the costs of a clutch mechanism manufactured by your company are too high. On inquiry, however, you are told that there are no detailed costs which can be provided for you. Describe two or three different courses of action which you might take.

With the situation the same as above except that you know cost data exist, the manager tells you that cost figures are not given out because it is feared that those who are not familiar with the serious problems involved in developing cost systems might use the figures wrongly and promote wrong decisions. Again, describe two or three courses of action which you might take.

The factory you are connected with is making parts which have the following costs:

Material	$10
Labor	5
Variable overhead	8
Fixed overhead	12
Total	$35

Vendor quotations for the same parts are $38.

On the basis of the curve for organized action in make-or-buy decisions, at what percentage of factory loading should the item be changed from a "make" part to a "buy" part?

Name and describe five wrong actions which might be taken as a result of using costs procured by a person who did not understand the conditions under which they were developed and the purpose for which the particular cost system was set up.

Recognizing that the traditional system of accounting for establishing costs is based upon adding material, labor, and overhead, and further recognizing that overhead is applied as a percentage of direct labor, describe the benefits and disadvantages of the system in which one overhead rate is used for all labor throughout the factory, regardless of whether a screwdriver or a $100,000 machine is the piece of capital equipment used.

Describe and discuss the advantages and disadvantages of using differing overheads in the form of a percentage of the labor, varying the percentages according to the amount of investment in capital equipment required for the particular labor operation.

What is your interpretation of the difference in meaning in this text between the word "costs" as normally used and the term "meaningful costs" used for the purpose of making decisions on engineering and manufacturing alternatives?

Discuss the major issues which must control a make-or-buy decision.

3-3. The following list shows a number of typical work positions in the normal business. Describe two or three types of information which you would expect to secure exclusively from the work areas involved.

Patent attorney	High-temperature metallurgist
Tax accountant	Manufacturing process engineer
Purchasing agent	Sales manager
Design engineer	Underwriters' specialist
Insulation engineer	Appearance-design specialist
Machinability engineer	Value analysis specialist
Shell-molding specialist	

Describe two or three practical courses of action to take when confronted with the following answers:

From the factory superintendent, "They won't buy it unless we put that finish on it."

From the project engineer, "There is only one reliable source in the country for the item. We must buy it from that company."

From the sales manager, "We would like to increase our manufacturing schedules, but we cannot get enough steel to support the increased production."

From the designer, "We cannot use that type of construction because it is not approved by Underwriters'."

From the buyer, "We cannot cast that part because it must withstand vibration."

From the manufacturing methods man, "We have to plan the job to be done on those machines because we have the machines."

From the design engineer, "We cannot design for the use of extrusions because they are not obtainable."

Write a list of twenty-five types of questions which might come up in connection with the design and manufacture of an electric iron or similar product, and state after each one the probable best source for information on it.

Describe a human relations problem which you might be confronted with in carrying out the technique of giving credence to answers only from the best source; also, describe the way you would handle the problem.

List and describe several reasons why you believe people who are not the best source for information tend to have readily available answers which they advance authoritatively.

How would you start in locating the best source for information concerning each of the following:

Brass die castings	Underwriters' requirements
High-temperature heat transfer	Air hammers
Appearance design	Aluminum tubing
Sensitive thermocouples	

3-4. Explain briefly what the "blast, create, refine" technique means to you. Under what circumstances would you use it?

State the main purpose of the "blast" portion of the technique.

State the main purpose of the "refine" portion of the technique. How would this technique be used in dealing with a chemical process? How would it be used with relation to the paper work in a department? How would you use it on an item which had been made satisfactorily in a specific way for a considerable length of time?

3-5. Describe your interpretation of creativity. What is the basic difference between the creative approach and the analytical approach?

Using the brainstorming technique, free of any tendency to immediately analyze the appropriateness of the suggestions, write a list of twenty-five suggested ways for accomplishing each of the following:

Closing a door	Conducting electric current
Blowing up a balloon	Starting a fire
Enclosing a volume	Addressing a friend
Mixing a liquid	

Select the two most unsuitable-appearing suggestions from each of the prepared lists. First, during the analytical phase, describe why they appear so unlikely; then describe a few directions which your thinking must take if an idea based on this selection is to be made to work.

3-6. Write down your understanding of "roadblocks." What other term might be used to convey this meaning?

Name and describe several reasons why roadblocks commonly exist whenever the endeavor is to produce an important change of any sort or to develop information which might lead to a change. In each of the following cases, state some of the first actions which you might take in order to overcome these roadblocks.

There is no better material.
We cannot pay for the tools.
It doesn't make sense.
The customers like it this way.
We must maintain interchangeability.
It cannot be cast.

It is impossible to separate out the costs of that operation.

There must be a good reason for it or we would not have made it that way.

3-7. "Every man takes the limits of his own field of vision for the limits of the world."—Arthur Schopenhauer.

Identify and explain five different procedures to follow in searching for the best specialized knowledge in existence.

Make a list of fifteen different areas of importance to a designer or manufacturer in which he might benefit by extreme penetration of knowledge through locating the best possible source of that specialized knowledge.

Given a situation in which you require a paper which will not burn, describe how you would locate specialized industrial knowledge on this subject, what you would tell the source of this knowledge after you have located it, and the types of answers you would expect.

Repeat the preceding problem for a product which must provide completely quiet electric-circuit interruption.

Repeat the problem except for a system of room air purification in which no provisions are made for circulation.

Repeat the problem for a case in which you are modifying the design of a toy and you want to make sure that the modifications not only decrease the cost of the toy but improve its appeal to parents.

Discuss the extent to which you believe men should be evaluated on their abilities in each of the following two divergent operating concepts: first, their ability to understand and accept an assignment and carry it through to its completion with little if any help; second, their ability to accept and understand an assignment and identify and call upon extensive resources which will promptly produce a highly satisfactory solution.

How might a management encourage men who, by availing themselves of outside assistance, quickly provide effective solutions to problems and thereby sacrifice the usual "we did it ourselves" satisfaction?

3-8. State what you understand a tolerance to be. Why do tolerances exist?

Do tolerances contribute to the use function of the product?

Do tolerances increase costs? Do they decrease costs?

Is the cost of each tolerance determinable? Is the function accomplished by each tolerance discernible?

Explain several bad results of working with wrong tolerances. Explain several good results assignable to the use of right tolerances.

Who normally determines tolerances?

Are the costs produced by each tolerance normally provided to the tolerance setter before he makes his decision?

Assuming that the cost of a particular tolerance on an item is extremely high, identify and describe five courses of action which might be taken to accomplish the same desired result at very much lower cost.

3-9. Describe what is meant by a "vendor's available functional product." List twenty-five examples.

Name and describe five reasons why such products are often not used even though they would accomplish the function reliably and simply at a much lower cost.

If your concern emphasized the projects identified below, how would you start out to determine what vendor's available functional products existed and what they would contribute to the best and most economical solution of your problem?

Lead pencil   Electrical solenoid
House paint   ¼-horsepower electric motor
Pair of shoes

Assume that you are a designer and manufacturer of electric fry pans and that you need an adjustable timer to control the heating temperature and the heating cycle. Write a typical sheet of information which you would provide to an appropriate supplier. Also describe the steps you would take to identify suitable available functional products for your requirement.

In what types of cases would you work it out for yourself instead of searching for applicable vendors' functional products.

3-10. Describe precisely your interpretation of the difference between the technique "utilize and pay for vendor's skills and knowledge" and the previous technique "utilize vendor's available functional products."

Do the same for the difference between the technique "utilize and pay for vendor's skills and knowledge" and the technique "use industry specialists to extend specialized knowledge."

How would you submit a problem to a vendor who was found not to have a suitable functional product but who was thought to have technical knowledge which excelled in the area so that his technical people would be likely to efficiently produce the functional product needed and provide it for the job?

Name three ways of paying vendors for the use of their specialized skills and knowledge.

Name three factors which, unless correctly handled, might cause a situation in which a vendor, though he made a contribution, still did not receive pay for it.

Identify ten areas in which you, as a manufacturer, might need specialized skills and knowledge from vendors who lead in various fields. Name the first step which you would take in locating such vendors.

Identify five problems which you, as the designer of a ¼-horsepower motor, might be studying. Name the sources, or types of sources, of applicable vendor skills and knowledge.

As a designer, you are in touch with a specialized vendor and have presented your problem to him thoroughly. As a result, he has assigned engineering talent to the problem and has provided you with an effective solution which would utilize a product he can provide. Then, with his effective solution before you, observe that it would be most simple and straightforward to do the manufacturing in your own plant according to his design. Describe the pros and cons of proceeding to do so and state the action which you would take in this case.

You are confronted with the same situation, except that, after the solution has been suggested by the specialized vendor, your purchasing agent states that he understands his job responsibility to be to get several bids before placing an order and, hence, that he expects, before awarding the order, to have the new design drawn up and presented for bid to other suppliers. Explain the pros and cons of doing this and state the action which you would take if you were the manager responsible for the decision.

3-11. Describe what you understand to be a specialty process.

What is the difference between a specialty process and a standard process?

When would you use a specialty process and when would you use a standard process?

State some approaches you might take to determine whether there indeed exists an applicable specialty process to accomplish your purpose.

Describe some of the advantages which accrue from utilizing a specialty process in a vendor's plant and some of the advantages which accrue from installing suitable equipment and performing the specialty process in your own facilities.

Recognizing that a particular design and a particular process usually go hand in hand, explain how you would endeavor to locate a specialty process to economically and reliably accomplish a function when the design, at the time you made it, seemed unsuitable for any specialty processes you had knowledge of.

Name twenty-five processes which are so little known by you that they rate as specialty processes.

What effect does a specialty process usually have on quality?

How are tolerances normally determined for a specialty process?

Explain the harmony or disharmony between the technique of utilizing specialty processes and the good accepted practice of utilizing standards wherever possible.

3-12. Describe some circumstances under which the use of standards saves money.

Describe some circumstances under which the use of standards costs extra.

List some general guides which will assist in determining the extent of standardization of a particular idea, item, or part of an item.

List some safeguards which might be established to protect against blindly choosing standards which are not the most economical answers.

List some safeguards which might be established to protect against indiscriminately establishing special items, ideas, or processes when there in fact exist standard ones which constitute the best answer.

List and describe the deviations on a dozen items which are normally standard to industry but which might be secured in the form of a modified standard for a particular application.

3-13. Identify and describe five situations which often make it difficult for each of the following individuals, under the circumstances listed, to make his decision using the primary criterion, "Would I spend my money this way?"

Buyer of a missile

Designer of an airplane guidance system

Manufacturer who has excessive equipment of certain types, insufficient equipment of certain other types, and no equipment of still other types

Draftsman detailing an electric relay

Foreman supervising a hundred employees

Project engineer responsible for an item which has good customer acceptance as it is

Chapter 4

Name and describe five purposes for which the value analysis techniques are used.

What is the primary purpose of the value analysis job plan and why is it desirable to use it?

Name the techniques you are likely to use in the following cases to identify unnecessary costs.

You are now using 1 million small alnico magnets per year in a thermostat.

You need a piece of insulated wire 2 feet long for conducting current.

You require 4 million eyelets per year for an electrical device.

You require 60 relief valves per year. These valves consist of one piece of very complicated machined steel and now cost $8 each.

You require 2,000 large springs per year.

You require 100 precision faceplates per year. They now cost $40 each.

You require 1,000 latches per year. The latch holds the cover secure on a metal box containing electrical equipment.

You are required to provide a function which is now obtained by using 700 cork gaskets, about a foot square and costing $4 each, per year.

You find that new design for a gear box will result in costs of $8 each for casting and $18 each for machining.

You find that you are paying $15,000 a year for the paper work in an office routine.

You are planning to make and market a chemical compound.

Chapter 5

Describe the special knowledge required by each of the following:

Doctor   Nuclear physicist
Lawyer   Heat-transfer specialist
Tax specialist   Plastics application specialist

What is the source of the special knowledge for each of the following, i.e., how does the specialist acquire it?

Doctor   Insulation specialist
Tax specialist   High-temperature metals specialist

(The reader will recognize that in some fields the special knowledge is available in, so to speak, a neat package, while in others, although it is just as essential to successful work in the profession, the special knowledge must be gleaned from a multiplicity of sources.)

Identify twenty-five sources from which the special knowledge required to effectively accomplish value work can be secured. (In the initial contact with the topic "special knowledge required" (Chapter 5), it might appear to the reader that it is being suggested that the value specialist have at his fingertips the same depth of knowledge in castings as the casting specialist or in mechanized circuitry as the specialist in that branch, etc. On further study, however, it will be seen that this is not the case. The specialist in value must recognize each technology for what it is and must know enough about it so that he can bring appropriate technical and economic information into a problem to attain a better solution.)

In each of the following cases, state the areas of special knowledge which you, as a value consultant, would arrange to bring into a product study for the purpose of accomplishing the product's functions at a much lower cost.

Automobile radiator
Bearings on a motor
Finish on a washing machine
Glass dome on a light fixture
Amplifier in a radio
Enclosing container for a domestic fuse or circuit-breaker box

(A word of warning is required. The reader must not assume that he can go to specialists for all of the required information. That would make the periods of preliminary exploration endlessly long, costly, and unfruitful. For use in the preliminary stages, the value analyst's fund of special knowledge must contain a wide range of information, complete with approximate costs, on materials, products, processes, and functional approaches.)

Write down a number of sources that the value specialist may turn to during his process of building up necessary special knowledge funds on the types and relative costs of:

Castings
Electrical insulations
Various machining processes
Various chipless manufacturing processes
Various materials-handling processes
Various metal surface protection processes
Available functional products; such as hinges, thermostats, motors, and doors

Chapter 6

Write down some of the technical factors which delay the application and use of newer and more economical means for accomplishing desired functions.

Discuss briefly the psychological deterrents which inhibit necessary actions.

From your own experience, state three examples of decisions which you influenced strictly for the benefit of your employer. Did the decision chosen in each case risk the entailment of personal loss for you?

Describe three decisions which you have made primarily on the basis of minimizing personal loss.

Describe the environment which can be promoted by the attitudes of each of the following persons to generally minimize personal loss and promote decisions most beneficial to the employer:

Purchasing agent   Manager of drafting
Manager of manufacturing   Manager of engineering
Office manager   Maintenance foreman

Describe, or quote, the comments which you, as a manager, might appropriately make to encourage more decisions for improving value to be made more promptly under each of the following circumstances:

Your tool engineer has just purchased a $1,000 machine which is in the process of installation. Today he discovers that a different type of tool, which, though also available, was not uncovered in his search prior to the placing of the order, would produce the items with the same reliability at $5,000 per year less cost. The new tool would cost $3,000. He now proposes to stop the installation, sell the purchased tool for whatever resale value it commands, buy the new tool, and have it installed.

Your purchasing agent has worked with a casting supplier in buying $10,000 worth of patterns and molds, helping to establish inspection routines, testing and approving samples of production, etc., and has just qualified this supplier for the furnishing of $100,000 worth of malleable castings per year. He then goes to a convention where he comes into contact with another supplier who has an automatic factory for making malleable castings and who, for a cost of $15,000 for molds, patterns, and tooling, would supply the required castings for $25,000 per year.

Your design engineer has been engaged for two years in developing a thermostatic relay to accomplish a group of functions. Tests have been completed and drawings have just been signed. The manufacturing people involved have studied the operations required and have planned the equipment. The manufacturing costs come to $8. Time is running out. Competition has just put such a product on the market. Your engineer comes to you and tells you that a different and very much simpler design approach will accomplish all of the functions reliably at a cost of $5. He advises you that there is nothing in this new design which did not exist two years ago and that it was merely a matter of associating better ideas for the accomplishment of function.

Your draftsman has just completed a month's work of drawing and detailing the parts of a product you expect to manufacture. He comes to you and advises that he can now see how to use an entirely different approach employing totally different relative shapes. This would necessitate spending another month redoing all of his work but would result in an equally reliable product for half the cost.

Chapter 7

7-1. State why value consultants must be concerned with accounting practice.

Name and describe five reasons why it is difficult to accumulate and tabulate appropriate costs so that they will be meaningful for the purpose of making decisions on engineering and manufacturing value alternatives.

Describe two reasons why all fixed overhead should be included in cost comparisons made for the purpose of determining whether to make or to buy.

Describe two reasons why only part of the fixed overhead should be included in cost accumulations for the purpose of deciding whether to make or to buy.

Assuming that you are working in an organization which has an accounting system designed primarily for the purpose of appropriate profit and tax accounting, what is the first of several steps you would take in order to arrive at meaningful cost for decision making on value alternatives?

7-2. Do you personally have any feeling that the objectives of a program to decrease cost also include reducing appearance and features that yield customer appeal? Describe and explain your answer.

If you were the manufacturer of a product which had a piece of overlying chrome decoration costing $1, how would you go about determining whether you should remove it or replace it with one which might cost $2?

List ten products which are purchased primarily because their appearance or attractiveness appeals to the customer.

List ten products that are purchased primarily because their use function appeals to the customer.

If your product was losing in sales, although it was competitively priced, how would you determine whether to add appearance functions or use functions?

If you were a manufacturer whose product is both considered too high in cost and recognized competitively as being unattractive in appearance, describe some of the first steps you would take in a program to provide, at the same time, very much lower costs and very much better appearance.

7-3. What do you understand to be meant by cost-reduction work?

Describe how you believe a cost-reduction program might be organized. Describe what you understand to be the meaning of value analysis work.

Contrast briefly the two kinds of programs or work.

Appropriate cost-reduction work is important and is to be encouraged. State five different ways in which the yield of cost reduction throughout a plant may be improved by the aid of appropriate value analysis work.

7-4. Describe briefly what you believe to be the engineer's primary job.

Note down the number of technologies in which the engineer must have penetrating and controlling knowledge. Recognizing that the engineer must call in consultants who can supplement his knowledge in each of several specific areas, name ten such areas (advanced mathematics, high-temperature metallurgy, etc.) which engineers generally recognize to contain so much essential knowledge and technique that the best answers can be attained only by assistance from experts.

Discuss why the identification of unnecessary cost is becoming an area in which the engineer requires special assistance if, indeed, you believe this to be the case.

Assume that you are a value consultant in a manufacturing concern. You are invited by the engineer to study his idea for a design and to make suggestions which might help accomplish the total functions for much lower cost. Describe how you would present your suggestions to him so that he would feel helped rather than criticized.

Assume that you, as a value consultant, have been invited by the engineer to review his design and have been able to make suggestions which he in turn has tested and has put into use with a resultant saving of $25,000 each year. Describe the pros and cons, from your viewpoint, of issuing a formal report to your manager that your activities have resulted in the saving of $25,000 per year.

Consider now the pros and cons from the engineer's viewpoint of your making such a formal report to your manager, assuming that he in turn will send it on to some manager who ranks above the engineer's manager.

Describe what you believe to be the best practice for reporting savings produced by you under such circumstances.

You, as a value consultant, have been invited by the engineer to develop and provide value alternatives. You have done so. One of them, in your judgment, is extremely workable and practicable and will save a sizable sum of money. You have given your report and conclusions to the engineer, and your work on the item is finished. A few weeks pass, and you see that no action has been taken. You now feel that you should return to him and further influence him to act on your suggestion. Discuss the advantages and disadvantages of doing so.

Under the same circumstances, discuss the advantages and disadvantages of not going back to the engineer and attempting to exert pressure on him.

7-5. In a few words, state what you believe the main job of manufacturing to be.

How do you believe that value analysis, in principle, can contribute to this job?

Describe some of the problems you would expect to have to work out and how you would go about doing so in each of the following situations:

Your evaluation of an important high-volume component being made in the factory shows that it can be purchased from an outside supplier for half the cost but that this will eliminate the work being done by an important segment of the plant, a group of people, and a battery of machines.

Your study shows that instead of making the part on the type of equipment which you have in operation in the plant and for which people have training it can be more economically made, for one-fifth of the cost, on another type of machine which the factory does not have.

Your study shows that rather than buying a group of parts, which you then assemble into a product, you can, instead, buy the completely assembled product from a manufacturer with a saving of one-third of the cost. This would cause important in-plant manufacturing adjustments and would result in floor space, people, and machines being idled for a time.

Your study shows that a large-volume part now purchased from vendors can be manufactured in-plant for one-half the cost, saving $100,000 per year. But to do so, an appropriation must be obtained to buy a $100,000 machine, and more people must be hired and trained.

Your studies show that an efficient hot-dip galvanizing plant, which you have had in operation for just two years, can be replaced with a modern zinc electroplating plant, the savings on which would liquidate the cost of new facilities in another two years, rendering the galvanizing plant totally obsolete.

7-6. Describe five services which the proper use of value analysis can provide for the management of the business.

List four techniques which it would be desirable for each of the following managers to know about, understand, and occasionally utilize.

General manager or president   Finance or accounting manager
Engineering manager   Purchasing agent
Manufacturing manager

Describe two situations in which a value consultant could be of substantial assistance to each of the individuals named above.

Assume that the managers listed below are faced with the problem of excessive costs, insufficient profits, and markets limited by high costs, as well as with a relatively short time in which to take corrective action. In each case, describe some of the instructions they should give their value consultants and the results they should expect from him.

General manager   Finance or accounting manager
Engineering manager   Manager of production
Manufacturing manager   Manager of drafting

7-7. In a few words, state what you consider the primary job of the purchasing agent and his buyers to be.

In your opinion, how can value analysis techniques generally benefit his work?

7-8. Recognizing that, in applying several of the techniques, it is necessary to have extensive purchasing knowledge and to make actual visitations to plants of competent vendors, and further recognizing that the buyer is definitely responsible for the selection of vendors and for price negotiations, answer the following questions:

How will you, as a value consultant, select the vendors on whom you will call?

Who, if anyone, will you take along with you?

What types of conversations will you have with them?

What types of commitments, if any, will you make to them?

What types of proposals will you solicit from them?

What types of information will you report to the buyer immediately upon your return?

Develop a few thoughts contrasting the two opposite results which might arise from a buyer's work with vendors: (*a*) the buyer might be further weakened in his job through continuously losing more and more touch with it, and (*b*) the buyer might be continuously strengthened in his job through learning more and more information which will better qualify him in vendor selection, negotiation of prices, discussion of needed functions, etc. In your description, list some of the items which will tend to weaken the buyer if the transaction is done inappropriately and some of the items which will tend to strengthen the buyer if done right.

7-9. Describe how the use of value analysis techniques can assist the salesman in determining what the customer really wants.

Describe how the use of the techniques can assist the salesman in describing the fair and reasonable price which the customer will expect to pay.

Describe how the use of the techniques can assist the salesman in eliminating cost elements which make no contribution to the use function or the appearance which the customer wants.

Describe how the use of the techniques can assist the customer in determining which products best suit his requirements.

Describe how the customer can utilize the value analysis techniques to arrive at an estimate of a reasonable price for him to pay for a product or function which he desires.

Chapter 9

In about fifty words, describe the kind of person whom you think is most likely to become proficient at value work.

How much experience and what type of experience do you believe a person needs to qualify for effective value work?

How would you expect the grade and degree of excellence of value work to be handicapped by deficiencies in each of the following respects:

Practical experience utilizing materials, processes, and engineering and manufacturing ideas
Good imagination
High degree of initiative
Self-organization and self-drive
Ability to deal with others
Sufficient emotional maturity to avoid frustration

Describe some of the parts of essential value analysis training which can best be learned by reading or listening to presentations, by doing, and by accumulating reference knowledge.

Chapter 10

Describe what is meant by integration.

Describe what is meant by value appraisal, when it should be done, and the benefits that can be expected from it.

Describe what is meant by product evaluation, when it should be done, and the principal problems connected with it.

Describe what is meant by value consultation, when it should be done, and how it is best carried out.

Why would a new value consultant have to do a very much more complete job of integration than he would do if he were new in some other job, such as purchasing agent, design engineer, or accountant?

Name some of the concerns and fears which will exist to some extent in the minds of people in the following types of work when they find that a value analyst or value consultant is starting on the job.

Buyer	Draftsman
Design engineer	Manager of manufacturing
Manager of engineering	Manager of costs
Manufacturing methods man	

In approximately fifty words, describe the most important things which, you, as a new value consultant, will tell each of the above individuals so that they will properly understand your work and its relationship to their work.

What is normally the purpose of any appraisal? Name several types of appraisals which are customary.

Who ordinarily requests an appraisal? To whom are the results of an appraisal ordinarily provided?

What actions will appraisals normally promote?

Note the similarity in the case of value appraisals and answer each of the following questions as they pertain to a value appraisal:

Who might be embarrassed by a value appraisal?

To what extent do you believe that product evaluation can be as well accomplished from a set of drawings as from an actual example of a product in its physical form?

Name and sufficiently describe some of the advantages of conducting product evaluations from drawings or blueprints in advance of production.

Name some of the benefits of conducting a product evaluation after experience has been obtained in the field and in manufacturing.

Consider the predicament an income tax consultant would be in if he were not called in by the accountants for the preparation of the income tax form. Discuss some of the steps he might take.

Discuss the same situation for a value consultant. Describe the benefits to the program of achieving better value which you, as a value consultant, are interested in promoting by training each of the following types of people:

Draftsmen	Buyers
Manufacturing methods engineers	Management people
Design engineers	Sales engineers
Cost men	

Describe several benefits which can result when sales people acquire a reasonable understanding of value analysis techniques, of what their value consultants are trying to accomplish, and of how the value consultants are trying to accomplish it.

Do the same for engineering personnel, for manufacturing methods personnel, and for purchasing personnel.

Do you believe that the work of the value analyst, or value consultant, is and must be distinct work carried out separately in order to be done correctly? Or do you believe that it is part of the work of others?

Describe your understandings and beliefs regarding value work in relation to the following activities:

Design engineering	Manufacturing planning
Manufacturing methods	Buying
Drafting	

Chapter 11

11-1. On the premise that results are secured where emphasis is placed and where competence is assigned, describe where you would place the emphasis, and why, in each of the following examples. (Bear in mind that this question does not ask that any important activity be slighted, but rather where the important concentrations of resources will bring the greatest yield. For example, will it be in improving performance, increasing quality, identifying and removing unnecessary costs, or another activity?)

Television sets	Supersonic aircraft
100-horsepower electric motors	Electric toasters
Computers	Atomic power plants

What are some of the techniques which might be used by the manager of a small business in order to secure important results in a particular area?

By contrast, what are some of the actions of the management of a small business which may demotivate, i.e., cause employees to place less importance on a particular activity?

Describe several important actions a management may take which unmistakably show emphasis on value work.

Describe the manner in which emphasis is applied to:

A design-engineering project
Preparation of annual tax statement
Preparation of monthly report of operations to management
Shipments of equipment manufactured

Using emphasis techniques suggested by these examples, as well as by others especially appropriate to value, describe a complete system for providing high emphasis on value.

11-2. Describe measurement systems which might be used to measure the degree of success with which the following are accomplished:

Sales work
Farming
Planning, preparing, and serving meals
Driving an automobile in an auto race
Design-engineering work
Purchasing work

Describe a system which might be used to measure the degree of excellence of value work.

Discuss the pros and cons—the good and the bad points—of this measuring system.

Assuming that two separate types of work are required to secure a high degree of value, namely, (*a*) efficient identification of unnecessary cost and (*b*) effective and prompt decision making to accomplish the value alternatives, does the system you have described measure the value work per se? That is, does it measure only the identification of unnecessary cost, or can the measurement be affected, plus or minus, by the work of others in the decision area?

If you were responsible for teaching value analysis techniques to others in your area, how would you want your work to be measured?

If you were responsible for value audit work, how would you want your work to be measured?

If you were responsible for integrating value analysis work into the organization and for gaining understanding, how would you want your work to be measured?

If your job was to provide guidance and counsel as needed before designs were made and before tooling was built, how would you want your work to be measured?

Prepare a twenty-item questionnaire which would give you, as a manager, important information about the organization, operation, and effectiveness of the value analysis program. Questions should be such that they can be answered with a "yes" or "no," with the use of two or three words, or with a short phrase.

Describe how you would endeavor to measure each of the following:

Are the correct number of people engaged in value work?

To what extent has each person the appropriate competence and training?

What important areas of work are being omitted?

What important areas of work are receiving overemphasis?

PROBLEMS

In order to help the reader supplement his acquisition of value analysis knowledge a number of problems from actual practice are offered in the following "do-it-yourself" exercises.

It should be noted that these problems are all limited to individual parts or components rather than to inclusive assemblies. This is intentional because students can hardly be expected to devote as much time to problem solving as exercises on a series of complete products would require.

The fact remains that there are no limitations on the complexity or size of projects that can be successfully improved by the value analysis approach. In reality, all problems demand analysis of components in themselves.

Procedure for Using the Problems

1. Make your plan for the problem.
2. Follow through each of the phases of the job plan.
3. Fill in some typical information which you have learned, or have developed, in each phase of the plan.
4. Fill in some typical information which you might learn, or have developed, by using each of the techniques.
5. Arrive at one or two suggested value alternatives which you believe may be quite good.
6. Prepare an appropriate suggestion sheet.

Special brass nut. Double thread, ½ inch square; made on automatic screw machine; 1 million per year; 3 cents each. Nut receives hand adjustment screw on electric blanket thermostat.

Fɪɢ. A-1

Steel control shaft. ¼ inch in diameter, 1¼ inches long; made on automatic screw machine; 1 million per year; 6 cents each. One end screws into brass nut above, other end mounts plastic knob. Center groove provides adjustment for the thermostat.

Fɪɢ. A-2

Appliance bottom cover. 7 inches deep, 6 inches in diameter; aluminum die casting; 75,000 per year; $1 each. Dust and protective cover.

Fɪɢ. A-3

Steel shipping plate (square washer). 4 inches square, ¼ inch thick; ⅝-inch center hole; made by shearing and punching; 15,000 per year; 32 cents each.

Hydraulic cylinder cap. Made from ⅜-inch-thick steel; 3 inches square; 1-inch blind hole drilled ¼ inch deep in center and four small mounting holes drilled in corners; 2,000 per year; 53 cents each. Used inside machine.

Fɪɢ. A-4

Brass motor brush holder casting. Sand-cast and machined; 1,500 per year; casting cost, $1; machining cost, $20. Size about 2 by 2 by 4 inches.

Fɪɢ. A-5

Steel controller shaft. Made from ½-inch-square steel, 10 inches long; ends turned ¼ inch in diameter; 2,000 per year; $1 each. This shaft operates at 1 rpm in electrical control equipment; small plastic cams are mounted along its length. Used in cabinet of electronic control.

Fig. A-6

Brass terminal. 1 inch long; machined from ³⁄₁₆-inch brass rod on automatic screw machine; becomes insert in plastic base; 50,000 per year; 6 cents each. Function is to make electrical connection.

Fig. A-7

Bearing plate. 1-inch-square steel; milled and drilled; 25,000 per year; 50 cents each.

Fig. A-8

Steel connection pin. ¹⁄₁₆-inch steel; 3-inch-long fastening groove machined at one end, point machined at other; made on screw machine; 10,000 per year; 11 cents each.

Fig. A-9

Steel spacer. Machined from bar stock 3 inches in diameter, 1½ inches long; 10,000 per year; 85 cents each. Used in heavy equipment assembly.

Fig. A-10

Brass toggle. 6 inches long; 25,000 per year; sand-casting, 60 cents; machining, 60 cents. Used in electronic control cabinet.

FIG. A-11

Porcelain cap. 3-inch inside diameter, 2-inch inside height; 150,000 per year; 40 cents each. For weather protection, outdoor switch gear.

FIG. A-12

Stud pin. Galvanized-steel screw with stainless-steel insert pin; over-all length, 3 inches; 50,000 per year; 25 cents each. For outdoor use on electrical equipment.

FIG. A-13

Flange. Made from steel bar by machining and turning flange, drilling and tapping two mounting holes; 1,500 per year; $1 each. Function is to hold a Calrod heater loosely through a 2-inch diameter hole in the side of an electric furnace.

FIG. A-14

Heavy lifting bail for industrial machine. Cast and machined; 30 per year; $50 each. Two were bolted to heavy machines for lifting during manufacture and installation.

FIG. A-15

End frame. Angle 1 foot long of 3/16-inch-thick material; 1 × 2-inch angle; holes made in it as shown; 4,000 per year; 30 cents each. Used as supporting structure for electrical equipment.

FIG. A-16

Cover fastener. Steel, 4-inch shank mounted in steel U strap; 4,000 per year; 45 cents each. Function is to secure cover on industrial equipment.

Fig. A-17

Plastic nut. Machined from ½-inch-thick plastic sheet; 1½-inches square; ½-inch hole drilled and tapped; 25,000 per year; 13 cents each. Used in electrical equipment.

Fig. A-18

Cork gasket. ⅟₁₆-inch-thick cork gasket material; 1-foot square; 700 per year; gasket material cost, 15 cents per square foot; total cost, $4 each.

Insert for coil-making machine. Machined from steel block about 3 inches long by 2½ inches wide by 2 inches deep; 500 per year; $80 each.

Fig. A-19

Adjustment screw. ¼ inch in diameter; made from brass bar by automatic screw machine; 200,000 per year; 1 cent each. Used in electronic control equipment.

Fig. A-20

Plastic cam block. 5 × 2 × 1 inch thick; machined from plastic block; 7,000 per year; $1.15 each. Used inside electrical-equipment cabinet.

Fig. A-21

Appliance gear assembly. Steel shaft 2 inches long with worm thread cut on one end; assembled into nylon gear; shaft, ¼ inch in diameter; gear, ¾ inch in diameter; 250,000 per year; 80 cents each. Used inside appliance gear case.

Fig. A-22

Steel washer. 1⅞ inches in diameter by ⅛ inch thick; ½-inch hole; made by screw machine from steel bar; 15,000 per year; 24 cents each. Used in electrical equipment.

Tapped resistor assembly. Made in factory assembly department; 300 per year; $7.50 each. Used in electrical instrument.

Fig. A-23

Thermocouple pin. 1 inch long; platinum plated; 80,000 per year; 50 cents each. Provides contact means for connecting and disconnecting thermostat.

Fig. A-24

Plastic coil form. About 1 inch square by ½ inch long; molded, then finish-machined; 15,000 per year; 40 cents each. Mounts coil in electronic control equipment.

Fig. A-25

Handle for electronic equipment. 4 inches between centers; handle extends 2 inches; made of $\frac{5}{16}$-inch stainless rod; stainless end fittings machined from $\frac{3}{4}$-inch stainless rod; 2,000 per year; $8 each. Used on front of panel to facilitate removal and interchange of electronic equipment.

Fig. A-26

Stainless-steel fastening screw. 1¼ inches long; made from ½-inch diameter stainless steel on automatic screw machine; contains shoulder and undercut section; 40,000 per year; 90 cents each. Used on panels of electronic equipment.

Fig. A-27

Steel pulley. Machined from 6-inch steel rod; 150 per year; $30 each. Used on machines in factory.

Fig. A-28

Aircraft electronics socket connector. Brass, ¾ inch long, $\frac{3}{16}$ inch in diameter; purchased part; 400,000 per year; $1.40 each.

Bronze arcing horn. 15 inches long by 2 inches wide; fabricated from formed sheet brass by brazing; other dimensions approximately as illustrated; 3,000 per year; $6.50 each. Function is to cool an arc so it will extinguish.

Fig. A-29

Plastic insulating washer. Machined from flat material; 2½ inches in diameter, ½ inch thick; hole drilled and countersunk; 6,000 per year; $1.23 each. Used inside enclosed-case electronic equipment.

Brass heater plug. Machined from hex bar 1½ inches across flats; approximately ½ inch thick; 10,000 per year; 80 cents each. Mounts Calrod heaters into furnace equipment.

FIG. A-30

Welded stud assembly. ⅛-inch steel welded assembly which includes eight washers and four nuts; 3,000 per year; $2 each. Holds cover in place on electronic equipment. 8 inches long with 2-inch studs.

FIG. A-31

Handle. Made from ¼-inch aluminum; 4-inch centers; threaded aluminum collars at each end form method of mounting; 4,000 per year; $1.40 each. Used for convenient handling of electronic equipment when it is out of master panel.

FIG. A-32

Switch blade. Made by sand-casting and milling the body, then brazing strip of brass ⅜ × ³⁄₃₂ inch thick and 4 inches long into body; over-all length, 7 inches; 600 per year; $3 each. Mounted in enclosed electric switch gear.

FIG. A-33

Flat steel cover. 15 inches in diameter, approximately round; ⅛ inch thick with five holes in one section; 200 per year; $5 each. Cover for switch on heavy electronic equipment in factory.

Toggle link. 1½ inches long; other dimensions in proportion; made as steel forging with later machining; 25,000 per year; 50 cents each. Used in electronic equipment mounted in cabinet.

FIG. A-34

Brass terminal clamp. Made by fabrication from brass extrusion; approximately ½ inch long, ¼ inch wide, ¼ inch high; is mechanical part that does not conduct current; 400,000 per year; 7 cents each. Used inside electrical control box.

FIG. A-35

Flange. 10-inch outside diameter, ¾ inch thick; made by burning, welding, and machining steel plate; 2,000 pieces per year; $12 each. Mounted on outside of electronic equipment which is later painted and used outdoors.

FIG. A-36

Control gear. Turned, machined, and hobbed from bar steel; approximately 4 inches in diameter, ¼ inch thick; hub ½ inch thick; 600 per year; $8 each. Slow-speed gear used in adjustment of electrical equipment; mounted inside enclosure.

FIG. A-37

Large hollow shaft. 18-inch outside diameter, 3-inch wall; 7 feet long; shaft ready for finish machining; 3 per year; $4,000 each. Used as shaft for rotating heavy machine in factory.

Fan. 15 inches in diameter; cast and machined from malleable iron; punched steel ring riveted to one side of blades; blade about 2 inches thick, hub about 3 inches thick; 1,600 per year; $17 each. Used for cooling air inside large electric motor.

FIG. A-38

Fan-blade assembly. Approximately 1 × 2-foot composite of three pieces of metal and one of plastic; 3,000 per year; $7 each. Function is to clamp on large revolving ring in electric generator and deflect air.

FIG. A-39

Screen for large electric motor. Made by cutting suitable metal frame approximately 7 inches on each of the radii, welding expanded metal over opening, and riveting in easy-opener lock; $\frac{1}{16}$-inch-thick steel; 4,500 per year; $6 each. Four screens fill end of 18-inch diameter motor opening.

FIG. A-40

Counterweight balance. Steel; cut from ring of $\frac{1}{8}$-inch steel, 1 inch across; each segment mounts on two studs; pieces approximately 3 inches long. 5,000 per year; 40 cents each. Mounts on large ring for counterbalance purposes.

FIG. A-41

Strain bolt assembly. 1 foot long; consists of machined iron casting threaded with suitable bushings and nuts; made of steel; 5,000 per year; $3.50 each. Used out of doors to support wires and cables.

FIG. A-42

Small crankshaft for air compressor. 7 inches long for two connecting rods; forged and machined; 9,000 per year; $5 each.

FIG. A-43

Spacer separating bearings of appliance. Steel spacer 2 inches long; diameters 1 inch outside, $\frac{3}{4}$ inch inside; steel tubing purchased, cut to length, and burred; 100,000 per year; 30 cents each. Function is to space two tapered roller bearings the appropriate distance apart.

FIG. A-44

Brass switch toggle. $1\frac{1}{4}$ inches long; made by screw machine from $\frac{3}{8}$-inch brass rod; 1 million per year; 9 cents each. For operating switch lever of lamp used in home.

FIG. A-45

BIBLIOGRAPHY

Value Analysis and Value Engineering

Miles, L. D.: "How to Cut Costs with Value Analysis," *American Machinist,*
     July, 1949.
Miles, L. D.: "Value Analysis," *Purchasing Magazine,* June, 1950.
"Value Analysis: Dollar Sign Engineering," *General Electric Review,* March,
     July, 1952.
Miles, L. D.: *Value Analysis: A Plant Wide Creative Cost Reduction Program
     under Purchasing Leadership,* Fifth Annual Industrial Engineering Insti-
     tute, University of California, 1952.
Miles, L. D.: "Value Analysis in Purchasing," *Pacific Purchaser,* October, 1954.
Miller, S.: "How to Get the Most from Value Analysis," *Harvard Business Re-
     view,* January–February, 1955.
Rawicz-Szczerbo, J.: *Value Analysis: A Specialist Approach to Cost-reduction
     in Industry,* University of Birmingham, England, 1955.
Waters, J. M.: "Value Engineering Means Required Function at Minimum
     Cost," *Bureau of Ships Journal,* April, 1955, pp. 9–11.
Purchasing Magazine, June, 1955 (value analysis issue).
"Value Analysis—Management Series," *Steel,* Sept. 19, 1955.
Value Engineering Seminar, U.S. Navy Bureau of Ships, Value Engineering
     Staff, January, 1956.
Reigart, J. M., and A. Sikorsky: "Quality Control and Value Engineering,"
     Quality Control Symposium Proceedings, Drexel Institute, Philadelphia,
     1956.
Fountain, R. E.: *The Importance of Value Analysis,* American Management
     Association, New York, 1956.
Mandelkorn, R. S.: "Value Engineering," *Proceedings of Society of Naval
     Architects & Marine Engineers Symposium, Chesapeake Section,* Wash-
     ington, Mar. 15, 1956.
Feichtinger, W. R.: "MIL-V-21237 (NORD) Value Engineering of Naval
     Ordnance Equipment," *Index of Specifications and Standards,* U.S. De-
     partment of the Navy, 1957.
Purchasing Magazine, May, 1957 (value analysis issue).
"Value Engineering Saves Navy $8 Million," *Electronic Week,* Dec. 2, 1957.
Aljian, George W. (ed): *Purchasing Handbook,* McGraw-Hill Book Company,
     Inc., New York, 1958, sec. 11.
Johnson, Richard C.: "Value Engineering in the Bureau of Ships," *Journal of
     the American Society of Naval Engineers,* February, 1958, pp. 77–85.
Purchasing Magazine, May 12, 1958 (value analysis issue).
Sikorsky, Albert: "Value Engineering," Armed Forces Communications Elec-
     tronics Association, Twelfth Annual Convention, Chicago, June 4–6, 1958.
"You Can Slash Costs by 25% with Value Analysis" (interview with L. D.
     Miles), *Management Methods,* June, 1958.
"Value Engineering—A Boon," *Electronic Design,* June 25, 1958, p. 15.

Fowlkes, Jack K.: "The Vendor's Role in Value Analysis," *The Midwest Purchasing Agent,* August, 1958.

Lowers, H. R.: "Criteria for Determining Application of Value Analysis," *Report of First Army Ordnance-Wide Value Analysis Seminar,* Watervliet, New York, Sept. 15–26, 1958, p. 359. *Value Engineering,* U.S. Department of Commerce, Value Engineering Maritime Administration, September, 1958.

"Incentive Problem in Value Engineering," *Ad Hoc Committee Report,* Conference of Oct. 8–10, 1958, Underwater Ordnance Division, American Ordnance Association.

Huizinga, Arys H.: "Value Engineering in Maritime Administration," *Symposium on Value Engineering,* annual meeting of the Society of Naval Architects & Marine Engineers, New York, Nov. 13–14, 1958.

Miles, L. D.: "Value Analysis—Value Engineering," *Symposium on Value Engineering,* annual meeting of the Society of Naval Architects & Marine Engineers, New York, Nov. 13–14, 1958.

Reigart, J. M., and M. D. Roderick: "Putting Value Engineering to Work," *Symposium on Value Engineering,* annual meeting of the Society of Naval Architects & Marine Engineers, New York, Nov. 13–14, 1958.

Sikorsky, A., and John B. Singel: "Value Engineering of Military Equipment," *Electronic Design,* Nov. 12, 1958, p. 140.

Sherwin, Fred S.: "Value Analysis Works Two Ways," *New England Purchaser,* December, 1958.

Lowers, H. R.: "Ordnance Value Analysis," *Ordnance,* May–June, 1959, p. 1013.

Johnson, Tom: "The Impact of Value Analysis," *American Machinist,* July 13, 1959.

Value Engineering, 1959 EIA Conference on Value Engineering, University of Pennsylvania, Oct. 6–7, 1959.

Value Engineering, vol. II (R. S. Mandelkorn, ed.), Proceedings of the Second EIA Conference on Value Engineering, Anaheim, Calif., Oct. 5–6, 1960.

Creativity

Kettering, Charles F.: "How Can We Develop Inventors," *American Society of Mechanical Engineers Reprint* PRD-35, 1943.

Easton, William H.: "Creative Thinking and How to Develop It," *Mechanical Engineering,* August, 1946.

Osborn, Alex: *Your Creative Power,* Charles Scribner's Sons, New York, 1951.

Cross, Hardy: *Engineers and Ivory Towers,* edited by Robert C. Goodpasture, McGraw-Hill Book Company, Inc., New York, 1952.

Black, Max: *Critical Thinking,* Prentice-Hall, Inc., Englewood Cliffs, N.J., 1952.

Osborn, Alex: *Applied Imagination,* Charles Scribner's Sons, New York, 1953.

Crawford, Robert P.: *The Techniques of Creative Thinking,* Hawthorn Books, Inc., New York, 1954.

Hodnett, Edward: *The Art of Problem Solving,* Harper & Brothers, New York, 1955.

Fuller, Edmund: *Tinkers and Genius*, Hastings House, Publishers, Inc., New York, 1955.

Ghiselin, Brewster: *The Creative Process*, Mentor Books, New York, 1955.

Von Fange, Eugene: *Professional Creativity*, Prentice-Hall, Inc., Englewood Cliffs, N.J., 1959.

RECOMMENDED ALLIED READING

On Value Definitions

Walsh, Correa Maylan: *The Four Kinds of Economic Value*, Harvard University Press, Cambridge, Mass., 1926.

On Brainstorming

"New Ways to Find New Ideas," *Time*, Feb. 18, 1957.

Clark, Charles: *Brainstorming*, Doubleday & Company, Inc., New York, 1958.

On Giving Credence to Information from the Best Source

Larrabee, Harold A.: *Reliable Knowledge*, Houghton Mifflin Company, Boston, 1945.

On Buy or Make

Oxenfeldt, Alfred R., and Myron W. Watkins: *Make or Buy*, McGraw-Hill Consultant Reports, McGraw-Hill Book Company, Inc., New York, 1956.

On Tolerance

Johnson, R. C.: "The Cost of Finishes and Tolerances," *Journal of the American Society of Naval Engineers*, November, 1958.

On Purchasing Practice and Vendor Relations

Aljian, George W.: *Purchasing Handbook*, McGraw-Hill Book Company, Inc., New York, 1958, secs. 3–11.

On Human Relations

Dubin, Robert: *Human Relations in Administration*, Prentice-Hall, Inc., Englewood Cliffs, N.J., 1951.

On Meaningful Costs

Beckett, John H.: "A Study of the Principles of Allocating Cost," *Accounting Review*, July, 1951.

Lewis, Ronello B.: "The Role of Accounting in Decision Making," *Accounting Review,* January, 1956.

Morse, Morton F., and Wilbur C. Haseman: "Direct Costing and Decision Making," *Accounting Review,* April, 1957.

On Work Simplification

Barnes, Ralph M.: *Motion Study and Time Study,* John Wiley & Sons, Inc., New York, 1949.

Healy, W. L., and A. H. Rau: *Simplified Drafting,* John Wiley & Sons, Inc., New York, 1953.

Lehrer, Robert N.: *Work Simplification: Creative Thinking about Work Problems,* Prentice-Hall, Inc., Englewood Cliffs, N.J., 1957.

Goodwin, Herbert F.: "Work Simplification: An Effective Program of Improvement," *Advanced Management,* vol. 22, no. 1, January, 1957.

On Change

Moore, Leo B.: "Too Much Management, Too Little Change," *Harvard Business Review,* January-February, 1956.

Moore, Leo B.: "How to Manage Improvement," *Harvard Business Review,* July–August, 1958.

CREEP[1]

Robert L. Dixon, Ph.D., CPA
PROFESSOR OF ACCOUNTING
UNIVERSITY OF MICHIGAN

Creep occurs when a business moves, slowly or speedily, into areas not fully explored. When this happens, a lot of problems arise. Do you want the enterprise to creep away from its original purpose or size? Have you set up your organization, control facilities, records, to enable you to deal with the spontaneous new creature your company can come to be? Creep is almost always found in successful companies, though it is sometimes the cause of failure. The accountant is the best, often the only, person able to detect creep; he may be the person to deal with the problems created.

A business enterprise, typically, is established for a limited purpose, such as the production of a single product or product group, the production of services, or the marketing of certain products. Usually this newly-established enterprise is simple in form, with specialized objectives. The profit motive leads to its creation, and it is expected that profit will be realized through pursuit of this specialized activity.

The case histories of some of the larger corporations, on the other hand,

[1] *The Journal of Accountancy,* July, 1953.

would undoubtedly show that a considerable proliferation of activities accompanies the aging process.

The addition of new activities to the one of initial specialization appears in various ways. Commonly it will appear in the form of integration through taking on the production of component parts formerly delegated to outsiders, or through extending back to the production of raw materials for use in the plant. The sales organization may be expanded to include wholesaling activities and may even be extended forward to include ownership and operation of retail outlets. This process may at the same time be accompanied by a horizontal expansion of activities in which an array of new products is added to the original specialty. In fact, the expansion, diversification, and proliferation may reach the stage where the original objective, through the multiplication of side activities, has become an obscure element in the total activity of the corporation.

Going along with this expansion process one is likely to find another, less spectacular but none the less significant, factor leading to the variegation of enterprise activity. This is the piecemeal attachment of relatively minor activities of service and supply. Examples of this are the establishment of a department for the production of tools; a department for the maintenance of machinery and electrical equipment; a department to service company-owned trucks and automobiles; an engineering department; a legal department; a carpentry and upholstering shop; a printing shop, and so on.

In many instances these accouterments are not added full grown as the result of a formal analysis and decision, but rather they edge into the picture, starting with the incidental, part-time activity of one or more employees, but ending up later as full-fledged departments of the plant.

In other instances these added activities are undertaken because *they seem to offer cost-saving opportunities*. The reasoning is somewhat as follows: because we have an established plant and organization an important portion of our costs is pretty well fixed; these costs will go on at approximately the same level whether our plant is fully or only partially used; it follows then that we can add odd jobs here and there, call them sideline or self-service activities, *without causing increases in these fixed costs*. In fact, in order to determine whether we should provide our own services and supplies in a particular case, we need consider only the *variable* costs of our existing organization, the variable costs of the added activity and, in cases where new equipment and new permanent personnel are required, certain added fixed costs. But the bulk of the fixed costs can be ignored since they will not be affected by the attachment of the additional operation. In many cases when the addition of a new activity is being considered, the management may go as far as to exclude overhead costs altogether in the computation of the costs to be added. They reason that addition of new activity should not relieve the old activities of any overhead costs.

Under the circumstances of this kind of cost calculation few vendor bids may hope to be successful, since by the self-service activity not only are the middlemen's profits and the distribution costs eliminated, but also the outside producer's profits, and even, in a sense, the producer's fixed costs. In fact, the situation practically offers a bonanza for the manufacturer. The added activities appear to be real bargains.

We are all aware of the advertising slogan, "Direct from the factory to you," but here we are able to go one step farther, in effect bringing the factory right into the home.

In some cases the opportunity for cost saving is so obvious that the self-service activity is allowed to develop, or is taken over in toto, without any preliminary, formal cost studies.

But in other cases the margin of saving may not be so obvious, and the cost accountant may prepare detailed cost studies. In these, if he follows the more orthodox theory, his report will be based on the estimated *incremental* costs, rather than the total costs, of the added activity.

Creep Factors

It was noted above that minor side activities tend in some cases to edge into the operations of a business firm where no special thought has been given to their short-run or long-run effects upon costs and efficiency; it is also true, however, that such activities are frequently added by positive action on the basis of cost studies.

Attention is directed to the proposed exclusion of fixed costs in the decision-making process. Certain observations with respect to this exclusion appear to be in order.

First, if the company is in a position to make permanent additions to its side activities without adding to its fixed costs, something must be out of order. Fixed costs reflect *capacity* to operate, and they appear throughout the entire business organization. Evidently if the fixed costs can be ignored in such a calculation, the company is overequipped and overstaffed for its regular work.

Second, although it is probably impossible to have a condition of absolute balance of staff and equipment throughout the organization, the situation would be rare in which the added activity can be imposed upon the below-capacity segments of the company without in any way impinging on the fully active segments.

Third, equipment to some extent, and human beings to a considerable extent, are capable of being pressed beyond capacity limits for periods of time, but beyond these time limits something must be done to relieve them.

Finally, if idle capacity does temporarily exist throughout the company, the addition of *extracurricular* activities may so pre-empt that available time that it will be difficult to re-establish full-time regular operations when business conditions come back to normal.

All of this means that the fixed costs simply cannot be ignored in making the produce-or-purchase decision, unless one is to be satisfied with a very short-sighted analysis. Fixed costs commensurate with the added activity will inevitably "creep" into the total cost picture, because even though there may be no *immediate* addition to the fixed costs, the added activity will encroach upon the available capacity, and sooner or later this will lead to an actual, though unanticipated and perhaps unrecognized, increase in fixed costs.

The creep effect upon fixed costs can develop in three general ways.

First, if the added activity is allowed to get out of hand in its growth it is obvious that more building space, more equipment, and more salaried personnel must eventually be added. This will be true even though the regular activity of the enterprise is maintained at a fairly fixed level. The question then is, would we have added this activity had we anticipated the fixed cost addition?

Second, even if the added activity is kept at a moderate level, when the main activity is increased fixed-cost increases will again be encountered. Thus, suppose a dozen men and some equipment are added in order that the company can repair its own transportation equipment. This may lead to no immediate addition of employees in the personnel department, the accounting department, or in the other administrative segments of the company; however, the later addition of one person to regular activities can bring into operation a chain of reactions in the form of salaried employee increases, salary increases, and fixed asset additions. The probabilities are that no one will recognize that the factor which really caused the fixed cost increases was the apparently bargain-price addition of the repair operations sometime earlier.

Finally, if the added activity is either kept level, or increased, it will be all the more difficult to cut down on fixed costs should subsequent reductions in the regular operations be necessary.

Side Effects of Creep

The principal aim in the section just concluded was to point out that the exclusion of fixed costs in the contemplation of a produce-versus-purchase decision constitutes a dangerously shortsighted treatment of the problem; that a full quota of fixed costs will almost inevitably creep into the picture regardless of the subsequent activity trends of the regular and added operations.

What might be called a side effect of creep, although it is actually a direct evidence of creep, is a tendency for the company to compensate unconsciously for overloads resulting from piecemeal additions of "bargain" activities. If, for example, an officer is hired to perform an administrative task under a particular set of conditions, and if then one by one a number of minor, peripheral activities are taken on by the company, the accumulation of these activities may more and more infringe upon the officer's time until through sheer necessity he is forced drastically to neglect his primary responsibilities.

Although no poll of managements has been taken on this point, it is suspected that they are not immune from creep, and one may well wonder if business efficiency and competitive vigor is not often impaired through the accumulation of these barnacles which appear to be bargain activities; in other words, activities which *apparently* do not add to the fixed costs.

Arguments Against Bargain Activities

At this point it may be well, again, to make clear just what sort of activity is being examined. This article does not pretend to weigh the wisdom of a decision to produce rather than purchase where the decision rests primarily (1) upon a question of public relations, or (2) on the basis of guaranteeing adequate supply when needed, or (3) on safeguarding quality, or (4) even decisions to produce rather than purchase during periods of depressed business conditions where the aim is to keep the working-force intact and to minimize idle capacity losses. Also it is recognized that new lines of production may properly be undertaken, and old ones dropped, in order to keep pace with changing market conditions. Rather, this is an appraisal of the wisdom of adding an activity, formerly provided by an outsider, on the basis of cost studies which appear to justify the added activity on the ground that fixed costs can be ignored.

The theme of this article is that a major danger in the addition of bargain activities is the creep danger. And this danger is likely to be overlooked in the case of any added activity, whether or not cost saving is the prime motive. In fact it is all the more likely to be overlooked where factors other than cost savings guide the decision.

Another type of danger lies in the fact that the company is not a specialist in the added activity, and that after it has become tied to it, with added personnel and equipment, the discontinued vendor may through research develop cost and sales price reductions which make the decision to produce completely untenable when looked upon with hindsight. Then it may be too late. Reversion to the purchase status is then blocked by prospective sacrifices in the disposal of equipment and the need for discharging personnel.

Public relations may constitute an argument on each side of the question. For instance, an entirely unsupportable contention may be made, particularly in the smaller community, that the local manufacturer should make himself as nearly autonomous as possible, since this means that he will thereby provide more jobs for local labor. Needless to say this is pure bunk. It is a form of disguised charity without the slightest scientific justification.

From the opposite point of view, it is evident that the maintenance of good public relations may actually dictate the avoidance of certain productive activities simply because the good will of the community compels the patronizing of small business firm suppliers.

From the economist's point of view, and unfortunately this argument is not likely to be very compelling with individual businessmen, it may be argued quite conclusively that a decision to produce, when based on a partial cost compilation (that is, with fixed costs excluded), is contrary to the public economic interest. In short, it constitutes mismanagement of economic resources. Just realize that the vendor's price, against which is being matched only a partial summation of costs, is high enough for him to cover not only his variable costs, but also fixed costs, and a profit margin on top of it all. If the vendor's offer, under this assumption, comes within gunshot of meeting the purchaser's variable cost computation, we are doing serious injury to our economic system if we make a decision to produce rather than buy from that vendor.

Another observation is this: activities are usually annexed, with cost saving as the reason, only when they are more or less intimately related to the primary functions of the company. Actually, however, it might be more reasonable, from the standpoint of impact on total profits, to take on completely extraneous operations—again with the assumption that the fixed-cost factor need not be a matter of concern. Thus, the automobile company might just as reasonably open a public restaurant, a dance hall, or a bowling alley, confident that the present executives can soak up such minor administrative burdens as would be involved, and that thereby they have an edge over existing recreational establishments which require a full complement of personnel.

Creep Avoidance

As has been mentioned earlier, some activities are added with clear recognition that no cost saving is attainable, simply because certain non-cost factors are of pressing importance. Others, the ones under consideration here, are annexed because, with fixed costs ignored, bargain rates appear to be achieved. Both kinds cause fixed cost pressures, and lead to unanticipated cost increases —although they may not be recognized in some cases until years later. The important question is then, having brought the nature of creep into the open, what can be done to avoid it?

Among a number of defensive measures undoubtedly existing, four will be suggested here.

First, in the company's organization chart make notations of the number of individuals in each department or other subdivision of the company. From these notations calculate a series of ratios which may be called responsibility indexes. Thus, calculate the ratio of productive and nonproductive employees to foremen in each of the productive and service departments of the plant; then, the ratio of foremen to plant manager or other personnel at the level above foremen. Similarly compute such ratios of responsibility through to top management, in each case using as the numerator of the ratio the number of persons who *report,* or for whom the person reported to is responsible.

Since the number of reporting persons will fluctuate, particularly at the lower levels of the organization, as productive activity fluctuates some judgment must be exercised in establishing certain of the ratios. Whether to use average ratios or ratios to reflect capacity might be debated; however, for present purposes it would seem that the ratios should be computed on a capacity basis. If, for example, the planned description of a given supervisory job is that it shall involve responsibility for receiving and analyzing reports from five persons, or responsibility for supervising the productive activities of twenty-five persons, any contemplation of additional activities should include recognition of probable immediate as well as long-run effects on the responsibility ratios. So far as possible this change should be taken into consideration in arriving at a decision.

A second safeguard in the insurance against creep consists of the exercise of caution that the comparative statement of costs is complete and correct. The costs of purchased supplies, services, etc., are likely to be compiled fairly completely, including an allowance for freight, handling, purchasing, and other incidents of the purchase. Certainly there is no justificaion for excluding, or overlooking, similar costs which will be incurred if the decision goes in favor of production rather than purchase. Interest on the additional investment should not be overlooked. If the question is one of production of component parts, the acquisition of raw materials is likely to cause a set of costs similar to those incurred in the purchasing of finished parts. A real risk is the likelihood of underestimating even the immediate costs of production.

A third factor to be considered in determining the advisability of adding a new activity is the relative merit of that particular activity as compared with alternatives. It would obviously be illogical to devote available equipment and energies to an operation which would provide a cost saving of a few hundred dollars when the same facilities, otherwise used, could accomplish savings of thousands. Even more foolish would be the addition of an activity of the minor cost-saving variety which might interfere with, or preclude, the later expansion of the company's main operations at a profit in excess of the expected cost-saving. Mistaken decisions of this sort constitute a principal creep danger, leading to a condition of overcrowded facilities and neglected responsibilities.

Creep, as has been emphasized, is not a short-run problem. It consists of the more or less gradual, unrecognized, cluttering up of business activity, accompanied by a parallel deterioration of company efficiency, a building up of fixed costs, and the undermining of profit potential. A fourth factor in the protection against creep is that of flexibility. New activities which are clearly temporary, which can be added and discarded on short notice without significant disruption, are much less likely to cause future trouble than are those which are less flexible. It is pretty well agreed that it is more difficult to dislodge an activity than it is to add one. For the classic object lesson on this point, consider the bureau of our federal and state governments. But, if an addition is to be made, at least as between two alternative activities which are otherwise equally attractive, the one which can later be abandoned the more easily is certainly the one to be chosen. It is therefore suggested that, among other things, serious consideration be given to the degree of permanence of any new plant, equipment, and, especially, personnel, which may be required in undertaking an added activity.

If careful analysis indicates that the proposed activity meets the test of flexibility—that is, if it can be dropped on short notice without serious sacrifice of personnel or of investment in inventories and fixed assets—and if the contemplated addition is purely and unquestionably for a short-run period, then a "partial costs" schedule is appropriate. In other words, under these circumstances it *is proper* to prepare a schedule which is limited to the incremental costs, *the costs which would be added,* and to ignore prorations of existing fixed overhead items. Because of the importance of situations of this class, the point will be considered further under the next section heading.

If, on the other hand, it is contemplated that the new activity may be more or less permanently attached, as where the company will take on its own full-scale printing operations, its own engineering, or toolmaking, or component parts supply, a partial costs schedule is entirely inappropriate. In fact, this point is the crux of the whole situation. For purposes of making the decision to add an activity which may be fairly permanent, the schedule of estimated costs of production should include not only an exhaustive list of the probable added costs, but also a complete assignment of all of the overhead charges, even including administrative overhead, which through regular cost accounting techniques are properly prorated against any regular segment of the enterprise.

Add Allowance for Profit

But this is not all. In addition to the full charge for prorated and added costs, an allowance should be added for profit. That is, in order to justify the addition of a permanent new activity on the grounds of cost savings, the best available supplier's price must be shown not only to exceed the estimated full cost of production, with no apportionable costs omitted, but it should be higher *by an amount at least equal to the rate of profit which the company is able to make through its principal operations.*

The reasons for this fairly extreme view have been expressed earlier in this article, and it should be repeated that the requirement that full costs plus profit be included is, in fact, no more than a minimum protection against creep. Clearly the relationship between today's costs and today's purchase prices may be only a temporary one, and it is altogether too probable that the nonspecialist producer will lag behind the specialist supplier whom he has discarded in the hope of achieving production economies. Thus, the decision can easily turn sour in spite of all of the measures which have been suggested by way of protection.

Justifiable Bargain Activities

It was stated above that where the added activity is clearly intended to be temporary it is proper to base the decision on a partial list of costs. The point here is that the nonpermanence of the activity tends to insure against the creeping up of fixed costs and managerial overloads. However, resolutions are too often forgotten, and unless positive plans are made in advance for the early abandonment of the activity, it will turn out to be a "sticky," if not permanent, activity, and the fixed costs will flow in to fill up the gaps in the cost analysis.

One form of added activity which, for example, may well be justifiable is that which can be started and stopped repeatedly to serve as fill-in work during periods of temporary lull in the principal activity of the company. Such fill-in work may even extend as long as the depression period of a business cycle, provided it can be stopped conveniently at the time of resumption of normal operations. Under such circumstances the presumption is that the regular working-force should be maintained and, from the cost point of view, the recovery of any portion of costs in excess of variable costs is preferable to their nonrecovery.

One may also justify the addition of activities on a partial cost, or bargain basis, when it is evident that substantial cost reductions will be achieved after a period of experience. In fact, costs during the initial period may be so unrepresentative of the future that they may in effect be disregarded.

Also, where a company is chronically operating below capacity, and has found itself absolutely unable to expand its market, there is justification for taking over certain activities of its suppliers, provided that an already unfavorable position is not further weakened, and provided that existing fixed costs cannot be cut down to a level commensurate with existing activity. Again, however, it should be emphasized that the company should not take over "just any old activity" in which its variable costs will be less than the best outside price. A very careful survey of all opportunities for cost saving should be made before any is chosen.

Elimination of Creep

Assuming that one has already suffered a good case of creep, what steps can be taken to cure the situation? Can we apply the same tests in deciding upon the elimination of activities that we use when consideration is being given to the addition of such activities? Are the same tests applicable in reverse?

Obviously a fringe activity should not be eliminated if the potential cost of acquiring the supplies, services, etc., from outsiders is so far in excess of the costs of self-service that over-all profits would thereby be diminished. But, in exploring this possibility, what costs of production should be included?

It was pointed out above that perhaps the most potent defense against creep is a requirement that outside suppliers be used, in the case of any relatively permanent program, unless it can be proved that their offering prices are higher than the buyer's total costs plus a margin of profit. Does this mean that an existing activity should be dropped in favor of outside supply if it is found that the existing activity when charged with full costs would not show profit if it were given credit for its output at regular market prices?

In general the answer would appear to be *yes*, although subject to one exception. The rule may be expressed somewhat as follows: A company should divest itself of any activity which has been undertaken because of its cost-saving potential if such activity would not be added under the suggested rules for the prevention of creep. The only exception is this: If specialized machinery, equipment, housing, or other specialized fixed assets have been purchased, and are of such nature that they have no alternative full use, the depreciation and other non-separable costs of such assets can be eliminated from the calculation except to the extent that the assets have a significant present market value. In other words, the cost of such assets is "sunk"; to the extent that such cost cannot be retrieved by sale or through other employment in the business, the cost may be said already to be invested in future production of the related product, and the sacrifice cannot, therefore, be avoided by the discontinuance of the activity. If, with depreciation of specialized assets modified or eliminated, it is found that a given activity, when charged with all costs usually prorated to a routine operation and "loaded" with a profit margin, is not able to compete with the price of comparable service as offered by outside suppliers, the activity should be abandoned.

The term "activity audit" might be adopted to describe a more or less continuous study of the ancillary activities of the business firm for purposes of detecting existing or potential creep.

Summary

A business firm, as it matures, is likely to accumulate an array of productive activities which were never contemplated when the company was founded. Many of these activities are added on a self-service basis as a matter of convenience, or they are added during periods of short supply, or to assure reliable quality, and for other reasons; such activities may well be continued provided that their full costs are adequately recognized and provided that management realizes what cost sacrifices are being made to achieve such convenience, etc. Many other activities, however, may have been taken on solely because of apparent cost savings, and additional activities may from time to time be contemplated. All such activities should be subjected to frequent activity audits to determine whether or not real cost advantages exist. Unless these activities are purely temporary, idle-time fillers, their continuance or addition cannot be justified on the grounds that they need be charged with only a part of the list of costs normally charged to regular, principal operations. This is true because fixed costs commensurate with the activity will inevitably creep into the operating costs structure.

Equally important, though not examined in detail in this article, are the additions of new lines of products which can be demonstrated *to show a profit* only because they are charged with costs on a partial, or incremental, basis. In course of time they too will cause creep.

Added activities, ranging all the way from minor service items to the production and sale of new product lines, not only create fixed costs but also tend to distract operating management from its principal objectives, and it may be no exaggeration to state that many business firms owe to creep not only the decline in their profit rates but also their ultimate failure.

Index